WITHDRAWN

FOOTE's LIFE

AND

𝔇ramatic 𝔚orks

IN TWO VOLUMES

———◆———

THE

DRAMATIC WORKS

OF

SAMUEL FOOTE, Esq;

TO WHICH IS PREFIXED

A LIFE OF THE AUTHOR

IN TWO VOLUMES

VOL. I

CONTAINING

TASTE	THE MAYOR OF GARRAT
THE ENGLISHMAN IN PARIS	THE ORATORS
THE AUTHOR	THE MINOR
THE ENGLISHMAN RE-	THE LYAR
TURNED FROM PARIS	AND
THE KNIGHTS	THE PATRON

BENJAMIN BLOM   New York/London

First Published London, 1809
by Benjamin Blom, Inc., Bronx, New York 10452
and 56 Doughty Street, London W.C. 1

Library of Congress Catalog Card Number 68-20223
Printed in the United States of America

THE

L I F E

O F

SAMUEL FOOTE, Efq.

THIS ingenious comic writer was born at Truro in Cornwall, but at what period of time we cannot take upon ourselves to say. His father, John Foote, was member of parliament for Tiverton in Devonshire, and enjoyed the posts of commissioner of the prize-office and fine-contract. His mother was heiress of the Dinely and Goodere families. The dreadful consequence of the misunderstanding between her two brothers, Sir John Dinely Goodere, bart. and Samuel Goodere, esq. captain of his majesty's ship the Ruby, is well known; on which a considerable part of the Goodere estate, which was better than fifty thousand pounds per annum, descended to Mr. Foote, her husband.

Our author was educated at Worcester college, in the university of Oxford, which owed its foundation to Sir Thomas Cockes Winford, Bart. a second cousin of our author. On his quitting the university, he commenced student of law in the Temple; but, as the dullnefs and gravity of this ftudy did not fuit the volatile vivacity of his temper and genius, he foon quitted it.

He married a young lady of a good family and fome fortune; but, their tempers being very oppofite to each other, a perfect harmony did not long fubfift between them. He now launched into all the fafhionable foibles of the age, gaming not excepted, and in a few years fpent his whole fortune. As he had long taken a difguft to the ftudy of the law, he was obliged to have recourfe to the ftage, and made his firft appearance in the character of Othello, but with no great fuccefs. He afterwards performed Fondlewife, in which he fucceeded much better; and, indeed, it was one of his favourite characters ever after. He next attempted Lord Foppington, but he liftened to the advice of his friends, and prudently gave it up. As Mr. Foote was never a capital actor in the plays of others, his falary of courfe could not be equal to his gay and extravagant mode of living: he at laft contracted fo many debts, that he was obliged to take refuge in the verge of the court, to fecure himfelf from the refentment of his creditors.

A very laughable ftratagem at length relieved him from his neceffities. Sir Francis Delaval had

had long been his intimate friend, and had dif-
fipated his fortune by fimilar extravagance. A
rich lady, an intimate acquaintance of Foote, was
fortunately at that time bent upon a matrimonial
fcheme. Foote ftrongly recommended to her to
confult, on this momentous affair, the conjuror in
the Old Bailey, whom he reprefented as a man
of furiprfing fkill and penetration. He employed
an acquaintance of his own to perfonate the conjuror, who depicted Sir Francis Delaval at full
length, defcribed the time when, the place where,
and the drefs in which fhe fhould fee him. The
lady was fo ftruck with the coincidence of every
circumftance, that fhe married the knight in a
few days after. For this fervice Sir Francis
fettled an annuity upon Foote, which enabled
him once more to appear upon the bufy ftage
of life.

Mr. Foote now affuming the double character
of author and performer, in 1747 opened his
Little Theatre in the Haymarket, with a dramatic piece of his own writing, called *The Diverfions of the Morning*. This piece confifted of
nothing more than the introduction of feveral
well-known characters in real life, whofe manner of converfation and expreffion our author
had very happily hit off in the diction of his
drama, and ftill more happily reprefented on the
stage,

ftage, by an exact and moft amazing imitation, not only of the manner and tone of voice, but even of the very perfons, whom he intended to *take off*. Among thefe characters there was in particular a certain phyfician, who was much better known from the oddity and fingularity of his appearance and converfation, than from his eminence in the practice of his profeffion. The celebrated Chevalier Taylor, the oculift, who was at that time in the height of his vogue and popularity, was alfo another object, and indeed defervedly fo, of Mr. Foote's mimicry and ridicule. In the latter part of this piece, under the character of a theatrical director, our author took off, with great humour and accuracy, the feveral ftiles of acting of every principal performer on the Englifh ftage.

Among thofe players, with whom Mr. Foote made free, was the facetious Harry Woodward, who returned the compliment in a little piece, called Tit for Tat, of which the following was the beginning :

" Call'd forth to battle, fee poor I appear,
" To try one fall with this fam'd auctioneer."

In the very fame piece Mr. Woodward, in the character of Foote, fays,

" But when I play'd Othello, thoufands fwore
" They never faw *fuch tragedy* before."

The

The Diverſions of the Morning at firſt met with ſome little oppoſition from the civil magiſtrates of Weſtminſter, under the ſanction of the act of parliament for limiting the number of play-houſes; but our author being patroniſed by many of the principal nobility and gentry, the oppoſition was over-ruled; and, after altering the title to that of *Giving Tea*, he proceeded without farther moleſtation, repreſenting it through a run of upwards of forty mornings to crowded and ſplendid audiences.

The enſuing ſeaſon he produced another piece of the ſame kind, which he called *An Auction of Pictures*. In this he introduced new and popular characters, all well known, particularly Sir Thomas de Veil, then the acting juſtice of peace for Weſtminſter; alſo Mr. Cock, the celebrated auctioneer, and the equally famous orator Henley. This piece was alſo well received by the public.

Notwithſtanding the favourable reception theſe pieces met with, they have never yet appeared in print, nor would they perhaps give any great pleaſure in the peruſal; for, conſiſting principally of characters, whoſe peculiar ſingularities could never be perfectly repreſented in black and white, they might probably appear flat and inſipid, when diveſted of the ſtrong colourings
which

which Mr. Foote had given them in his perfonal reprefentations. It may not be improper
here to obferve, that he himfelf reprefented all
the principal characters in each piece, which
ftood in need of his mimic powers to execute,
fhifting from one to the other with all the dexterity of a Proteus, to the wonder and aftonifh-
ment of his genteel and numerous auditors.

However, he now proceeded to write pieces
with more dramatic accuracy and regularity,
his *Knights* being the produce of an enfuing
feafon; yet in this alfo, though his plot and
characters feemed lefs immediately perfonal, it
was apparent, that he kept fome particular real
perfonages ftrongly in his eye in the performance, and the town took on themfelves to fix
them where the refemblance appeared to be the
moft ftriking.

Mr. Foote continued from time to time to
entertain the public, by felecting for their ufe
fuch characters, as well general as individual,
as feemed moft likely to contribute to the exciting our laughter, and beft anfwer the principal end of dramatic writings of the comic kind,
fuch as relax the mind from the fatigue of bufinefs or anxiety.

The

The following is a catalogue of his performances.

1. *Taste*, a comedy of two acts, acted at
Drury-Lane, 8vo. 1752. This piece and its
profits were given by its author to Mr. Worfdale
the painter, who acted the part of Lady Pentweazle in it with great applause. The general
intention of it is, to point out the numerous im-
positions that persons of fortune and fashion
daily suffer in the pursuit of what is called *taste*,
or a love of Vertù, from the tricks and confede-
racies of painters, auctioneers, medal dealers,
&c. and to shew the absurdity of placing an
inestimable value on, and giving immense prices
for a parcel of maimed busts, erazed pictures,
and inexplicable coins, only because they have
the mere name and appearance of antiquity,
while the more perfect and really valuable performances of the most capital artists of our own
age and country, if known to be such, are totally
despised and neglected, and the artists themselves
suffered to pass through life unnoticed and dif-
couraged. These points our author has in this
farce set forth in a very just, and at the same time
in a very humorous light; but whether the generality of the audience did not relish, or perhaps
did not understand this refined satire, or that,
understanding it, they were so wedded to the
infatuation

infatuation of being impofed upon, that they
were unwilling to fubfcribe to the juftice of it,
are points we cannot determine ; but it met
with fome oppofition for a night or two, and
during the whole run of it, which was not a
long one, it found at beft but a cold and dif-
tafteful reception.

2. *The Englifhman in Paris*, a comedy of two
acts, 8vo. 1753, performed at Covent-Garden
theatre. This piece met with great fuccefs; its
firft appearance was for Macklin's benefit, when
that performer acted the part of Buck, and
Mifs Macklin Lucinda, which feemed written
entirely to give her an opportunity of difplay-
ing her various qualifications of mufic, finging,
and dancing, in all which fhe obtained univerfal
applaufe. The author himfelf afterwards re-
peatedly performed the part of Buck ; yet it is
difficult to fay, which of the two did the character the greateft juftice. This piece feems
defigned to expofe the abfurdity of fending our
youth abroad, to catch the vices and follies of
our neigbouring nations ; yet there is fomewhat
of an inconfiftency in the portrait of the Englifhman, that fcarcely renders the execution
anfwerable to the intention. This little comedy
was imagined to be a burlefque on M. de Boiffy's
François à Londres. On a comparifon, however,
                                                there

there does not appear to be the flighteft refemblance.

3. *The Knights*, a comedy of two acts, 8vo.
1754. This piece made its firft appearance at
the Little Theatre in the Haymarket, about the
year 1747, and at that time terminated with a
droll concert of vocal mufic between two cats,
in burlefque of the Italian comic operas. As
this, however, was only temporary, the author,
to adapt it more properly to dramatic tafte, and
render it a more perfect farce, has wound up a
conclufion for it, which however, even as it now
ftands, is fcarcely fo conclufive or fo natural as
it could be wifhed; but this fault is amply made
amends for by its poffeffing, in the higheft degree,
a much more effential excellence of comedy,
which is great ftrength of character, and the moft
accurate and lively colouring of nature. His two
knights, Sir Penurious Trifle, and Sir Gregory Gazette, the firft of which has the ftrongeft paffion for
perpetually entertaining his friends with a parcel
of ftale, trite, infignificant ftories, and the latter,
who is poffeffed with a moft infatiable thirft for
news, without even capacity fufficient to comprehend the full meaning of the moft familiar
paragraph in a public journal, are very ftrongly
painted. The firft of them received additional
life from the admirable execution of the author
in

in his reprefentation of the character, in which
indeed it has been reported, that he mimicked
the manners of a certain gentleman in the weft
of England; and the other feems to have af-
forded a hint to Mr. Murphy in his Upholfterer,
to expatiate ftill more largely on this extravagant
and abfurd kind of folly. His other characters
Tim and Mifs Suck, with the fcene of court-
fhip introduced between them, though not abfolutely new in the firft conception, yet are
managed after a new manner, and always give
great entertainment in their reprefentation. It
was afterwards acted at Drury-Lane.

4. *The Englifhman returned from Paris*, a
comedy of two acts, 8vo. 1756. Acted at
Covent-Garden. This is a fequel to *The Englifhman in Paris*, wherein the Englifhman, who before was a brute, is now become a coxcomb;
from being abfurdly averfe to every thing
foreign, he is grown into a deteftation of every
thing domeftic; and rejects the very woman,
now poffeffed of every advantage, whom he before was rufhing headlong into marriage with,
when deftitute of any. This piece is much
more dramatic and complete than the other, and
has a greater variety of characters in it, two
more efpecially, Crab and Macruthen, which
are finely drawn; but the circumftance of the
cataftrophe

cataftrophe being brought about by Lucinda's pretending to have poïfoned Sir John Buck in a difh of tea, is taken from Mrs. Centlivre's *Artifice.*

5. *The Author*, a comedy of two acts, 8vo. 1757. Acted at Drury-Lane. This piece was written only for the fake of affording to the writer of it an opportunity of exerting his talents of mimickry, at the expence of a gentleman of family and fortune, Mr. Aprice, whofe particularities of character, although entirely inoffenfive, were rendered the butt of public ridicule in the part of Cadwallader. The eager fondnefs which the world ever fhew to perfonal flander, added to the inimitable humour of this writer and performer in the reprefentation, for fome time, brought crowded houfes to it; till at length the refemblance appearing too ftrong, and the ridicule too pungent, not to be feen and felt by the gentleman thus pointed out, occafioned an application for the fuppreffion of the piece, which was therefore forbidden to be any more performed.

6. *The Diverfions of the Morning*, a farce, acted at Drury-Lane in 1768, but not printed. This was partly compiled from *Tafte* and Mr. Whitehead's *Fatal Conftancy.*

7. *The Minor*, a comedy of three acts, 8vo. 1760. This piece was firſt repreſented in the ſummer ſeaſon, at the Little Theatre in the Haymarket; and though it was performed by an entirely young, and unexperienced company, it brought full houſes for thirty-eight nights in that time of the year. As the principal merit of all our anthor's writings conſiſts in the drawing of peculiar characters well known in real life, which he heightened by his own manner of perſonating the originals on the ſtage, it will be neceſſary to inform poſterity, that in the characters of Mrs. Cole and Mr. Smirk, the author repreſented thoſe of the celebrated Mother Douglas, and Mr. Langford, the auctioneer; and that in the concluſion, or rather epilogue to the piece, ſpoken by Shift, which the author performed together with the other two characters, he took off, to a great degree of exactneſs, the manner and even perſon of that noted preacher, and chief of the Methodiſts, Mr. George Whitefield. Indeed, ſo happy was the ſucceſs of this piece, in one reſpect, that it ſeemed more effectually to open our eyes, thoſe of the populace eſpecially, in regard to the abſurdities of that ſet of enthuſiaſts, than all the more ſerious writings that had ever been publiſhed againſt them.

8. *The*

8. *The Lyar*, a comedy of three acts, 8vo. 1764. This comedy was originally intended to have been performed during the summer partnership between Mr. Murphy and the author; but the run of thofe pieces they had before brought on, and the unexpected neceffity of playing the *Wifhes*, having exhaufted the time limitted for their reprefentation, this was obliged to be deferred till the enfuing winter, when it was reprefented, for the firft time, at the theatre in Covent-Garden. Its fuccefs was very indifferent; and indeed it muft be confeffed, that it was in itfelf far from equal to the generality of our author's works. Though there were here and there fome ftrokes of humour in it, which were not unworthy of their author, and fome few touches of temporary fatire, yet the character of the Lyar had certainly neither native originality enough in it to pleafe as a novelty, nor additional beauties fufficient either in his drefs or demeanour, to excite a frefh attention to him as a new acquaintance. In fhort, on the whole, it was rather tedious and unentertaining, having neither enough of the *vis comica* to keep up the attention of an audience through fo many acts as a farce, nor a fufficiency of incident and fentiment to engage their hearts, if confidered under the denomination of a comedy, yet it has fince been often acted as a farce.

9. *The*

9. *The Orators*, a comedy of three acts, 8vo.
1762. This piece, which met with very good
fuccefs, was performed at the Little Theatre in
the Haymarket, in the middle of the day, during
fome part of the fummer of 1762. Our author
has thrown into the defign of this piece a great
variety of characters, fome of which have been
fuppofed to be drawn from real life, particularly
one of a late printer of Ireland, who, with all
the difadvantages of age, perfon, and addrefs,
and even the deficiency of a leg, was perpetually
giving himfelf airs of the greateft importance,
continually repeating ftories of his wit, and boaft-
ing of being a favourite of the fair fex. Such a
character is furely a genuine object of ridicule,
and the ftage feems to demand it as a facrifice at
the fhrine of common fenfe.

10. *The Mayor of Garrat*, a comedy of two
acts, performed at the theatre in the Haymarket
in 1763, and printed in 8vo. in 1769. In this
very humorous and entertaining piece, the character of Major Sturgeon, a city militia officer,
is entirely new, highly wrought up, and was
performed in a moft capital ftile by Mr. Foote
himfelf.

11. *The Patron*, a comedy of three acts, performed at the Haymarket in 1764. The hint is
                                        borrowed

borrowed from one of Marmontel's Tales. The character of the Patron, said to be Lord Melcombe, is that of a superficial pretender to wit and learning, who, being a man of fashion and fortune, affords his countenance and protection to a set of contemptible writings, for the sake of the incense offered by them to his vanity. The character of a mere antiquarian, a favourite object of ridicule with Mr. Foote, is here introduced with great pleasantry, Mr. Rust having fallen in love with a fine young lady, because he thought the tip of her ear resembled the Princess Popœa. Sir Peter Pepperpot, a rich West India merchant, comes in likewise, with his account of barbecues and turtle feasts; and a miserable poet, with a low Moorfields bookseller, serve to complete the entertainment.

12. *The Commiffary*, a comedy, acted with great success, at the Haymarket in 1765. Among other real characters drawn from life, the late celebrated Dr. Arne was ridiculed in this comedy.

13. *Prelude* on opening the Theatre, 1767.

14. *The Devil upon two Sticks*, a comedy, acted at the Haymarket in 1768, printed in 8vo. in 1778. This was one of the most successful of our author's performances; but though it abounds with wit, humour, and satire of the most pleasant

and

and inoffenſive kind, yet it ſeems to have loſt its exiſtence with its parent.

15. *The Lame Lover*, a comedy, aſted at the Haymarket in 1770. Though this piece was by no means inferior to any other of his writing, yet it did not meet with the deſerved ſucceſs. Sir Luke Limp, the Serjeant, and his ſon, are admirably drawn charaſters.

16. *The Maid of Bath*, a comedy, aſted at the Haymarket in 1771, and printed in 8vo. in 1778. The ground-work of this very intereſting performance is taken from a tranſaſtion which happened at Bath, in which a perſon of fortune was ſaid to have treated a young lady celebrated for her muſical talents in a very ungenerous manner. The delinquent is here held up to ridicule under the name of Hint, and it will be difficult to point out a charaſter drawn with more truth and accuracy than this, eſpecially in the ſecond aſt. The parts of Lady Catherine Coldſtream, Sir Chriſtopher Cripple, and Billy Button, are all highly finiſhed, and render this piece one of the moſt pleaſing of all our author wrote.

17. *The Nabob*, a comedy, aſted at the Haymarket in 1772, and printed in 8vo. in 1778. This piece is a ſevere ſatire on the greater part

of

of thofe gentlemen who have acquired wealth in the Eaft Indies. At the time this play was produced. a general odium had been excited againft the members of the Eaft India company, which was kept alive by every art that virulence and party could fuggeft. Mr. Foote, ever attentive to avail himfelf of popular fubjects, feized the prefent occafion to entertain the town at the ex-expence of fome individuals. The character of Sir Matthew Mite was intended for a gentleman who had rifen from the low fituation of a cheefe-monger.

18. *Piety in Pattens*, a farce, acted at the theatre in the Haymarket in 1773; but never printed.

19. *The Bankrupt*, acted at the Haymarket in 1776. This piece, like moft others written by our author, contains little elfe than detached fcenes without any plot. It exhibits, however, fome ftrong delineations of character, and is by no means a bad performance.

20. *The Cozeners*, a comedy of three acts, acted at the Haymarket in 1774, and printed in 8vo. in 1778. The character of Simony in this piece was defigned as a vehicle for fatire on the late Dr. Dodd. It may be obferved, as fome apology for our author's ftage ridicule, that he rarely

pointed

pointed it at any perſons who met with public reſpect, or deſerved to meet with it.

21. *The Capuchin*, a comedy, acted at the Haymarket in 1776, and printed in 8vo. in 1778.

22. *A Trip to Calais*, a comedy, intended for repreſentation in 1776, at the Haymarket; but containing a character deſigned for a lady of quality, ſhe had intereſt enough to prevent its obtaining a licence.

Mr. Foote, after having written theſe pieces, ſuffered his name to be put to a work, entitled, The Comic Theatre, in five volumes, 12mo. being a tranſlation of a number of French comedies. Of theſe, however, we are aſſured, the firſt only, The Young Hypocrite, is to be attributed to him.

All Mr. Foote's works are to be ranked only among the *petites piéces* of the theatre. In the execution they are ſomewhat looſe, negligent, and unfiniſhed; the plans are often irregular, and the cataſtrophes not always concluſive; but, with all theſe deficiencies, they contain more ſtrength of character, more ſtrokes of keen ſatire, and more touches of temporary humour, than are to be found in the writings of any other modern dramatiſt. Even the language ſpoken by

his

his characters, incorrect as it may fometimes appear, will, on a clofe examination, be found entirely dramatical, as it abounds with thofe natural minutiæ of expreffion, which frequently form the very bafis of character, and which render it the truest mirror of the converfation of the times in which he wrote and publifhed them.

Being on a party of pleafure, in the year 1766, with the late Duke of York, Lord Mexborough, and Sir Francis Delaval, Mr. Foote had the mif-fortune to break his leg, by a fall from his horfe, in confequence of which he was obliged to undergo an amputation. This accident, fo fenfibly affected the Duke, that he made a point of obtaining for Mr. Foote a patent for life, whereby he was allowed to perform, at the Little Theatre in the Haymarket, from the 15th of May to the 15th of September every year.

Our author now became a greater favourite of the town than ever; his very laughable pieces, with his more laughable performances, conftantly filled his houfe, and his receipts were fome feafons almoft incredible. Parfimony was never a vice to be afcribed to Mr. Foote; his hofpitality and generofity were ever confpicuous; he was vifited by the firft nobility, and he was fome-times honoured even by royal guefts.

In

In 1766, the Duchefs of K———, who had long been a general topic of converfation, our wit thought would furnifh a good fubject for a three-act piece; he fet about it, and during the time of writing it, often mentioned it to his friends, to fome of whom he read the chaaracter of Lady Kitty Crocodile, which was intended for her grace. We are told, that the fatire was highly feafoned, and the play one of the beft he ever wrote. Her grace hearing of her being intended as a principal character in Foote's piece preparing for reprefentation, applied by her friends to the Lord Chamberlain; and when the play came before his lordfhip for his approbation, it was critically fcanned, and a permiffion refufed. Mr. Foote, however, certain that no objection could be laid to it on her grace's part, fent her the manufcript to read; but fhe was inexorable. Upon this, a paper war commenced between her grace and the wit, to the no fmall entertainment of the town.

The attack made upon his character by one of his domeftics, whom he had difmiffed for his mifbehaviour, is too well known to need being mentioned here. It may be fufficient to fay he was honourably acquitted of that charge. It is, however, believed by fome, that the fhock he received from it accelerated his death, particularly

the

the very active part the agents of a certain duchefs took in that criminal profecution. It is
more probable, that his natural volatility of
fpirits would fupport him againft all impreffions
from attacks of that nature.

Our author, finding his health decline, entered into an agreement with Mr. Colman for
his patent of the theatre, according to which he
was to receive from that gentleman 1600l. per
annum, befides a ftipulated fum whenever he
chofe to perform. Mr. Foote, afterwards made his
appearance in two or three of his moft admired
characters; but being fuddenly feized with a pa-
ralytic ftroke one night whilft upon the ftage, he
was compelled to retire, and from that time the
public loft their juftly-admired Ariftophanes.
He was advifed to bathe, and accordingly went
down to Brighthelmftone, where he feemed to
recover his former health and fpirits.

A few weeks before his death he returned to
London; but, with the advice of his phyficians,
fet out with an intention to fpend the winter
at Paris, and in the fouth of France. He had
got no farther than Dover, when he was fuddenly
attacked by another ftroke of the palfy, which
in a few hours terminated his exiftence. He died
on the 21ft of October, 1777, about the 56th
year

year of his age, and was privately interred in the cloifters of Weftminfter-abbey. He left a natural fon, a minor, to whom he bequeathed moft of his fortune.

We have very good authority for faying, that the day on which Mr. Foote fet out for Dover, about an hour before he went into his chaife, he walked into every room in his houfe, and examined, with an accuracy not ufual to him, every article of furniture he had, but more particularly his pictures, of which he had a large and elegant collection. When he came to the portrait of Wefton, he made a full ftop, as if by fome fecret impulfe, and rivetted his eyes upon the countenance of his old acquaintance for above ten minutes, without uttering a fyllable. Then turning away, with a tear in his eye, he exclaimed, " Poor Wefton." But the words had fcarce dropped from his lips, when, with a tone as it were of reproach for his feeming fecurity, he repeated, " Poor Wefton ! It will be very " fhortly, Poor Foote, or the intelligence of " my fpirits deceive me !"

As a private man, Mr. Foote was fincere, generous, and humane. As no man ever contributed more to the entertainment of the public, fo no man oftener made the minds of his companions

panions expand with mirth and good humour; and, in the company of men of high rank and superior fortune, who courted his acquaintance, he always preferved an eafy and noble indepen- dency. That he had his foibles and caprices, no one will pretend to deny; but they were amply counterbalanced by his merit and abilities, which will tranfmit his name to pofterity with diftinguifhed reputation.

There are in print many fmart fayings and repartees attributed to Mr. Foote; but, as we cannot vouch for their authority, we fhall not infert them here. The two following lines are among the verfes that have been written on his death:

> Foote from his earthly ftage, alas! is hurl'd;
> Death *took him off*, who *took off* all the world.

1 *Head from* Herculaneum, *whether* Jupiter Tonans, *or* Venus
  of Paphos, *doubted*.
2 *The Foot, with the Toes entire, of* Juno Lucina.
3 *The Hand of the* Apollo *of* Delphos
4 *The Calf of the left Leg of the Infant* Hercules.
5 *The Caduceus of* Mercurius Infernals.

TASTE

A

COMEDY

IN TWO ACTS:

PERFORMED AT THE

THEATRE ROYAL, DRURY-LANE:

WRITTEN BY THE LATE

SAMUEL FOOTE, *Esq.*

Be rich in ancient Brass, tho not in Gold,
And keep his Lares, tho' his House be sold;
To heedless Phœbe his fair Bride postpone,
Honour a Syrian Prince above his own;
Lord of an Otho, If I vouch it true,
Blest in one Niger, till he knows of two.

POPES'S DUNCIAD.

LONDON:

Printed for W. Lowndes, J. Bakker and H. Lowndes.

1799.

Price One Shilling.

Rebel to this univerfal Tyrant, who, not contented with exciting all that is pitiful or terrible in human Nature, has claimed the privilege of occafioning every thing that is ridiculous or contemptible in it ; and thus, from the abject Submiffion of our dramatic *Poets*, is both *Tragedy* and *Comedy* fubjected to the Power of *Love*. It may be thought prefumptuous in me to have dignified fo fhort a Performance with the Name of a *Comedy* ; but when my Reafons why it cannot be called a *Farce* are confidered, the Critics muft indulge me with the Ufe of that Title ; at leaft till they can furnifh me with a better. As the Follies and Abfurdities of Men are the fole Objects of *Comedy*, fo the Powers of the Imagination (Plot and Incident excepted) are in this Kind of Writing greatly reftrained. No unnatural Affemblages, no Creatures of the Fancy, can procure the Protection of the *Comic* Mufe ; Men and Things muft appear as they are. It is employed either in debafing lofty Subjects, or in raifing humble Ones. Of the two Kinds we have Examples in the *Tom Thumb* of Mr. *F——*, and a Traveftie of the *Ulyffes*, where *Penelope* keeps an Ale-houfe, *Telemachus* is a Tapfter, and the *Heroe* a Recruiting Serjeant. In both thefe Inftances you fee Nature is reverfed ; but as I flatter myfelf in the following Sheets her Steps have been trod

with

with an undeviating Simplicity, give me leave to hope, that though I have not attained the *Togata*, yet I have reached the *Tabernaria* of the *Romans*. I once intended to have thrown into this Addreſs, the Contents of many of our Converſations on the Subject of *Comedy* ; for in whatever Diſſipations the World may ſuppoſe our Days to have been conſumed, many, many Hours have been conſecrated to other Subjects than generally employ the Gay and the Giddy. I hope the preſent Occaſion will demonſtrate, that pleaſure has not been always my Purſuit ; and unleſs I am greatly miſtaken, it will ſoon be diſcovered, that, joined to the acknowledged beſt Heart in the World, Mr. *Delaval* has a Head capable of directing it. As I am now above the reach of common Obligations, an Acknowledgement of theſe Qualities, in the Perſon of a Man who has honoured me with his Friendſhip, is the ſole Cauſe of the Trouble you now receive. Long has been our Union, may it never be divided till the fatal Stroke, that demoliſhes all ſublunary Connections, ſhall reach One of us, which One will, I hope, be

Your obliged, and

affectionate Servant,

SAMUEL FOOTE.

PREFACE.

I Was always apprehensive that the Subject of the following Piece was too abstracted and singular for the Comprehension of a mix'd Assembly. Juno, Lucina, Jupiter, Tonans, Phidias, Praxiteles, with the other Gentlemen and Ladies of Antiquity, were, I dare say, utterly unknown to my very good Friends of the Gallery; nor, to speak the Truth, do I believe they had many Acquaintances in the other Parts of the House. But tho' I despair of gratifying the Populum Tributim of the THEATRE, yet I flatter myself the Primores Populi will find me no disagreeable Companion in the Closet, et satis magnum Theatrum mihi estis.

I was neither prompted by a lucrative, nor an ambitious Motive to this Undertaking. My Design was to serve a Man, who had ever great Merit with his Friends, and to whom, on the Score of some late Transactions, I think the Public vastly indebted. That my good Intentions for Mr. WORSDALE have proved successful, is entirely owing to the Generosity and Humanity of the Managers of Drury-Lane THEATRE; they have given him a Benefit,
and

and are jointly entitled to my Thanks; but as to Mr. GARRICK, I have more personal Obligations. I take this Opportunity of assuring him, that I shall ever retain the most grateful Remembrance of his Assistance, Assiduity, and kind Concerns, at the Birth, Pogress, and untimely End of this my last and favourite offspring.

The Objects of my Satire were such as I thought, whether they were considered in a moral, a political, or a ridiculous Light, deserved the Notice of the Comic Muse. I was determined to brand those Goths in Science, who had prostituted the useful Study of Antiquity to trifling superficial Purposes; who had blasted the Progress of the elegant Arts amongst us, by unpardonable Frauds and absurd Prejudices; and who had corrupted the Minds and Morals of our Youth, by persuading them, that what only serves to illustrate Literature was true Learning, and active Idleness real Business. How far this End has been obtained, is now, in the following Sheets, more generally submitted to the Public.

PROLOGUE.

PROLOGUE.

Written by Mr. GARRICK,

And spoken by him in the Character of an
Auctioneer.

BEFORE this Court, I PETER PUFF appear,
  A Briton born, and bred an Auctioneer ;
Who for myself, and eke a hundred others,
My useful, honest, learned bawling Brothers,
With much Humility and Fear implore ye,
To lay our present desp'rate Case before ye.——
  'Tis said this Night a certain Wag intends
To laugh at us, our Calling, and our Friends :
If Lords and Ladies, and such dainty Folks,
Are cur'd of Auction-hunting by his Jokes !
Should this odd Doctrine spread throughout the
      Land,
Before you buy, be sure to understand.
Oh ! think on us what various Ills will flow,
When great Ones only purchase——what the know.
Why laugh at TASTE? *It is a harmless Fashion,*
And quite subdues each detrimental Passion ;
The Fair Ones Hearts will ne'er incline to Man,
While thus they rage for——China and Japan.
The Virtuoso, *too, and* Connoisseur,
Are ever decent, delicate, and pure ;
The smallest Hair their looser Thoughts might hold,
                        Just

Juſt warm when ſingle, and when married cold:
Their Blood at Sight of Beauty gently flows ;
Their Venus *muſt be old, and want a Noſe!*
No am'rous Paſſion with deep Knowledge thrives;
'Tis the Complaint, indeed, of all our Wives !
Tis ſaid Virtù *to ſuch a height is grown,*
All Artiſts are encourag'd——but our own.
Be not deceiv'd, I here declare on Oath,
I never yet ſold Goods *of foreign growth :*
Ne'er ſent Commiſſions out to Greece *or* Rome;
My beſt Antiquities are made at Home.
I've Romans, Greeks, Italians *near at hand,*
True Britons *all—and living in the* Strand.
I ne'er for Trinkets rack my Pericranium,
They furniſh out my Room from Herculaneum.
But huſh ——
Should it be known that Engliſh *are employ'd,*
Our Manufacture is at once deſtroy'd ;
No matter what our Countrymen deſerve,
They'll thrive as Ancients, but as Moderns ſtarve
If we ſhould fall—to you it will be owing;
Farewell to Arts—*they're going, going, going;*
The fatal Hammer's in your Hand, oh Town !
Then ſet Us *up—and knock the* POET *down.*

Dramatis

Dramatis   Personæ.

Carmine,	*Mr.* Palmer.
Puff,	*Mr.* Yates.
Brush,	*Mr.* Cross.
Novice,	*Mr.* Blake.
Lord Dupe.	*Mr.* Shuter.
Alderman Pentweazle,	*Mr.* Taswell.
Caleb,	*Mr.* Costollo.
Boy,	*Master* Cross.
Lady Pentweazle,	*Mr.* Worsdale.

TASTE.

A

COMEDY.

ACT I.

SCENE I. *A Painting Room.*

Enter CARMINE, *followed by the Boy:*

CARMINE. LAY these Colours in the Window, by the Pallet. Any Visitors or Messages?

Boy. 'Squire *Felltree* has been here, and insists upon Miss *Racket's* Pictures being immediately finish'd, and carry'd Home——As to his Wife and Children, he says, you may take your own Time.

Carm. Well——

Boy. Here has been a Message-too, from my Lady *Pen*——— I can't remember her Name, but 'tis upon the Slate. She desires to know if you will be at Home about Noon.

Carm. Fetch it.   (*Exit.* Boy.

Was the Whole of our Profession confined to the mere Business of it, the Employment would be pleasing as well as profitable; but as matters are

now

now managed, the Art is the laſt Thing to be regarded. Family Connections, private Recommendations, and an eaſy, genteel Method of Flattering, is to ſupply the Delicacy of a *Guido*, the colouring of a *Rubens*, and the Deſign of a *Raphael*—all their Qualities centring in one Man, without the firſt Requiſites, would be uſeleſs; and with theſe, one of them is neceſſary.

Enter Boy *with the Slate.*

Carm. Let's ſee———Oh! Lady *Pentweazel* from *Blowbladder-ſtreet*———Admit her by all Means; and if *Puff* or *Varniſh* ſhould come, I am at home. (*Exit* Boy.
Lady *Pentweazel!* ha! ha! Now here's a Proof that Avarice is not the only, or laſt Paſſion old Age is ſubject to———this ſuperannuated Beldame gapes for Flattery, like a Neſt of unfledged Crows for Food; and with them, too, gulps down every Thing that's offer'd her—no Matter how coarſe; well, ſhe ſhall be fed; I'll make her my introductory Key to the whole Bench of *Aldermen.*

Enter Boy *with* Puff.

Boy. Mr. *Puff,* Sir.
Carm. Let us be private. What have you there?
Puff. Two of *Rembrandt's* Etching by *Scrape,* In *May's Buildings*; a paltry Affair, a Poor Ten Guinea Job; however, a ſmall game———you know the Proverb———What became of you Yeſterday?
Carm. I was detained by Sir *Poſitive Bubble.* How went the Pictures? The *Guido,* what did that fetch?

Puff.

Puff. One Hundred and Thirty.

Carm. Hum! Four Guineas the Frame, Three the Painting; then we divide juft One Hundred and Twenty three.

Puff. Hold——not altogether fo faft——*Varnifh* had Two Pieces for bidding againft *Squander*; and *Brufh* Five for bringing Sir *Tawdry Trifle.*

Carm. Mighty well; look ye, Mr. *Puff*, if thefe people are eternally quarter'd upon us, I declare off, Sir; they eat up the Profit. There's that damn'd *Brufh*———but you'll find him out. I have upon his old Plan given him Copies of all the Work I executed upon his Recommendation; and what was the Confequence? He clandeftinely fold the Copies, and I have all the Originals in my Lumber-Room.

Puff. Come, come, *Carmine*, you are no great Lofer by that. Ah! that Lumber-Room! that Lumber-Room out of repair, is the beft conditioned Eftate in the County of *Middlefex.* Why now there's your *Sufannah*; it could not have produced you above Twenty at moft, and by the Addition of your Lumber-Room Dirt, and the falutary Application of the Spaltam Pot, it became a *Guido*, worth a Hundred and Thirty Pounds; befides, in all Traffic of this Kind, there muft be Combinations.— *Varnifh* and *Brufh* are our Jackalls, and it is but fair they fhould partake of the Prey. Courage, my Boy! never fear! Praife be to Folly and Fafhion, there are, in this Town, *Dupes* enough to gratify the Avarice of us all.

Carm. Mr. *Puff*, you are ignorant and Scurrilous, and very impertinent Mr. *Puff*; and Mr. *Puff*, I have a ftrange Mind to leave you to yourfelves,

and

and then see what a Hand you would make of it——
Sir, if I do now and then add some Tincts of Antiquity to my Pictures, I do it in Condescension to
theFoible of the World; for, Sir, Age, Age, Sir,
is all my Pictures want to render 'em as good Pieces
as the Masters from whom they are taken; and let
me tell you Sir, he that took my *Susannah* for a
Guido, gave no mighty Proofs of his Ignorance,
Mr. *Puff*.

Puff. Why, thou Post-painter, thou Dauber,
thou execrable White-washer, thou——Sirrah, have
you so soon forgot the wretched State from whence
I dragg'd you. The first Time I set eyes on you,
Rascal! what was your Occupation then? Scrib-
bling, in scarce legible Letters, Coffee, Tea, and
Chocolate on a Bawdy-house Window in *Goodman's
Fields*.

Carm. The Meanness of my Original demon-
strates the greatness of my Genius.

Puff. Genius! Here's a Dog. Pray, how high
did your Genius soar? To the daubing diabolical
Angels for Alehouses, Dogs with Chains for Tan-
ner's Yards, Rounds of Beef and roasted Pigs for
Porridge Island.

Carm. *Hanibal Scratchi* did the same.

Puff. From that contemptible State did not I
raise you to the *Cat* and *Fiddle* in *Petticoat-lane*; the
Goose and *Gridiron* in *Paul's Church-yard*; the first
live Things you ever drew, Dog?

Carm. Pox take your Memory. Well, but,
Mr. *Puff*—you are so—

Puff. Nor did I quit you then: Who Sirrah, recommended you to *Prim Stiff*, the Mercer upon *Lud-
gate-hill*; how came you to paint the *Queen* there?
(*Loud Knocks at the Door.*
Carm.

Carm. Mr. *Puff*, for Heaven's fake! dear Sir, you are fo warm, we fhall be blown——

Enter Boy.

Boy. Sir, my Lady *Pen*——
Carm. Send her to the—Show her up Stairs. Dear *Puff*——
Puff. Oh! Sir, I can be calm; I only wanted to let you fee I had not forgot, though perhaps you may.
Carm. Sir, you are very obliging. Well, but now as all is over, if you will retreat a fmall Time—Lady *Pentweazel* fits for her Picture, and fhe's——
Puff. I have fome Bufinefs at next Door; I fuppofe in half an Hour's Time——
Carm. I fhall be at Leifure. Dear *Puff*—
Puff. Dear *Carmine*—— *(Exit Puff.*
Carm. Son of a Whore——Boy, fhew the Lady up Stairs.

Enter Lady Pentweazel.

Lady. Fine Pieces!—very likely Pieces! and, indeed, all alike. Hum! Lady *Fuffock*—and, ha! ha! ha! Lady *Glumftead*, by all that's ugly—Pray now, Mr. *Carmine*, how do you Limners contrive to overlook the Uglinefs, and preferve the Likenefs?
Carm. The Art, Madam, may be convey'd in two words; where nature has been fevere, we foften; where fhe has been kind, we aggravate.
Lady. Very *ingenus*, and very kind, truly. Well, good Sir, I bring you a Subject that will demand the whole of the firft Part of your Skill; and if you are at Leifure, you may begin directly.

Carm.

Carm. Your Ladyſhip is here a little ungrateful to Nature, and cruel to yourſelf; even Lady *Pent-weazel's* Enemies (if ſuch there be) muſt allow ſhe is a fine Woman.

Lady. Oh! your Servant, good Sir. Why I have had my Day, Mr. *Carmine*; I have had my Day.

Carm. And have ſtill, Madam. The only Difference I ſhall make between what you were, and what you are, will be no more than what *Rubens* has diſtinguiſhed between *Mary de Medicis*, a Virgin and a Regent.

Lady. Mr. *Carmine*, I vow you are a very judicious Perſon. I was always ſaid to be like that Family. When my Piece was firſt done, the Limner did me after *Venus de Medicis*, which I ſuppoſe might be one of *Mary's* Siſters; but Things muſt change; to be ſitting for my Picture at this Time of Day; ha! ha! but my Daughter *Sukey*, you muſt know, is juſt married to Mr. Deputy *Dripping* of *Candlewick-Ward*, and would not be ſaid nay; ſo it is not ſo much for the Beauty as the Similitude. Ha! ha!

Carm. True, Madam; ha! ha! but if I hit the Likeneſs, I muſt preſerve the Beauty,—Will your Ladyſhip be ſeated? *(She ſits.*

Lady. I have heard, good Sir, that eveıy Body has a more betterer and more worſerer Side of the Face than the other—now which will you chuſe?

Carm. The Right Side, Madam—the Left—now, if you pleaſe, the Full—Your Ladyſhip's Countenance is ſo exactly proportion'd, that I muſt have it all; no Feature can be ſpared?

Lady.

Lady. When you come to the Eyes, Mr. *Carmine*, let me know, that I may call up a Look.

Carm. Mighty well, Madam——Your Face a little nearer to the Left, nearer me—yonr Head more up—Shoulders back—and Cheſt forward.

Lady. Bleſs me, Mr. *Carmine*, don't mind my Shape this Bout; for I am only in Jumps.——Shall I ſend for my Tabbys?

Carm. No, Madam, we'll ſupply that for the preſent—Your Ladyſhip was juſt now mentioning a Daughter—Is ſhe—your Face a little more towards me—Is ſhe the ſole Inheritor of her Mother's Beauty; Or——have you——

Lady. That? ha! ha! ha!—why that's my youngeſt of all, except *Caleb.* I have had, Mr. *Carmine*, live born, and chriſten'd—ſtay—don't let me lye now—One—Two—Three—Four—Five—Then I lay fallow——but the Year after I had Twins——they came in Mr. *Pentweazel's* Sheriffalty; then *Roger*, then *Robin*, then *Reuben* ——in ſhort, I have had Twenty as fine Babes as ever trod in Shoe of Leather.

Carm. Upon my Word, Madam, your Ladyſhip is an admirable Member of the Commonwealth; 'tis a thouſand Pities that, like the *Romans*, we have not ſome Honours to reward ſuch diſtinguiſhed Merit.

Lady. Ay, ay, Mr. *Carmine*, if Breeding amongſt *Chriſtians* was as much encouraged as amongſt Dogs and Horſes, we need not be making Laws to let in a Parcel of outlandiſh Locuſts to eat us all up.

Carm. I am told, Madam, that a Bill for ſome ſuch Purpoſe is about to paſs, and that we begin now
to

to have almoſt as much Regard for the Propoga-
tion of the Species, as the Preſervation of the
Game in theſe Kingdoms—Now, Madam, I am
come to the Eyes—Oh! that Look, that, that, I
muſt deſpair of imitating.

Lady. Oh! Oh! good Sir, have you found out
that? Why all my Family by the Mother's Side
were famous for their Eyes: I have a Great Aunt
among the Beauties at *Windſor*; ſhe has a Siſter at
Hampton-Court, a *perdigious* fine Woman—ſhe had
but one Eye, indeed, but that was a Piercer; that
one Eye got her three Huſbands—we were called
the gimlet-eyed Family. Oh! Mr. *Carmine*, you
need not mind theſe Heats in my Face; they always
diſcharge themſelves about *Chriſtmas*—my true
Carnation is not ſeen in my Countenance. Thats
Carnation! here's your Fleſh and Blood!

(*ſhewing her Arm.*

Carm. Delicate, indeed! finely turn'd, and of
a charming Colour.

Lady. And yet it has been employed enough to
ſpoil the beſt Hand and Arm in the World.——
Even before Marriage never idle; none of your
galloping, goſſiping, *Ranelagh* Romps, like the
forward Minxes of the preſent Age. I was always
employed either in painting your *Lamſkips*, playing
upon the *Haſpicols*, making Paſte, or ſomething or
other——All our family had a *Geno*; and then I
ſung! Every Body ſaid I had a monſtrous fine
Voice for Muſic.

Carm. That may be diſcern'd by your Ladyſhip's
Tones in Converſation.

Lady. Tones—you are right, Mr. *Carmine*;
that was Mr. *Purcel's* Word. Miſs *Molly Griſkin*,
ſaid he (my maiden Name) you have Tones.

Carm.

Carm. As your Ladyſhip has preſerved every Thing elſe ſo well, I dare ſwear you have not loſt your Voice. Will you favour me with an Air!

Lady. Oh! Sir, you are ſo polite, that it's im-poſſible——But I have none of your new Play-houſe Songs——I can give you one that was made on myſelf by *Lawrence Luteſtring*, a Neighbour's Son.

Carm. What you pleaſe, Madam.

Lady.

As I was a walking by the Side of a River,
I met a young Damſel ſo charming and clever;
Her Voice to pleaſe could not fail,
She ſung like any Nightingale.

                  Fal de rol; hugh, hugh, &c.

Bleſs me! I have ſuch a Cough; but there are Tones.

Carm. Inimitable ones.

Lady. But, Mr. *Carmine*, you Limners are all *ingenus* Men—you ſing.

Carm. A Ballad, or ſo, Madam; Muſic is a Siſter Art; and it would be a little unnatural not to cultivate an Acquaintance there.

Lady. Why truly we ought not to be aſhamed of our Relations, unleſs they are poor; and then, you know——

Enter Boy.

Boy Alderman *Pentweazle* and Mr. *Puff.*

Lady. Oh! he was to call upon me; we go to the Auction. Deſire him to walk up—Mr. *Pent-weazle,* you muſt know, went this Morning to meet *Caleb,* my youngeſt Boy, at the *Bull* and *Gate.* The Child has been two Years and three

                      Quarters

Quarters at School with Dr. *Jerk*, near *Doncaster*, and comes To-day by the *York* Waggon; for it has always been my Maxum, Mr. *Carmine*, to give my Children Learning enough; for, as the old Saying is,

When House and Land are gone and spent,
Then Larning is most excellent.

Carm. Your Ladyship is quite right. Too much Money cannot be employed in so material an Article.

Lady. Nay, the Cost is but small; but poor fourteen Pounds a Year for Head, Back, Books, Bed, and Belly; and they say the Children are all wonderful Latiners, and come up, lack-a-day, they come up as fat as Pigs ——Oh! here they are; Odds me! he's a Thumper. You see, Mr. *Carmine*, I breed no Starvelings Come hither, Child. Mind your Haviours. Where's your best Bow? Turn out your Toes. One would think he had learnt to dance of his Father. I'm sure my Family were none so awkward. There was my Brother *George*, a perfect Picture of a Man; he danced, Lud! But come, all in good Time—Hold up thy Head, *Caleb*.

Ald. Pr'ythee, sweet Honey, let the Child alone. His Master says he comes on wonderful in his Learning; and as to your Bows and your Congees, never fear, he'll learn them fast enough at Home.

Lady. Lack-a-day! well said—We now—If he does, I know who must teach him. Well, Child, and dost remember me? Hey? Who am I?

Caleb. Anon!

Lady. Dost know me?

Caleb. Yes; you be Mother.

Lady.

Lady. Nay, the Boy had always a good Memory. And what haſt learnt, *Caleb*, hey?

Caleb. I be got into *Æſop's Fables*, and can ſay all *As in præſenti* by Heart.

Lady. Upon my Word—that's more than ever thy Father could.

Ald. Nay, nay, no Time has been loſt; I queſtioned the Lad as we came along; I aſk'd him himſelf———

Lady. Well, well, ſpeak when you are ſpoken to, Mr Alderman. How often muſt I———Well, *Caleb*, and hadſt a good deal of Company in the Waggon, Boy?

Caleb. O Law! Powers of Company. Mother. There was Lord *Gorman's* fat Cook, a Blackamore Drumming Man, two Actor People, a Recruiting Serjeant, a Monkey and I:

Lady. Upon my Word, a pretty Parcel.

Caleb. Yes, indeed; but the———the fat Cook got drunk at *Coventry*, and ſo fell out at the tail of the Waggon; ſo we left ſhe behind. The next Day the Serjeant ran away with the Showman's Wife; the t'other two went after; ſo only the Monkey and I came to Town together.

Carm. Upon my Word, the young Gentleman gives a good Account of his Travels.

Lady. Ay, ay, Mr. *Carmine*, he's all over the blood of the *Griſkins.* I warrant the Child will make his Way. Go, *Caleb*, go and look at them pretty Paintings— Now, Mr. *Carmine*, let us ſee if my good Man can find me out.

Ald. Lack-a-day; well, I profeſs they are all ſo handſome, that I am puzzled to know which is thine, Chuck.

Puff.

Puff. I am furprized at your Want of Difcernment, Mr. Alderman ; but the poffeffion of a Jewel deftroys its Value with the Wearer ; now to me it feems impoffible to err ; and tho' Mr. *Carmine* is generally fuccefsful, in this Inftance he is particularly happy. Where can you meet with that Mixture of Fire and Softnefs, but in the Eyes of Lady *Pentweazle?*

Lady. Oh, Sir!

Puff. That Clearnefs and Delicacy of Complexion, with that Flow of Ruddinefs and Health.

Lady. Sir ! Sir ! Sir !

Puff. That Fall of Shoulders, Turn of Neck, fet on Head, full Cheft, taper Waift, plump—

Lady. Spare me, fweet Sir !——You fee Mr. *Pentweazle,* other People can find out my Charms, tho' you overlook them—Well, I profefs, Sir, you are a Gentleman of great Difcernment ; and if Bufinefs fhould bring you into the City ; for alas ! what Pleafure can bring a Man of your refined Tafte there ?——

Puff. Oh ! Ma'am !

Lady I fay, Sir, if fuch an Accident fhould happen, and *Blowbladder-ftreet* has any Charms—

Puff. Oh ! Ma'am ! Ma'am ! Ma'am ! Ma'am—

Lady. It is not impoffible but we may receive you, tho' not equal to your Merits——

Puff. Ma'am !

Lady. Yet in fuch a Manner as to fhew our Senfe of them. Sir, I'm your very obedient.

Puff. Your Ladyfhip's moft——

Lady. Not a Step.

Puff. Ma'am.

Lady.

Lady. Sir————Mr. Alderman, your Bow to the Gentlemen.   The very fineſt.

Puff. Ma'am !

Lady. Sir————Your moſt obedient.

Puff. Your devoted.   (*Ex. Ald. and* Wife.

Carm. Ha ! ha ! Well ſaid, *Puff.* What a Calamity thou haſt drawn upon the Knight ! Thou haſt ſo tickled the Vanity of the Haradan, that the poor Helpmate will experience a double portion of her Contempt.

Puff. Rot them.

Carm. Come, *Puff,* a matrimonial Aſſiſtant to a rich Alderman is no contemptible Employment.

Puff. Ay, if it were a *Sine-cure.*

Carm. No, that you muſt not expect ; but unleſs I am greatly miſtaken in the Language of the Eyes, her Ladyſhip's were addreſs'd to you with moſt perſuaſive Tenderneſs.

Puff. Well, of that hereafter————But to our Buſineſs.   The Auction is about beginning ; and I have promiſed to meet Mr. *David Duſledorpe,* Sir *Poſitive Bubble,* and Lord Dupe, to examine the Pictures, and fix on thoſe for which they are to bid—— But ſince we have ſettled the *German* Plan ; ſo *Varniſh* or *Bruſh* muſt attend them.

Carm. Oh ! by all means purſue that.   You have no Conception how the dear Foreign Accent is to your true Virtuoſo ; it announces Taſte, Knowledge, Veracity, and in ſhort, every Thing—But can you enough diſguiſe the Turn of your Face, and Tone of your Voice ? a Diſcovery of Mr. *Puff* in *Mynheer Groningen* blaſts us at once.

Puff. Never fear me.   I wiſh you may have equal Succeſs in the Part of *Canto.*

Carm.

Carm. Pho! mine's a Trifle. A man muft have very flender Abilities indeed, who can't for ten Minutes imitate a Language and Deportment that he has been Witnefs to for ten Years.

Puff. But you muft get their Tones, their Tones; 'tis eafy enough. Come, hand up here that there *Corregio*; an inimitable Piece. Gentlemen and Ladies: the very beft Work of the beft Mafter, Subject agreeable, highly finifhed, and well pre-ferved;—a Seat for the Ladies;—hand it to Sir *Pofitive*: a going for Fifty: fpeak, or it's gone for Fifty: Joy to your Ladyfhip. Come the next; but remember, let your Bob be bufhy, and your Bow low.

Carm. Enough, enough; we are Strangers to each other, you know.

Puff. Abfolute. Oh! but what Pictures of yours are in the Sale?

Carm. There's my Holy Family by *Raphael*; the Marriage in *Cana* by *Reuben Rouge*; *Tom Jack-fon's Teniers*; and for Bufts, *Taylor's* Head without a Nofe from *Herculaneum.*

Puff. Are the Antique Seals come Home?

Carm. No; but they will be finifh'd by next Week.

Puff. You muft take care of *Novice's* Collection of Medals he'll want them by the End of the Month.

Carm. The Coins of the firft Emperor are now fleeping in Copperas; and I have an *Otho*, a *Galba*, *Nero*, and two *Domitians* reeking from the Dung-hill---The Reft we can have from Doctor *Mummy*; a never failing Chap, you know.

Puff. Adieu

Carm.

Carm. Yours, Sir——a troublefome Fellow, this—confounded Memory-----ufeful, tho'----- Rounds of Beef and roafted Pigs !---muft get rid of him------Ay, but when ?----Why when ?---- when I have gain'd my Point. But how, how then ?---Oh, then it does not fignify Two Pence.

The End of the FIRST ACT.

A C T II.

Enter Puff, *as* Monfieur Baron de Groningen, Carmine *as* Canto, *and* Brufh.

CANTO. COME, buftle, buftle. *Brufh* you introduce *Puff*, *Puff*, how are you in your *German ?*

Puff. I canno fpeak for *Englandt*, but I can mak underftand very mightily. Will that do ?

Brufh. To a Hair. Remember you are come hither to purchafe Pictures for the Elector of *Bavaria*. *Carmine*, you muft clap Lord *Dupe's* Coat of Arms on that Half Length of *Erafmus*; I have fold it him, as his Great Grandfather's third Brother, for Fifty Guineas.

Canto. It fhall be done---Be it my Province to eftablifh the Baron's Reputation as a Connoiffeur.--

Brufh

Brush has seen you Abroad at the Court of the reigning Prince of *Blantin*.

Puff. Yes; I was do Bufinefs mightily for Prince *Blantin*.

Brush. Your Portraits go firft, *Carmine, Novice,* Sir *Pofitive Bubble, Jack Squander,* Lord *Dupe,* and *Mordecai Lazarus,* the *Jew* Broker, have appointed me to examine with them the Hiftory Pieces.---Which are moft likely to ftick?

Canto. Here's a Lift.

Brush. Hufh, hide the *Erafmus,* I hear the Company on the Stairs,

(Exit Carmine, *and re-enters anon.*

Enter Lord Dupe, Bubble, Squander, *&c.*

Lord. Mr. *Brush.* I am your devoted Servant. You have procured my Anceftor.

Brush. It is in my Poffeffion, my Lord; and I have the Honor to affure your Lordfhip, that the Family Features are very difcernable; and allowing for the Difference of Drefs, there's a ftrong likenefs between you and your Predeceffor.

Lord. Sir, you have obliged me. All thefe you have mark'd in the Catalogue are Originals?

Brush. Undoubted. But my Lord, you need not depend folely on my Judgement; here's Mynheer Baron *de Groningen,* who is come hither to furvey, and purchafe for the Eleftor of *Bavaria;* an indifputable Connoiffeur; his Bidding will be a Direftion for your Lordfhip. 'Tis a Thoufand Pities that any of thefe Mafters fhould quit *England.* They were condufted hither at an immenfe Expence. and if they now leave us, what will it be but a
public

public Declaration, that all Taste and liberal knowledge is vanish'd from amongst us?

Lord. Sir---leave the Support of the National Credit to my Care. Could you introduce me to Mynhéer?---Does he speak *English?*

Brush. Not fluently, but so as to he understood. Mynheer, Lord *Dupe*—the Patron of Arts, the *Petronius* for Taste, and for well-timed Generosity, the *Leo*—and the *Mecænas*—of the present Age, desires to know you.

Puff. Sir, you honour me very mightily. I was hear of Lord *Dupes* in *Hollandt*. I was tell he was one Delatant, one Curieuse, one Precieuse of his Country.

Lord. The *Dutch* are an obliging, civilized, well-bred, pretty Kind of People. But, pray Sir, what occasions us the Honour of a Visit from you?

Puff. I was come to bid for Paints for de Elector of *Bavaria.*

Lord. Are there any here that deserve your Attention?

Puff. O! dare are good Pieces; but dare is one I likes mightily; the off Sky, and Home Track is fine, and the Maister is in it.

Lord. What is the Subject?

Puff. Dat I know not; vat I minds, vat you call the Draws and the Colors.

Lord. Mr. *Canto,* what is the Subject?

Canto. It is, my Lord St. *Anthony* of *Padua* exercising the Devil out of a Ram-cat; it has a Companion somewhere---Oh! here, which is the same Saint in a Wilderness, reading his Breviary by the Light of a Glow-worm.

Brush.

Brush. Invaluable Pictures, both ! and will match your Lordship's *Corregio* in the Saloon.

Lord. I'll have them. What Pictures are those, Mr. *Canto ?*

Canto. They are not in the Sale ; but I fancy I could procure them for your Lordship.

Lord. This, I presume, might have been a Landskip ; but the Water, and the Men, and the Trees, and the Dogs, and the Ducks, and the Pigs, they are obliterated, all gone.

Brush. An indisputable Mark of its Antiquity ; its very Merit ; besides a little Varnish will fetch the Figures again.

Lord. Set it down for me—The next.

Canto. That is a *Moses* in the Bulrushes. The blended Joy and Grief in the Figure of the Sister in the Corner, the Distress and Anxiety of the Mother here, and the Beauty and Benevolence of *Pharoah's* Daughter, are Circumstances happily imagined, and boldly exprefs'd.

Brush. Lack-a-day, 'tis but a modern Performance ; the master is alive, and an *Englishman*.

Lord. Oh ! then I would not give it House-room.

Puff. Here is a pretty Piece I find stick up here in de Corner : I was see in *Hollandt*, at *Loo*, a Piece mighty like ; there was little Mices, that was nibble, nibble, nibble, upon vat you call Frumage, and little Shureis all with Brush tails ran up the trees ; and there was great things vat you call—Pshaw, that have long Bearts, and cry Ba.

Brush. What Goats ;

Puff. Ay, dat was de name.

Lord. I should think, by the Cheese and the Goats, Mynheer, yours was a *Welch* Piece, instead of a *Dutch*. *Puff.*

Puff. Ah, 'twas good Piece.   I wifh to my Heart
Lord *Dupes* was have that Piece.

Enter Novice.

Novice. Where's Mr. *Brufh?*   My dear *Brufh,*
am I too late ?

Brufh. In pretty good Time.

Nov. May I lofe my *Otho,* or be tumbled from
my Phaëton the firft Time I jehup my Sorrels, if
I have not made more Hafte than a young Surgeon
to his firft Labour.   But the Lots, the Lots, my
dear *Brufh,* what are they ? I'm upon the Rack of
Impatience till I fee them, and in a Fever of Defire till I poffefs them.

Brufh. Mr. *Canto,* the Gentleman would be glad
to fee the Bufts, Medals, and precious Reliques of
Greece and ancient *Rome.*

Canto. Perhaps, Sir, we may fhow him fom
thing of greater Antiquity—Bring them forward
The firft Lot confifts of a Hand without an Arm,
the firft joint of the Fore-Finger gone, fuppofed to
be a Limb of the *Apollo Delphos*—The fecond,
Half a Foot, with the Toes entire, of the *Juno
Lucina*—The third, the *Caduceus* of the *Mercurius
Infernalis*—The fourth, the Half of the Leg of
the Infant *Hercules*—all indifputable Antiques, and
of the *Memphian* Marble.

Puff. Let me fee *Juno's* Half Foot.   All the
Toes entire ?

Canton. All.

Puff. Here is a little Swelt by this Toe, that
looks bad Proportion.

All. Hey, hey.

Puff.

Puff. What's dat?

Canto. That! Pſhaw! that! Why that's only a Corn.

All. Oh!

Puff. Corn! dat was extreme natural; dat is fine; the Maiſter is in it.

All. Very fine! Invaluable!

Puff. Where is de *Hercules*' Calf? Upon my Word 'tis a very large Calf; big, big, big, all de Way up, all de Way down.

Lord. believe this *Hercules* was an *Iriſh* Man.

Nov. But where are your Buſts? Here, here; Gentlemen; here's a Curioſity; a Medal of *Oriuna,* got for me by Doctor *Mummy*; the only one in the viſible World; there may be ſome under Ground!

Lord. Fine, indeed! Will you permit me to taſte it? It has the Reliſh.   *(All taſte.*

Nov. The Reliſh! 'Zooks it coſt me a hundred Guineas.

Puff. By Gar, it is a dear Bit tho'.

Nov. So you may think; but three Times the Money ſhould not purchaſe it.

Lord. Pray, Sir, whoſe Buſt is it that dignifies this Coin?

Nov. The Empreſs *Oriuna,* my Lord.

Lord. And who, Sir, might ſhe be? I don't re-collect to have heard of the Lady before.

Nov. She, my Lord? Oh! ſhe was a kind of a What-dy'e-call'em—a Sort of a Queen, or Wife, or ſomething or other to ſomebody, that liv'd a damn'd while ago—*Mummy* told me the whole Story; but before Gad, I've forgot it. But come, the Buſts.

Canto.

Canto. Bring forward the Head from *Herculaneum.* Now Gentlemen, here is a Jewel.

All. Ay, ay, let's fee.

Canto. 'Tis not entire, tho'.

Nov. So much the better.

Canto. Right, Sir—the very Mutilations of this Piece are worth all the moſt perfect Performances of modern Artiſts—Now, Gentlemen, here's a Touchſtone for your Taſte !

All. Great! great, indeed !

Nov. Great! Amazing! Divine! Oh, let me embrace the dear diſmember'd Buſt! a little farther off. I'm raviſhed! I am tranſported! What an Attitude! But then the Locks! How I adore the Simplicity of the Antients! How unlike, the preſent priggiſh, prick-ear'd Puppets! How gracefully they fall all adown the Cheek ! ſo decent, and ſo grave, and—Who the Devil do you think it is, *Bruſh ?* Is it a Man or a Woman ?

Canto. The Connoiſſeurs differ. Some will have it to be the *Jupiter Tonans* of *Phidias,* and others the *Venus* of *Paphos* from *Praxiteles* ; but I don't think it fierce enough for the firſt, nor handſome enough for the laſt.

Nov. Yes, handſome enough.

All. Very handſome ; handſome enough.

Canto. Not quite—therefore I am inclined to join with Signor *Julio de Pampedillo,* who, in a Treatiſe dedicated to the King of the *Two Sicilies,* calls it the *Serapis* of the *Ægyptians,* and ſuppoſes it to have been fabricated about Eleven Hundred and Three Years before the Mosaic Account of the Creation.

Nov. Prodigious ! and I dare ſwear true.

All.

All. Oh, true, very true.

Puff. Upon my Honour, 'tis a very fine Buſt; But where is de Noſe?

Nov. The Noſe, what care I for the Noſe; Where is de Noſe? Why, Sir, if it had a Noſe I would not give Sixpence for it—How the Devil ſhould we diſtinguiſh the Works of the Antients, if they were perfect?——The Noſe, indeed! Why I don't ſuppoſe now, but, barring the Noſe, *Roubiliac* could cut as good a Head every Whit—— *Bruſh*, who is this man with his Noſe? The Fellow ſhould know ſomething of ſomething too, for he ſpeaks broken *Engliſh.*

Bruſh. It is Mynheer *Groningen*, a great Connoiſſeur in Painting.

Nov. That may be, but as to Sculpture, I am his very humble Servant. A Man muſt know damn'd little of Statuary, that diſlikes a Buſt for want of a Noſe.

Canto. Right, Sir—The Noſe itſelf without the Head, nay, in another's Poſſeſſion, would be an Eſtate—But here are behind Gentlemen and Ladies, an Equeſtrian Statue of *Marcus Aurelus* without the Horſe; and a complete Statue of the Emperor *Trajan*, with only the Head and Legs miſſing; both from *Herculaneum.*——This Way, Gentlemen and Ladies.

Enter Lady Pentweazel, Alderman, *and* Caleb.

Lady. Now, Mr. *Pentweazel*, let us have none of your *Blowbladder* Breeding. Remember you are at the Court end of the Town. This is a Quality Auction.

Ald. Where ot Courſe nothing is ſold that is uſeful——I am tutor'd, ſweet Honey.

Lady.

Lady. *Caleb*, keep behind, and don't be medling.   Sir——   (*To Brush.*

Brush. Your Pleafure, Ma'am.

Lady. I fhould be glad you would inform me if there are any Lots of very fine old China.   I find the Quality are grown infinitely fond of it; and I am willing to fhow the World, that we in the City have Tafte.

Brush. 'Tis a laudable Refolution, Ma'am, and, I dare fay, Mr. *Canto* can fupport——Blefs me what's that?   (Caleb *throws down a china Difh.*

Lady. That Boy, I fuppofe! Well, if the mifchievous Brat has not broke a——and look how he ftands——Sirrah, Sirrah, did I not bid you not meddle?——Leave fucking your Thumbs.   What, I fuppofe you learnt that Trick of your Friend the Monkey in the Waggon?

Caleb. Indeed I did not go to do it, Mother.

Ald. Pr'ythee, fweet Honey, don't be fo paffionate.   What's done can't be undone.   The Lofs is not great; come, come.

Brush. Mr. Alderman is in the Right. The Affair is a Trifle, but a Twenty Guinea Job.

Lady. Twenty Guineas! You fhould have twenty of my Teeth as——

Canto. You mean if you had them——Your Ladyfhip does not know the Value of that Piece of China. It is the right old Japan of the Peagreen Kind. Lady *Mandarin* offer'd me, if I could match it, Fourfcore Guineas for the Pair.

Lady. A fine Piece, indeed!

Puff. 'Tis ver fine.

Caleb. Indeed, Father, I did not break it. 'Twas crack'd in the Middle, and fo fell a two in my Hand.

Puff. Hands off. If I muft fuffer, it fhall not be fingly. Here is the obfequious Mr. *Brufh,* and the very courtly Mr. *Canto,* fhall be the Partners of my Diftrefs. Know then, we all are Rogues, if the taking Advantage of the Abfurdities and Follies of Mankind can be call'd Roguery. I own I have been a Cheat, and I glory in it. But what Point will you Virtuofi, you Connoiffeurs, gain by the Detection ? Will not the publifhing of our Crimes trumpet forth your Folly ?

Lord. Matchlefs Impudence !

Puff, My noble Lord here the *Dilettanti,* the *Curieu,* the *Precieu* of this Nation, what Infinite Glory will he acquire from this Story, that the *Leo,* the *Mecænas,* the *Petronius,* notwithftanding his exquifite Tafte, has been drawn in to purchafe, at an immenfe Expence, a Cart-load of—Rubbifh !

Lord. Gentlemen and Ladies—I have the Honour to take my leave.

Puff. Your Lordfhip's moft obedient—When fhall I fend your *Corregio;* your St. *Anthony* of *Padua,* your *Ram Cat,* my good Lord ?

Lord. Rafcal ! *(Exit.*

Nov. This won't do, Sir.—Tho, my Lord has not Spirit enough. damn me if I quit you.

Puff. What, my fprightly Squire ! Pray favour me with a Sight of your *Oriuna.*—It has the Relifh; an Indifputable Antique ; being a *Briftol* Fathing, coin'd by a Soap-boiler to pay his Journeymen in the Scarcity of Cafh, and purchafed for Two-pence of a travelling Tinker by, Sir, your humble Servant, *Timothy Puff.* Ha, ha, ha !

Nov. My *Oriuna* a *Briftol* Farthing !

Puff. Moft affuredly.

Nov.

Nov. I'll be reveng'd   *Going*

Puff. Stay, ftay, and take your Buft, my fweet Squire; your *Serapis*. Two Heads, they fay, are better than one; lay them together. But the Locks! how gracefully they fall all adown! fo decent, and fo—ha, ha, ha!

Nov. Confound you!

Puff. Why, Sir, if it had a Nofe, I would not give Sixpence for it—Pray, how many Years before the Creation was it fabricated, Squire?

Nov. I fhall live to fee you hang'd, you Dog.

                              (Exit.

Puff. Nay, but, Squire; ha, ha, ha!——Now, Madam, to your Ladyfhip I come; to whofe Difcernment, aided by the Sagacity of your Son *Caleb*, I owe my Difcovery.

Ald. Look you, don't think to abufe my Lady, I am one of the——

Puff. Quorum—I know it, Mr. Alderman; but I mean to ferve your Worfhip by humbling a little the Vanity of your Wife.

Lady. Come along, Chuck. I'll not ftay to hear the rafcality of the Fellow.

Puff Oh, my Lady *Pentweazle*, correct the Severity of that Frown, left you fhould have more of the *Medufa* than the *Medicis* in your Face.

Lady. Saucy Jackanapes!

Puff. What, then, I have quite loft my City Acquaintance; why, I've promifed all my Friends Tickets for my Lord Mayor's Ball, through your Ladyfhip's Intereft.

Lady. My intereft, indeed, for fuch a—

Puff. If *Blowbladder-ftreet* has any Charms— Sir—Ma'am—Not a ftep—The fineft Gentleman! ha, ha,

ha, ha, ha!—And what can you say for yourself,
you cowardly ill-looking Rascal? (*to* Canto.)
Desert your Friend at the first Pinch—-your Ally
—-your Partner—-No Apology, Sir—I have done
with you. From Poverty and Shame I took you; to
that I restore you. Your Crime be your Punishment. (*Turning to the Audience.*)
Could I be as secure from the Censure of this Assembly as I am safe from the Resentment of *Dupe*,
Novice, *Squander*; from the alluring Baits of my
amorous City Lady; and the dangerous Combination of my false Friend I should be happy.

'Tis from your Sentence I expect my Fate;
Your Voice alone my Triumph can complete.

F I N I S.

THE

ENGLISHMAN IN PARIS.

A

COMEDY,

IN TWO ACTS,

AS IT IS PERFORMED AT THE

THEATRE-ROYAL IN DRURY-LANE.

WRITTEN BY

SAMUEL FOOTE, Esq.

LONDON :
PRINTED FOR W. LOWNDES, 38, BEDFORD STREET.

1808.

MY Bookseller informs me, that the bulk of his Readers, regarding in a work of this kind the Quantity more than the Quality, will not be contented without an additional half-sheet ; and he apprehends that a short Dedication will answer the purpose.

But as I have no obligations to any great man or woman in this country, and as I will take care that no production of mine shall want their patronage, I don't know any person whose good offices I so much stood in need of as my Bookseller's : Therefore, Mr. VAILLANT, I think myself obliged to you for the correctness of the Press, the beauty of the Type, and the goodness of the Paper, with which you have decorated this work of

Your humble Servant,

SAM. FOOTE.

Pall-Mall, April 21, 1753.

PROLOGUE,

BETWEEN

Mr. MACKLIN and his WIFE.

———————

She.

TO contradict me!—Blockhead! Ideot! Fool! Sot!

 He. But amidft thefe hard names, our dispute is forgot,
To contradict you I know is high-treason;
For the will of a wife is always her reason.

 She. No, sir, for once, I'll give up my pretension,
And submit to the Pit our cause of dissention.

 He. I agree; for the Pit is our natural lord.
LADIES, ———————   ———————

 She. —Hey! How come you to claim the first word?
GENTLEMEN, my husband and I have had a difpute,
Where the difference lies 'twixt a man and a brute;
Which we beg, whilst the folks for the farce are preparing,
You would please to decide, and give us the hearing.
—Hem! Hem!—

After Plutarch of Rome! and Virgil of Greece!
And Iliads, and Eniends, and authors like thefe;
I boldly affirm, deny it who can,
That in laughter confists the true essence of man:
Whilst my husband—

 He. ——— Nay, pray let me state my own case, ⎫
And I'll make it as clear as the nose in your face, ⎬
That hissing in man preserves the first place.   ⎭
To begin then with Critics:—'Tis their capital bliss,
Than to laugh—don't you find it more pleafing to hiss?
In this all agree;—Jews! Infidels! Turks!

 She. I grant it, sweet sir,—if you mean at your works.

Yet even 'gainst that I've a potent objection;
For every rule still has its exception:
Tho' they hiss'd at your farces, your Pasquin, and stuff,
At your Tragedy sure they laugh'd hearty enough.
And again, Mr. Wiseman, regard the world round,
'Tis in mankind alone that laughter is found;
Whilst your favourite hissing, sage sir, if you please,
You enjoy but in common with serpents and geese.

She. And arn't you ashamed—('tis no time to dissemble,)
O Critics! these creatures in this to resemble?

He. Not a jot; in this place 'tis of singular use,
Of bad poets and players to reform the abuse.
In the practice, kind sirs! were I fit to advise,
The hissing like geese I would have you despise,
And copy the serpent,——be subtle and wise,
But free from his venom.——Well, sirs! what d'ye say?
Is your judgment——

She. —————— Let us wait 'till the end of the play:
In the progress of that we shall easily find,
Whether laughing or hissing is most to their mind.

He. I'm sure they will hiss.

She. And I hope they'll be kind.

DRAMATIS PERSONÆ.

BUCK,	Mr. Palmer.
SIR JOHN BUCK,	Mr. Wrighten.
SUBTLE,	Mr. Waldron.
CLASSIC,	Mr. Packer.
MARQUIS,	Mr. Lamash.
DANCING-MASTER,	Mr. R. Palmer.
ROGER,	Mr. Griffith.
MRS. SUBTLE,	Mrs. Love.
LUCINDA,	Miss Collet.

Servants, &c.

ENGLISHMAN IN PARIS.

—

ACT I.   SCENE I.

Enter Mr. Subtle and Mr. Classic.

Mr. Subtle.

WELL, well, that may be; but still I say that a Frenchman——

Classic. Is a fop; it is their national disease; not one of the qualities for which you celebrate them, but owes its origin to a foible; their taste is trifling, their gaiety grimace, and their politeness pride.

Mr. Sub. Hey-dey! Why what the duce brings you to Paris then?

Class. A debt to Friendship; not but I think a short residence here a very necessary part in every man of fashion's education.

Mr. Sub. Where's the use?

Class. In giving them a true relish for their own domestic happiness, a proper veneration for their national liberties; a contempt for adulation; and an honour for the extended, generous commerce of their country.

Mr. Sub. Why there, indeed, you have the preference, master Classic; the traders here are a sharp set; cozening people; foreigners are their food; civilities with a—Aye! aye! a congee for a crown, and a shrug for a shilling; devilish dear, master Classic, devilish dear.

Class. To avoid their exactions, we are, Mr.
Subtle, recommended to your protection.

Mr. Sub. Aye! and wisely they did who recommended you: buy nothing but on mine or my
lady's recommendation, and you are safe. But
where was your charge? Where was Mr. Buck last
night? My lady made a party at cards on purpose
for him, and my ward Lucinda is mightily taken
with him; she longs to see him again.

Class. I am afraid with the same set his father
sent him hither to avoid; but we must endeavour to
inspire him with a taste for the gallantries of this
court, and his passion for the lower amusements of
ours will diminish of course.

Mr. Sub. All the fraternity of men-makers are
for that purpose without; taylors, peruquiers,
hatters, hosiers——Is not that Mr. Buck's English
servant?

Enter Roger.

Class. Oh! aye, honest Roger. So, the old
doings, Roger; what time did your master come
home?

Rog. Between five and six, pummell'd to a jelly:
Here been two of his old comrades follow'd un already; I count we shall ha' the whole gang in a
se'nnight.

Class. Comrades, who?

Rog. Dick Daylight and Bob Breadbasket the
bruisers: They all went to the shew together,
where they had the devil to pay; belike they had
been sent to Bridewell, hadn't a great gentleman
in a blue string come by and releas'd them.—I
hear master's bell; do, master Classic, step up and
talk to'un; he's now sober, and may hearken to
reason.

Class. I attend him. Mr. Subtle, you won't be
out of the way.

Mr. Sub. I shall talk a little with the trades-

men. A smoaky fellow this Classic; but if Lucinda plays her cards well, we have not much to fear
from that quarter: contradiction seems to be the
life and soul of young Buck.—A tolerable expedition this, if it succeeds — Fleece the Younker!—
Pshaw, that's a thing of course!——but by his
means to get rid of Lucinda, and securely pocket
her patrimony;——aye! that indeed——

Enter Mrs. Subtle.

Oh! wife! Have you open'd the plot? Does the
girl come into it greedily, hey?

Mrs. Sub. A little squeamish at first; but I
have opened her eyes. Never fear, my dear, sooner
or later women will attend to their interest.

Mr. Sub. Their interest! aye, that's true; but
consider, my dear, how deeply our own interest is
concern'd, and let that quicken your zeal.

Mrs. Sub. D'ye think I am blind? But the girl
has got such whimsical notions of honour, and is
withal so decent and modest: I wonder where the
duce she got it; I am sure it was not in my house.

Mr. Sub. How does she like Buck's person.

Mrs. Sub. Well enough! But prythee, husband,
leave her to my management, and consider we
have more irons in the fire than one. Here is the
Marquis de Soleil to meet Madam de Farde to-
night,——and where to put 'em, unless we can
have Buck's apartment—Oh! by the bye, has
Count Cog sent you your share out of Mr. Punt-
well's losings a Thursday?

Mr. Sub. I intend calling on him this morning.

Mrs. Sub. Don't rail! He's a slippery chap you
know.

Mr. Sub. There's no fear. Well, but our
pretty countrywoman lays about her handsomely!
Ha!——Hearts by hundreds! Hum!

Mrs. Sub. Aye! that's a noble prize, if we could
but manage her; but fhe's so indiscreet, that fhe'll

be blown before we have made half our market. **I**
am this morning to give audience on her score, to
two counts and a foreign minifter.

Mr. Sub. Then ftrike whilft the iron's hot: but
they'll be here before I can talk to my people ; fend
'em in prythee.

Enter Tradesmen.

Mr. Sub. So, gentlemen ; Oh ! hufh ! we are
interrupted : if they afk for your bills, you have left
them at home.

Enter Buck, Classic, and Roger.

Buck. Ecod, I don't know how it ended, but I
remember how it begun. Oh ! master *Subtle*, how
do'st, old buck, hey? Give's thy paw! And little
Lucy, how fares it with she? Hum !

Mr. Sub. What has been the matter, squire ?
Your face seems a little in deshabille.

Buck. A touch of the times, old boy! a small
skirmish ; after I was down tho', a set of cowardly
sons of — ; there's George and I will box any five
for their sum.

Mr. Sub. But how happen'd it ? The French
are generally civil to strangers.

Buck. Oh! damn'd civil! to fall seven or eight
upon three : seven or eight ! Ecod we had the whole
house upon us at last.

Mr. Sub. But what had you done ?

Buck. Done ! Why nothing at all ! But wounds !
how the powder flew about, and the monsieurs
scour'd.

Mr. Sub. But what offence had either they or
you committed ?

Buck. Why I was telling domine last night ;
Dick Daylight, Bob Breadbasket, and I, were
walking through one of their *rues* I think they call
them here, they are streets in London ; but they
have such devilish out-of-the-way names for things,

that there is no remembering them : so we see
crowds of people going into a house, and Comedy
pasted over the door ; in we troop'd with the rest,
pay'd our cash, and sat down on the stage : presently they had a dance ; and one of the young women
with long hair trailing behind her, stood with her
back to a rail just by me : ecod what does me ! for
nothing in the world but a joke, as I hope for
mercy, but ties her locks to the rail ; so when 'twas
her turn to figure out, souse she flapp'd on her back ;
'twas devilish comical, but they set up such an uproar, one whey-fac'd son of a bitch, that came to
loose the woman, turn'd up his nose, and call'd me
bête ; ecod, I lent him a lick in his lanthorn jaws,
that will make him remember the spawn of old
Marlborough, I warrant him. Another came up to
second him, but I let drive at the mark, made the
soup-maigre rumble in his bread-basket, and laid
him sprawling. Then in pour'd a million of them ;
I was knock'd down in a trice ; and what happen'd
after I know no more than you. But where's Lucy ?
I'll go see her.

Class. Oh fie ! Ladies are treated here with a
little more ceremony : Mr. Subtle too has collected
these people, who are to equip you for the conversation of the ladies.

Buck. Wounds ! all these ! What, Mr. Subtle,
these are Mounseeres too I suppose ?

Mr. Sub. No ! squire, they are English-men.
Fashion has ordain'd, that as you employ none but
foreigners at home, you must take up with your
own countrymen here.

Class. It is not in this instance alone we are particular, Mr. Subtle ; I have observ'd many of our
pretty gentlemen, who condescend to use entirely
their native language here, sputter nothing but bad
French in the side-boxes at home.

Buck. Look you, sir, as to you, and your wife,
and miss Lucy, I like you all well enough ; but the

devil a good thing else have I seen since I lost sight
of Dover; the men are all puppies, mincing and
dancing, and chattering, and grinning; the women
a parcel of painted dolls: their food's fit for hogs;
and as for their language, let them learn it that like
it, I'll none on't; no, nor their frippery neither: so
here you may all march to the place from whence
you—Harkee! What are you an Englishman?

Barber. Yes, sir.

Buck. Domine! look here, what a monster the
monkey has made of himself! Sirrah, if your string
was long enough, I'd do your business myself, you
dog, to sink a bold Briton into such a sneaking, snivelling—the rascal looks as if he had not had a piece
of beef and pudding in his paunch these twenty
years; I'll be hang'd if the rogue ha'nt been fed
upon frogs ever since he came over. Away with
your trumpery!

Class. Mr. Buck, a compliance with the customs
of the country in which we live, where neither our
religion or morals are concern'd, is a duty we owe
ourselves.

Mr. Sub. Besides, squire, Lucinda expects that
you should usher her to public places, which it
would be impossible to do in that dress.

Buck. Why not?

Mr. Sub. You'd be mobb'd.

Buck. Mobb'd! I should be glad to see that—
No! no! they ha'nt spirit enough to mob here;
but come, since these fellows here are English, and
it is the fashion, try on your fooleries.

Mr. Sub. Mr. Dauphine, come produce —Upon
my word, in an elegant taste, sir: this gentleman
has had the honour—

Dauph. To work for all the beaux esprits of the
court. My good fortune commenc'd by a small alteration in a cut of the corner of the sleeve for count
Crib; but the addition of a ninth plait in the skirt
of marshal Tonerre, was applauded by madam la

duchess Rambouillet, and totally establish'd the reputation of your humble servant.

Buck. Hold your jaw and dispatch.

Mr. Sub. A word with you—I don't think it impossible to get you acquainted with madam de
Rambouillet.

Buck. An't she a papist?

Mr. Sub. Undoubtedly.

Buck. Then I'll ha' nothing to say to her.

Mr. Sub. Oh! fie! Who minds the religion of a
pretty woman? Besides, all this country are of the
same.

Buck. For that reason I don't care how soon I
get out of it: come, let's get rid of you all as soon
as we can. And what are you, hey?

Barb. Je suis peruquier, monsieur.

Buck. Speak English, you son of a whore.

Barb. I am a periwig-maker, sir.

Buck. Then why could not you say so at first?
What are you asham'd of your mother tongue? I
knew this fellow was a puppy by his pig-tail. Come
let's see your handy work.

Barb. As I found you were in a hurry, I have
brought you, sir, something that will do for the
present: but a peruque is a different *ouvrage*,
another sort of a thing here, from what it is *en Angleterre*; we must consult the colour of the complexion, and the *tour de visage*, the form of the face;
for which end, it will be necessary to regard your
countenance in different lights:—A little to the
right, if you please.

Buck. Why you dog, d'ye think I'll submit to be
exercised by you?

Barb. Oh mon Dieu! monsieur, if you don't, it
will be impossible to make your wig *comme il faut.*

Buck. Sirrah, speak another French word, and
I'll kick you down stairs.

Barb. Gad's curse! Would you resemble some
of your countrymen, who at their first importation

with nine hairs of a side to a brawny pair of cheeks, look like a Saracen's head ! Or else their water-gruel jaws, sunk in a thicket of curls, appear, for all the world, like a lark in a soup-dish !

Mr. Sub. Come Squire, submit ; 'tis but for once.

Buck. Well, what must I do ?

> [*Places him in a chair.*

Barb. To the right, sir ;—now to the left ;—now your full ;—and now, sir, I'll do your business.

Mr. Sub. Look at yourself a little ; see what a revolution this has occasion'd in your whole figure.

Buck. Yes ! a bloody pretty figure indeed ! But 'tis a figure I am damnably asham'd of : I would not be seen by Jack Wildfire or Dick Riot for fifty pounds, in this trim, for all that.

Mr. Sub. Upon my honour, dress greatly im-proves you. Your opinion, Mr. Classic.

Class. They do mighty well, sir ; and in a little time Mr. Buck will be easy in them.

Buck. Shall I ! I am glad on't, for I am damnably uneasy at present, Mr. Subtle. What must I do now ?

Mr. Sub. Now, sir, if you'll call upon my wife, you'll find Lucinda with her, and I'll wait on you presently.

Buck. Come along, domine ! But harkee, Mr. Subtle, I'll out of my tramels, when I hunt with the king.

Mr. Sub. Well ! Well !

Buck. I'll on with my jemmys ; none of your black bags and jack boots for me.

Mr. Sub. No ! No !

Buck. I'll shew them the odds on't ! old Silver-tail ! I will ! Hey !

Mr. Sub. Ay ! ay !

Buck. Hedge, stake, or stile ! over we go !

Mr. Sub. Ay ! but Mr. Classic waits.

Buck. But d'ye think they'll follow ?

Mr. Sub. Oh no! impossible!

Buck. Did I tell you what a chace she carry'd me last Christmas Eve? We unkennell'd at ——

Mr. Sub. I am busy now; at any other time.

Buck. You'll follow us. I have sent for my hounds and horses.

Mr. Sub. Have you?

Buck. They shall make the tour of Europe with me: and then there's Tom Atkins the huntsman, the two whippers-in, and little Joey the groom comes with them. Dammy, what a strange place they'll think this? But no matter for that; then we shall be company enough of ourselves. But you'll follow us in?

Mr. Sub. In ten minutes!—An impertinent jackanapes! But I shall soon ha' done with him. So, gentlemen; well, you see we have a good subject to work upon. Harkee, Dauphine, I must have more than 20 per cent. out of that suit.

Dauph. Upon my soul, Mr. Subtle, I can't.

Mr. Sub. Why I have always that upon new.

Dauph. New! sir! Why as I hope to be—

Mr. Sub. Come, don't lie; don't damn yourself, Dauphine; don't be a rogue; did not I see at madam Fripon's that waistcoat and sleeves upon colonel Crambo?

Dauph. As to the waistcoat and sleeves, I own —but for the body and lining—may I never see—

Mr. Sub. Come, don't be a scoundrel; five and thirty, or I've done.

Dauph. Well, if I must, I must.

Mr. Sub. Oh! Solitaire! I can't pay that draft of Mr. —— these six weeks; I want money.

Soli. Je suis dans le meme cas——Je—

Mr. Sub. What d'ye mutiny, rascal? About your business, or———— [*Exeunt.*
I must keep these fellows under, or I shall have a fine time on't; they know they can't do without me,

Enter Mrs. Subtle.

Mrs. Sub. The Calais letters! my dear.

Mr. Sub. *(reads)* Ah! ah! Calais—the Dover packet arrived last night, loading as follows: six taylors, ditto barbers, five milliners, bound for Paris to study fashions; four citizens come to settle here for a month by way of seeing the country; ditto their wives; ten French valets, with nine cooks, all from Newgate, where they had been sent for robbing their masters; nine figure-dancers, exported in September ragged and lean, imported well clad and in good case: twelve dogs, ditto bitches, with two monkies, and a litter of puppies, from mother Midnight's in the Haymarket: A precious cargo!— *Postscript.* One of the coasters is just put in with his grace the duke of ——, my lord —, and an old gentleman, whose name I can't learn. Gadso! well, my dear, I must run, and try to secure these customers; there's no time to be lost: mean while——

Enter Classic.

So, master Classic; what, have you left the young couple together?

Class. They want your ladyship's presence, madam, for a short tour to the Tuilleries. I have received some letters which I must answer immediately.

Mr. Sub. Oh! Well! Well! no ceremony; we are all of a family you know. Servant.   [*Exit.*

Class. Roger!

Enter Roger.

Rog. Anon!

Class. I have just received a letter from your old master; he was landed at Calais, and will be this evening at Paris. It is absolutely necessary that this circumstance should be conceal'd from his son; for which purpose you must wait at the Piccardy gate, and deliver a letter I shall give you, into his own hand.

Rog. I'll warrant you.

Class. But, Roger, be secret.

Rog. Oh! lud! Never you fear!

Class. So, Mr. Subtle, I see your aim. A pretty lodging we have hit upon ; the mistress a commode, and the master a—But who can this ward be ? Possibly the neglected punk of some riotous man of quality. 'Tis lucky Mr. Buck's father is arriv'd, or my authority would prove but an insufficient match for my pupil's obstinacy. This mad boy! How difficult, how disagreeable a task have I undertaken? And how general, yet how dangerous an experiment is it to expose our youth, in the very fire and fury of their blood, to all the follies and extravagance of this fantastic court ? Far different was the prudent practice of our forefathers:

They scorn'd to truck, for base, unmanly arts,

Their native plainness, and their honest hearts ;

Whene'er they deign'd to visit haughty France,

'Twas arm'd with bearded dart, and pointed lance.

No pompous pageants lur'd their curious eye,

No charms for them had fops or flattery ;

Paris they knew, their Streamers wav'd around,

There Britons saw a British Harry crown'd.

Far other views attract our modern race,

Trulls, toupees, trinkets, bags, brocades, and lace ;

A flaunting form, and a fictitious face.

Rouse! re-assume! refuse a Gallic reign,

Nor let their arts win that their arms could never gain.

END OF THE FIRST ACT.

A C T II.

Enter Mr. Classic and Roger.

Roger.

OLD maister's at a coffee-house next street, and will tarry till you send for 'un.

Class. Bye and bye, in the dusk, bring him up the back stairs.   You must be careful that nobody sees him.

Rog. I warrant you.

Class. Let sir John know, that I would wait on him myself, but I don't think it safe to quit the house an instant.

Rog. Ay, ay.   [*Exit Roger.*

Class. I suppose, by this time, matters are pretty well settled within, and my absence only wanted to accomplish the scene; but I shall take care to ————Oh! Mr. Subtle and his lady.

Enter Mr. and Mrs. Subtle.

Mrs. Sub. Oh! delightfully! Now, my dearest, I hope you will no longer dispute my abilities for forming a female.

Mr. Sub. Never, never : How the baggage leer'd !

Mrs. Sub. And the booby gap'd !

Mr. Sub. So kind, and yet so coy ; so free, but then so reserv'd : Oh! she has him !

Mrs. Sub. Ay! ay! the fish is hook'd; but then safely to land him.——Is Classic suspicious ?

Mr. Sub. Not that I observe ; but the secret must soon be blaz'd.

Mrs. Sub. Therefore dispatch : I have laid a trap to enflame his affection.

Mr. Sub. How ?

Mrs. Sub. He shall be treated with a display of Lucy's talents ; her singing, dancing.

Mr. Sub. Pshaw! her singing and dancing!

Mrs. Sub. Ah! you don't know, husband, half the force of these accomplishments in a fashionable figure.

Mr. Sub. I doubt her execution.

Mrs. Sub. You have no reason; she does both well enough to flatter a fool; especially with love for her second: Besides, I have a coup de maitre, a sure card.

Mr. Sub. What's that?

Mrs. Sub. A rival.

Mr. Sub. Who?

Mrs. Sub. The language-master: He may be easily equipt for the expedition; a second-hand tawdry suit of cloaths will pass him on our countryman for a marquis; and then, to excuse his speaking our language so well, he may have been educated early in England. But hush! the squire approaches; don't seem to observe him.

Enter Buck.

For my part, I never saw any thing so alter'd since I was born: In my conscience, I believe she's in love with him.

Buck. Hush! [*Aside.*]

Mr. Sub. D'ye think so?

Mrs. Sub. Why, where's the wonder? he's a pretty, good-humour'd, sprightly fellow; and, for the time, such an improvement! Why he wears his cloaths as easily, and moves as genteely, as if he had been at Paris these twenty years.

Mr. Sub. Indeed! How does he dance?

Mrs. Sub. Why he has had but three lessons from Marseil, and he moves already like Dupré. Oh! three months stay here will render him a perfect model for the English court.

Mr. Sub. Gadso! No wonder then, with these qualities, that he has caught the heart of my ward;

but we must take care that the girl does nothing imprudent.

Mrs. Sub.   Oh! dismiss your fears; her family, good sense, and more than all, her being educated under my eye, render them unnecessary: Besides, Mr. Buck is too much a man of honour to———

[*He interrupts them.*]

Buck.   Damn me, if I an't.

Mrs. Sub.   Bless me! sir! you here! I did not expect———

Buck.   I beg pardon; but all that I heard was, that Mr. Buck was a man of honour.   I wanted to have some chat with you, madam, in private.

Mr. Sub.   Then I'll withdraw.   You see I dare trust you alone with my wife.

Buck.   So you may safely; I have other game in view.   Servant, Mr. Subtle.

Mrs. Sub.   Now for a puzzling scene; I long to know how he'll begin.   Well, Mr. Buck, your commands with me, Sir.

Buck.   Why, madam,—I ah—I ah——but let's shut the door: I was, madam,——ah! ah! Can't you guess what I want to talk about.

Mrs. Sub.   Not I, indeed, Sir.

Buck.   Well, but try; upon my soul I'll tell you if you're right.

Mrs. Sub.   It will be impossible for me to divine: But come, open a little.

Buck.   Why, have you observed nothing?

Mrs. Sub.   About who?

Buck.   Why, about me!

Mrs. Sub.   Yes; you are new dress'd, and your cloaths become you.

Buck.   Yes! Pretty well; but it an't that.

Mrs. Sub.   What is it?

Buck.   Why, ah! ah!——Upon my soul, I can't bring it out.

Mrs. Sub.   Nay, then it's to no purpose to wait; Write your mind.

Buck. No! No! Stop a moment, and I will tell.

Mrs. Sub. Be expeditious, then.

Buck. Why, I wanted to talk about Miss Lu-cinda.

Mrs. Sub. What of her?

Buck. She's a bloody fine girl; and I should be glad to——

Mrs. Sub. To——Bless me! What! Mr. Buck! And in my house! Oh! Mr. Buck, you have deceiv'd me! Little did I think, that, under the appearance of so much honesty, you could go to—— ruin the poor girl.

Buck. Upon my soul you're mistaken.

Mrs. Sub. A poor orphan too! Deprived in her earliest infancy of a father's prudence, and a mother's care.

Buck. Why I tell you——

Mrs. Sub. So sweet, so lovely an innocence; her mind as spotless as her person.

Buck. Hey-day!

Mrs. Sub. And me, Sir! Where had you your thoughts of me? How dar'd you suppose that I would connive at such a—

Buck. The woman's bewitch'd!

Mrs. Sub. I! whose untainted reputation the blistering tongue of slander never blasted. Full fifteen years, in wedlock's sacred bands, have I liv'd unreproached; and now to ——

Buck. Odds fury! She's in heroics!

Mrs. Sub. And this from you too, whose fair outside and bewitching tongue had so far lull'd my fears, I dar'd have trusted all my daughters, nay, myself too, singly, with you.

Buck. Upon my soul! and so you might safely.

Mrs. Sub. Well, sir, and what have you to urge in your defence?

Buck. Oh! oh! What you are got pretty wel to the end of your line, are you? And now, if you'l be quiet a bit, we may make a shift to understand one another a little.

Mrs. Sub. Be quick, and ease me of my fears.

Buck. Ease you of your fears! I don't know how the devil you got them. All that I wanted to say was, that Miss Lucy was a fine wench; and if she was as willing as me, ——

Mrs. Sub. Willing! Sir! What demon ——

Buck. If you are in your airs again, I may as well decamp.

Mrs. Sub. I am calm; go on.

Buck. Why that if she lik'd me, as well as I lik'd her, we might, perhaps, if you lik'd it too, be married together.

Mrs. Sub. Oh! Sir! if that was indeed your drift, I am satisfy'd. But don't indulge your wish too much; there are numerous obstacles; your father's consent, the law of the land, ——

Buck. What laws?

Mrs. Sub. All clandestine marriages are void in this country.

Buck. Damn the country: In London now a footman may drive to May-Fair, and in five minutes be tack'd to a countess; but there's no liberty here.

Mrs. Sub. Some inconsiderate couples have indeed gone off post to protestant states; but I hope my ward will have more prudence.

Buck. Well, well, leave that to me. D'ye think she likes me?

Mrs. Sub. Why, to deal candidly with you, she does.

Buck. Does she, by ——

Mrs. Sub. Calm your transports.

Buck. Well! But how? She did not, did she! Hey! Come now, tell ——

Mrs. Sub. I hear her coming; this is her hour for music and dancing.

Buck. Could I not have a peep?

Mrs. Sub. Withdraw to this corner.

Enter Lucinda, with Singing and Dancing-Masters.

Luc. The news, the news, monsieur Gamut; I die, if I have not the first intelligence! What's doing at Versailles? When goes the court to Marli? Does Rameau write the next opera? What say the critics of Voltaire's Duc de Foix? Answer me all in a breath!

Buck. A brave-spirited girl! She'll take a five-barr'd gate in a fortnight!

Gamut. The conversation of the court your lady-ship has engross'd, ever since you last honour'd it with your appearance.

Luc. Oh! you flatterer! have I! Well and what fresh victims? But 'tis impossible; the sun-shine of a northern beauty is too feeble to thaw the icy heart of a French courtier.

Gam. What injustice to your own charms and our discernment!

Luc. Indeed! nay, I care not; if I have fire enough to warm one British bosom, rule! rule! ye Paris belles! I envy not your conquests.

Mrs. Sub. Meaning you.

Buck. Indeed!

Mrs. Sub. Certain!

Buck. Hush!

Luc. But come, a truce to gallantry, Gamut, and to the business of the day: Oh! I am quite enchanted with this new instrument; 'tis so lan-guishing and so portable, and so soft and so silly: But come, for your last lesson.

Gam. D'ye like the words?

Luc. Oh! charming! They are so melting, and easy, and elegant. Now for a coup d' essai.

Gam. Take care of your expression; let your eyes and address accompany the sound and sen-timent.

Luc. But, dear Gamut, if I am out, don't interrupt me ; correct me afterwards.

Gam. Allons, commencés.

SONG.

I.

PAR un matin Lisette se leva,
Et dans un bois seulette s'en alla.

Ta, la, la.

II.

Elle cherchoit des nids de ça de la,
Dans un buisson le rossignol chanta.

Ta, la, la.

III.

Tout doucement elle s'en approcha,
Savez vous bien, ce qu'elle denicha.

Ta, la, la.

IV.

C'étoit l'Amour, l'Amour l'attendoit la,
Le bel oiseau dit elle que voila.

Ta, la, la.

V.

La pauvre enfant le prit, le caressa,
Sous son mouchoir en riant le plaça.

Ta, la, la.

VI.

Son petit cœur aussitot s'enflama,
Elle gemit, et ne sçait ce quelle a.

Ta, la, la.

VII.

Elle s' en va se plaindre à son papa,
En lui parlant la belle soupira.

Ta, la, la.

VIII.

Le bon papa qui s'en doutoit deja,
Lui dit je sçais un remede à cela.

Ta, la, la.

IX.

Il prit l'Amour, les ailes lui coupa,
D'un double noeud fertement le lia,

Ta, la, la.

X.

Dans la voliere aussitot l'enferma,
Chantez Fripon autant qu'il vous plaira.

Ta, la, la.

XI.

Heureusement la belle s'en tira,
Mais on n'a pas toujours ce secret la.

Ta, la, la.

XII.

Jeune beauté que l'Amour guetera,
Craignez le tour qu' à Lissette il joua.

Ta, la, la.

Gam. Bravo ! Bravo !

Buck. Bravo ! Bravissimo ! My lady, what was the song about ?   [*Aside to my lady.*

Mrs. Sub. Love : 'Tis her own composing.

Buck. What, does she make verses then ?

Mrs. Sub. Finely. I take you to be the subject of these.

Buck. Ah ! D'ye think so ? Gad ! I thought by her ogling 'twas the music-man himself.

Luc. Well, Mr. Gamut ; tolerably well, for so young a scholar.

Gam. Inimitably, madam ! Your ladyship's progress will undoubtedly fix my fortune.

Enter Servant.

Luc. Your servant, sir.

Ser. Madam, your dancing-master, monsieur Kitteau.

Luc. Admit him.

Enter Kitteau.

Monsieur Kitteau, I can't possibly take lesson this

morning, I am so busy ; but if you please, I'll just hobble over a minuet by way of exercise.

Enter a Servant.   *[After the Dance.*

Ser. Monsieur le marquis de ———

Luc. Admit him this instant.

Mrs. Sub. A lover of Lucinda, a Frenchman of fashion, and vast fortune.

Buck. Never heed ; I'll soon do his business, I'll warrant you.

Enter Marquis.

Luc. My dear marquis!

Marq. Ma chere adorable ! 'Tis an age since I saw you.

Luc. Oh! An eternity! But 'tis your own fault, though.

Marq. My misfortune, *ma princesse!* But now I'll redeem my error, and root for ever here.

Buck. I shall make a shift to transplant you, I believe.

Luc. You can't conceive how your absence has distress'd me. Demand of these gentlemen the melancholy mood of my mind.

Marq. But now that I am arriv'd, we'll dance and sing, and drive care to the — Ha! monsieur Kitteau! have you practis'd this morning?

Luc. I had just given my hand to Kitteau before you came.

Marq. I was in hopes that honour would have been reserved for me. May I flatter myself that your ladyship will do me the honour of venturing upon the fatigue of another minuet this morning with me ?   *[Takes her hand.*

Enter Buck briskly.

Buck. Not that you know of, monsieur.

Marq. Hey! *Diable ! Quelle bête !*

Buck. Harkee, monsieur Ragout, if you repeat

that word *bête*, I shall make you swallow it again, as I did last night one of your countrymen.

Marq. *Quel sauvage!*

Buck. And another word; as I know you can speak very good English, if you will. When you don't, I shall take it for granted you're abusing me, and treat you accordingly.

Marq. Cavalier enough! But you are protected here. Mademoiselle, who is this officious gentleman? How comes he interested? Some relation, I suppose.

Buck. No; I'm a lover.

Marq. Oh! oh! a rival! Eh morbleu! a dangerous one too. Ha! ha! Well, monsieur, what, and I suppose you presume to give laws to this lady; and are determin'd, out of your very great and singular affection, to knock down every mortal she likes, *A-la-mode d'Angleterre*; hey! monsieur Roast-Beef!

Buck. No; but I intend that lady for my wife; consider her as such, and don't chuse to have her soil'd by the impertinent addresses of every French fop, *A-la-mode de Paris*, monsieur Fricassy!

Marq. Fricassy!

Buck. We.

Luc. A truce; a truce, I beseech you, gentlemen: It seems I am the golden prize for which you plead; produce your pretensions; you are the representatives of your respective countries: begin, marquis, for the honour of France; let me hear what advantages I am to derive from a conjugal union with you.

Marq. Abstracted from those which I think are pretty visible; a perpetual residence in this Paradise of pleasures; to be the object of universal adoration; to say what you please, go where you will, do what you like, form fashions, hate your husband, and let him see it; indulge your gallant, and let t'other know it; run in debt, and oblige the

poor devil to pay it. He! ma chere! There are
pleasures for you!

Luc. Bravo! marquis! These are allurements
for a woman of spirit. But don't let us conclude
too hastily; hear the other side: what have you to
offer, Mr. Buck, in favour of England?

Buck. Why, madam, for a woman of spirit,
they give you the same advantages in London as at
Paris, with a privilege forgot by the marquis, an
indisputable right to cheat at cards in spite of detection.

Marq. Pardon me, sir, we have the same; but
I thought this privilege so known and universal,
that 'twas needless to mention it.

Buck. You'll give up nothing, I find; but to
tell you my blunt thoughts in a word, if any woman can be so abandon'd, as to rank amongst the
comforts of matrimony, the privilege of hating her
husband, and the liberty of committing every folly
and every vice contained in your catalogue, she
may stay single for me; for damn me, if I'm a husband fit for her humour; that's all.

Marq. I told you, mademoiselle!

Luc. But stay, what have you to offer as coun-
terbalance for these pleasures?

Buck. Why, I have, madam, courage to protect
you, good nature to indulge your love, and health
enough to make gallants useless, and too good a
fortune to render running in debt necessary. Find
that here if you can.

Marq. Bagatelle!

Luc. Spoke with the sincerity of a Briton; and
as I don't perceive that I shall have any use for the
fashionable liberties you propose, you'll pardon,
marquis, my national prejudice; here's my hand,
Mr. Buck.

Buck. Servant, Monsieur.

Marq. Serviteur!

Buck. No offence!

Marq. Not in the least; I am only afraid the reputation of that lady's taste will suffer a little; and to shew her at once the difference of her choice, the preference, which, if bestowed on me, would not fail to exasperate you, I support without murmuring; so that favour, which would probably have provok'd my fate, is now your protection. *Voila la politesse Françoise,* madam; I have the honour to be——*Bon jour, monsieur.* Tol de rol.

[*Exit Marq.*

Buck. The fellow bears it well. Now if you'll give me your hand, we'll in, and settle matters with Mr. Subtle.

Luc. 'Tis now my duty to obey.

[*Exeunt.*

Enter Roger, peeping about.

Rog. The coast is clear; sir, sir, you may come in now, master Classic.

Enter Mr. Classic and the Father.

Class. Roger, watch at the door. I wish, Sir John, I could give you a more chearful welcome, but we have no time to lose in ceremony; you are arrived in the critical minute; two hours more would have plac'd the inconsiderate couple out of the reach of pursuit.

Father. How can I acknowledge your kindness? You have preserved my son; you have sav'd——

Class. I have done my duty; but of that——

Rog. Maister and the young woman's coming.

Class. Sir John, place yourself here, and be a witness how near a crisis is the fate of your family.

Enter Buck and Lucinda.

Buck. Pshaw! What signifies her? 'Tis odds whether she'd consent, from the fear of my father. Besides, she told me, we could never be married here ; and so pack up a few things, and we'll off in a post-chaise directly.

Luc. Stay, Mr. Buck. let me have a moment's reflection.————What am I about! contriving in concert with the most profligate couple that ever disgrac'd human nature, to impose an indigent orphan on the sole representative of a wealthy and honorable family! Is this a character becoming my birth and education? What must be the consequence? Sure detection and contempt, contempt even from him, when his passions cool.————I have resolv'd, sir.

Buck. Madam.

Luc. As the expedition we are upon the point of taking is to be a lasting one, we ought not to be over-hasty in our resolution.

Buck. Pshaw! Stuff! When a thing's resolv'd, the sooner 'tis over the better.

Luc. But before it is absolutely resolv'd, give me leave to beg an answer to two questions.

Buck. Make haste then.

Luc. What are your thoughts of me?

Buck. Thoughts! Nay, I don't know; why that you are a sensible, civil, handsome, handy girl, and will make a devilish good wife. That's all I think.

Luc. But of my rank and fortune?

Buck. Mr. Subtle says they are both great; but that's no business of mine, I was always determin'd to marry for love.

Luc. Generously said! My birth, I believe, won't disgrace you; but for my fortune, your friend, Mr. Subtle, I fear, has anticipated you there.

Buck. Much good may it do him; I have enough for both. But we lose time, and may be prevented.

Luc. By whom?

Buck. By domine; or perhaps father may come.

Luc. Your father!—You think he would prevent you then.

Buck. Perhaps he'would.

Luc. And why?

Buck. Nay, I don't know; but pshaw! 'zooks!
this is like saying one's catechise.

Luc. But don't you think your father's consent
necessary?

Buck. No! Why 'tis I am to be married, and
not he. But come along, old fellows love to be
obstinate; but ecod I am as mulish as he; and to tell
you the truth, if he had propos'd me a wife, that
would have been reason enough to make me dislike
her; and I don't think I should be half so hot
about marrying you, only I thought 'twould plague
the old fellow damnably. So, my pretty partner,
come along; let's have no more ————

Enter Father and Classic.

Fath. Sir, I am oblig'd to you for this declaration, as to it I owe the entire subjection of that paternal weakness which has hitherto suspended the
correction your abandon'd libertinism has long provok'd. You have forgot the duty you owe a father,
disclaim'd my protection, cancell'd the natural co-
venant between us; 'tis time I now should give you
up to the guidance of your own guilty passions, and
treat you as a stranger to my blood for ever.

Buck. I told you what would happen, if he
should come; but you may thank yourself.

Fath. Equally weak as wicked, the dupe of a
raw, giddy girl. But proceed, sir; you have nothing farther to fear from me; compleat your project, and add her ruin to your own.

Buck. Sir, as to me, you may say what you
please; but for the young woman, she does not deserve it; but now she wanted me to get your consent, and told me that she had never a penny of portion into the bargain.

Fath. A stale, obvious artifice! She knew the discovery of the fraud must follow close on your inconsiderate marriage, and would then plead the merits of her prior candid discovery. The lady, doubtless, sir, has other secrets to disclose; but, as her cunning reveal'd the first, her policy will preserve the rest.

Luc. What secrets?

Buck. Be quiet, I tell you; let him alone, and he'll cool of himself by and by.

Luc. Sir, I am yet the protectress of my own honour; in justice to that, I must demand an explanation. What secrets, sir!

Fath. Oh! perhaps a thousand! But I am to blame to call them secrets; the customs of this gay country give sanction, and stamp merit upon vice; and vanity will here proclaim what modesty would elsewhere blush to whisper.

Luc. Modesty!—You suspect my virtue then!

Fath. You are a lady; but the fears of a father may be permitted to neglect a little your plan of politeness: Therefore to be plain; from your residence in this house, from your connection with these people, and from the scheme which my presence has interrupted, I have suspicions———of what nature, ask yourself.

Luc. Sir, you have reason, appearances are against me, I confess, but when you have heard my melancholy story, you'll own you have wrong'd me, and learn to pity her whom now you hate.

Fath. Madam, you misemploy your time; there tell your story, there it will be believ'd; I am too knowing in the wiles of women, to be soften'd by a syren tear, or impos'd on by an artful tale.

Luc. But hear me, sir, on my knee, I beg it, nay I demand it; you have wrong'd me, and must do me justice.

Class. I am sure, madam, sir John will be glad to find his fears are false, but you can't blame him.

Luc. I don't, sir, and I shall but little trespass on his patience. When you know, sir, that I am the orphan of an honourable and once wealthy family, whom her father, misguided by pernicious politics, brought with him, in her earliest infancy, to France, that dying here, he bequeath'd me, with the poor remnant of our shatter'd fortune, to the direction of this rapacious pair; I am sure you'll tremble for me.

Fath. Go on!

Luc. But when you know that plunder'd of the little fortune left me, I was reluctantly compell'd to aid this plot; forced to comply under the penalty of deepest want; without one hospitable roof to shelter me, without one friend to comfort or relieve me, you must, you can't but pity me.

Fath. Proceed!

Luc. To this when you are told, that, previous to your coming, I had determined never to wed your son, at least without your knowledge and consent, I hope your justice then will credit and acquit me.

Fath. Madam, your tale is plausible and moving; I hope 'tis true; here come the explainers of this riddle.

Enter Mr. and Mrs. Subtle.

Mr. Sub. Buck's father!

Fath. I'll take some other time, sir, to thank you for the last proofs of your friendship to my family; in the mean time, be so candid as to instruct us in the knowledge of this lady, whom, it seems, you have chosen for the partner of my son.

Mr. Sub. Mr. Buck's partner —— I chose—— I —— I——

Fath. No equivocation or reserve; your plot's reveal'd, known to the bottom; who is the lady?

Mr. Sub. Lady, sir,——the lady's a gentlewoman, sir.

Fath. By what means ?

Mr. Sub. By her father and mother.

Fath. Who were they, sir ?

Mr. Sub. Her mother was of —————— I forget her maiden name.

Fath. You han't forgot her father's?

Mr. Sub. No! No! No!

Fath. Tell it then.

Mr. Sub. She has told it you, I suppose.

Fath. No matter, I must have it, sir, from you; here's some mystery.

Mr. Sub. 'Twas Worthy.

Fath. Not the daughter of sir Gilbert!

Mr. Sub. You have it.

Fath. My poor girl ! I indeed have wrong'd, but will redress you ; and pray, sir, after the many pressing letters you received from me, how came this truth concealed ? but I guess your motive. Dry up your tears, Lucinda, at last you have found a father.   Hence ye degenerate, ye abandon'd wretches, who, abusing the confidence of your country, unite to plunder those ye promise to protect.

Luc. Am I then justified ?

Fath. You are, your father was my first and firmest friend ; I mourn'd his loss ; and long have sought for thee in vain, Lucinda.

Buck. Pray han't I some merit in finding her ? She's mine by the custom of the manor.

Fath. Yours—first study to deserve her ; she's mine, sir, I have just redeem'd this valuable treasure ; and shall not trust it in a spendthrift's hands.

Buck. What would you have me do, sir ?

Fath. Disclaim the partners of your riot, polish your manners, reform your pleasures, and, before you think of governing others, learn to direct yourself.   And now, my beauteous ward, we'll for the

land where first you saw the light, and there endeavour to forget the long, long bondage you have
suffer'd here. I suppose, sir, we shall have no difficulty in persuading you to accompany us ; it is not
in France I am to hope for your reformation. I
have now learn'd, that he who transports a profligate son to Paris, by way of mending his manners,
only adds the vices and follies of that country to
those of his own.

FINIS.

EPILOGUE,

MISS MACKLIN.

Escaped from my guardian's tyrannical sway,
By a fortunate voyage on a prosperous day,
I am landed in England, and now must endeavour,
By some means or other, to curry your favour.
   Of what use to be freed from a Gallic subjection,
Unless I'm secure of a British protection?
Without cash,—but one friend—and he too just made,
Egad I've a mind to set up some trade.
Of what sort! in the papers I'll publish a puff
Which won't fail to procure me custom enough:
" That a lady from Paris is lately arriv'd,
" Who with exquisite art has nicely contriv'd
" The best paint for the face,—the best paste for the hands,
" A water for freckles, for flushings, and tans.
" She can teach you the *melior coeffeure* for the head,
" To lisp—amble—and simper—and put on the red;
" To rival, to rally, to backbite, and sneer,
" Um—no; that they already know pretty well here.
   " The Beaux she instructs to bow with a grace,
" The happiest shrug,—the newest grimace;
" To *parler François*,—fib, flatter, and dance,
" Which is very near all that they teach ye in France.
   " Not a buck, nor a blood, through the whole English
      " nation,
" But his roughness she'll soften, his figure she'll fashion.
" The merest John Trot in a week you shall zee
" *Bien poli, bien frizé, tout à fait un Marquis.*"

EPILOGUE.

What d'ye think of my plan, is it form'd to your goût ?
May I hope for disciples in any of you ?
Shall I tell you my thoughts, without guile, without art,
Though abroad I've been bred, I have Britain at heart.
Then take this advice, which I give for her sake,
You'll gain nothing by any exchange you can make ;
In a country of commerce, too great the expence,
For their baubles and bows, to give your good sense.

DRAMATIC AND POETICAL WORKS,

PRINTED FOR

W. LOWNDES.

Anstey's New Bath Guide, 18mo
British Poets, 124 vols 18mo
Cibber's Dramatic Works, 5 vols 12mo
Congreve's Works, 2 vols 12mo
English Theatre, 14 vols 12mo
Farquhar's Works, 2 vols 12mo
Francis's Horace, Lat. & Eng. 4 vols 18mo
Gay's Fables, demy 8vo, foolscap 8vo, and 18mo
Goldsmith's Poetical Works, foolscap 8vo
Hill's Dramatic Works, 2 vols 8vo
Jodrell's Select Dramatic Pieces, 8vo
Jonson's (B.) five Acting, Plays 12mo
Milton's Paradise Lost, 12mo and 18mo
Milton's Poetical Works, 7 vols 8vo & 4 vols 12mo
Moore's Dramatic Works, 12mo
Philips's (John) Poems, foolscap 8vo
Poetical Elegant Extracts, royal 8vo, or Epitomized
    in square 12mo
Pomfret's Poems on Several Occasions, 12mo
Rowe's (N.) Works, 2 vols 12mo
Rowe's Lucan's Pharsalia, 3 vols 18mo
Shakspeare's Plays with Notes, 21 vols, 10 vols or
    9 vols 8vo and in 9 vols 18mo
Smart's Poems, 2 vols foolscap 8vo
Steele's Dramatic Works, 12mo
Thomson's Seasons, royal, demy or foolscap 8vo
Thomson's Works by Murdock, 3 vols 8vo
Vanbrugh's Plays, 2 vols 12mo
Young's Works, 3 vols 8vo

THE

A U T H O R;

A

COMEDY,

IN TWO ACTS,

AS IT IS PERFORMED AT THE

THEATRE-ROYAL IN DRURY-LANE.

WRITTEN BY

SAMUEL FOOTE, Esq.

———————————

LONDON:
PRINTED FOR W. LOWNDES, 38, BEDFORD STREET.

———

1808.

PROLOGUE,

WRITTEN AND SPOKEN BY

Mr. FOOTE.

—————

SEVERE their tafk, who in this critic age,
With frefh materials furnifh out the stage!
Not that our fathers drain'd the comic store;
Frefh characters spring up as heretofore——
Nature with novelty does still abound;
On every side frefh follies may be found.
But then the taste of every guest to hit,
To pleafe at once, the gall'ry, box, and pit;
Requires at least—no common share of wit.

 Thofe, who adorn the orb of higher life,
Demand the lively rake, or modifh wife;
Whilst they, who in a lower circle move,
Yawn at their wit, and flumber at their love.
If light, low mirth employs the comic scene,
Such mirth as drives from vulgar minds the spleen;
The polifh'd Critic damns the wretched ftuff,
And cries,—" 'twill pleafe the gall'ries well enough."
Such jarring judgments who can reconcile,
Since fops will frown, where humble traders smile?

 To dafh the poet's ineffectual claim,
And quench his thirst for univerfal fame,
The Grecian fabulist, in moral lay,
Has thus addrefs'd the writers of this day.

 Once on a time, a fon and fire we're told,
The stripling tender, and the father old,
Purchas'd a jack-afs at a country fair,
To eafe their limbs, and hawk about their ware:
But as the fluggifh animal was weak,
They fear'd, if both fhould mount, his back wou'd break:

PROLOGUE.

Up gets the boy ; the father leads the afs,
And through the gazing crowd attempts to pafs ;
Forth from the throng, the grey-beards hobble out,
And hail the cavalcade with feeble fhout.
" This the refpect to reverend age you fhew ?
" And this the duty you to parents owe ?
" He beats the hoof, and you are fet astride ;
" Sirrah ? get down, and let your father ride."
As Grecian lads were feldom void of grace,
The decent, duteous youth, refign'd his place.
Then a frefh murmur through the rabble ran ;
Boys, girls, wives, widows, all attack the man.
" Sure never was brute beast fo void of nature !
" Have you no pity for the pretty creature ?
" To your own baby can you be unkind ?
" Here—Suke, Bill, Betty—put the child behind."
Old Dapple next, the clowns compaffion claim'd ;
" 'Tis wonderment, them boobies ben't afham'd.
" Two at a time upon a poor dumb beaft !
" They might as well have carried he at leaft."
The pair, still pliant to the partial voice,
Difmount and bear the afs—then what a noife !———
Huzzas—loud laughs, low gibe, and bitter joke,
From the yet filent fire, thefe words provoke.
" Proceed, my boy, nor heed their farther call,
" Vain his attempt, who strives to pleafe them all !"

EPILOGUE:

WRITTEN BY A LADY,

SPOKEN BY MRS. CLIVE.

WELL—thank my stars, that I have done my task,
And now throw off this aukward, ideot mask.
Cou'd we suppose this circle so refin'd,
Who seek those pleasures that improve the mind,
Cou'd from such vulgarisms feel delight;
Or laugh at characters, so unpolite?
Who come to plays, to see, and to be seen;
Not to hear things that shock, or give the spleen;
Who shun an Opera, when they hear 'tis thin.
" Lord! do you know?" says lady Bell—" I'm told
" That Jacky Dapple got so great a cold
" Last Tuesday night—there wa'n't a creature there;
" Not a male thing to hand one to one's chair.
" Divine Mingotti! what a swell has she!
" O! such a Sustinuto upon B!
" Ma'am, when she's quite in voice she'll go to C.
" Lord," says my lady English—" here's a pother!
" Go where she will, I'll never see another."
Her ladyship, half choak'd with London air,
And brought to town to see the sights—and stare.
" Fine singing that!—I'm sure it's more like screaming:
" To me, I vow, they're all a pack of women!
" Oh Barbare!—Inhumana Tramontane!——
" Does not this creature come from Pudding Lane?
" Look, look, my lord!—She goggles!— Ha, ha, pray be
       quiet;
" Dear lady Bell, for shame! You'll make a riot.
" Why will they mix with us to make this rout?
" Bring in a bill, my lord, to keep 'em out.
" We'll have a taste act, faith!"—my lord replied;
" And shut out all, that are not qualified."
Thus ridicule is bounded like a ball,
Struck by the great, then answer'd by the small;
While we, at times, return it to you all.
A skilful hand will ne'er your rage provoke;
For though it hits you, you'll applaud the stroke;
Let it but only glance, you'll never frown;
Nay, you'll forgive, tho't knocks your neighbour down.

2.

DRAMATIS PERSONÆ.

AT DRURY LANE, 1782.

GOVERNOR CAPE,	Mr. Wrighten.
YOUNG CAPE,	Mr. Aikin.
SPRIGHTLY,	Mr. R. Palmer.
CADWALLADER,	Mr. Bannister.
POET,	Mr. Waldron.
VAMP,	Mr. Moody.
PRINTER'S DEVIL,	Mr. Burton.
ROBIN,	Mr. Chaplin.
MRS CADWALLADER,	Mrs. Wrighten.
MISS ARABELLA,	Mrs. Sharp.

AUTHOR.

ACT I.

Enter Governor Cape, and Robin.

Governor.

AND he believes me dead, Robin?

Rob. Most certainly.

Gov. You have given him no intimation that his fortunes might mend.

Rob. Not a distant hint.

Gov. How did he receive the news?

Rob. Calmly enough: when I told him that his hopes from abroad were at an end, that the friend of his deceased father thought he had done enough in putting it in his power to earn his own livelihood, he replied 'twas no more than he had long expected; charged me with his warmest acknowledgments to his conceal'd benefactor; thanked me for my care, sigh'd and left me.

Gov. And how has he lived since?

Rob. Poorly, but honestly: To his pen he owes all his subsistence. I am sure my heart bleeds for him: consider, sir, to what temptations you expose him.

Gov. The severer his trials, the greater his triumph. Shall the fruits of my honest industry, the purchase of many perils, be lavish'd on a lazy luxurious booby, who has no other merit than being born five-and-twenty years after me? No, no, Robin; him, and a profusion of debts were all that the extravagance of his mother left me.

Rob.   You loved her, sir.

Gov.   Fondly—nay, foolishly, or necessity had not compell'd me to seek for shelter in another climate. 'Tis true, fortune has been favourable to my labours, and when George convinces me that he inherits my spirit, he shall share my property; not else.

Rob.   Consider, sir, he has not your opportunities.

Gov.   Nor had I his education.

Rob.   As the world goes, the worst you cou'd have given him. Lack-a-dav, learning, learning, sir, is no commodity for this market; nothing makes money here, sir, but money; or some certain fashionable qualities that you would not wish your son to possess.

Gov.   Learning useless? impossible!—Where are the Oxfords, the Halifaxes, the great protectors and patrons of the liberal arts?

Rob.   Patron!—The word has lost its use; a guinea subscription at the request of a lady, whose chambermaid is acquainted with the author, may be now and then pick'd up——protectors!—Why I dare believe there's more money laid out upon Islington turnpike in a month, than upon all the learned men in Great Britain in seven years.

Gov.   And yet the press groans with their productions. How do they all exist?

Rob.   In garrets, sir; as, if you will step to your son's apartment in the next street, you will see.

Gov.   But what apology shall we make for the visit?

Rob.——That you want the aid of his profession; a well penn'd address now, from the subjects of your late government, with your gracious reply, to put into the news-papers.

Gov.   Aye; is that part of his practice?—Well, lead on, Robin.

Scene draws and discovers Young Cape with the Prin-
ter's Devil.

Cape. Prythee go about thy business—vanish,
dear devil

Devil. Master bid me not come without the
proof; he says as how there are two other answers
ready for the press, and if your's don't come out a
Saturday 'twon't pay for the paper; but you are
always so lazy: I have more plague with you—
There's Mr. Guzzle, the translator, never keeps me
a minute—unless the poor gentleman happens to
be fuddled.

Cape. Why, you little sooty, sniv'ling, diabolical puppy, is it not sufficient to be plagu'd with
the stupidity of your absurd master, but I must be
pester'd with your impertinence?

Devil. Impertinence!—marry, come up, I keep
as good company as your worship every day in the
year——There's master Clench, in Little Britain,
does not think it beneath him to take part of a pot
of porter with me, tho' he has wrote two volumes
of lives in quarto, and has a folio a coming out in
numbers.

Cape. Harky', sirrah, if you don't quit the room
this instant, I'll shew you a shorter way into the
street than the stairs.

Devil. I shall save you the trouble—give me
the French book that you took the story from for
the last journal.

Cape. Take it——*(throws it at him.)*

Devil. What, d'ye think it belongs to the circulating library, or that it is one of your own performances, that you——

Cape. You shall have a larger——*(Exit Devil.*
'Sdeath! a pretty situation I am in! and are these
the fruits I am to reap from a long, laborious and
expensive——

Re-enter Devil.

Devil. I had like to have forgot, here's your week's pay for the news-paper, five and five pence, which with the two-and-a-penny, master pass'd his word for to Mrs. Suds, your washer-woman, makes the three half crowns.

Cape. Lay it on the table.

Devil. Here's a man on the stairs wants you; by the sheepishness of his looks, and the shabbiness of his dress, he's either a pick-pocket, or a poet— Here, walk in, Mr. What-d'ye-call-'um, the gentleman's at home.

(Surveys the figure, laughs, and exit.)

Enter Poet.

Poet. Your name, I presume, is Cape.

Cape. You have hit it, sir.

Poet. Sir, I beg pardon ; you are a gentleman that write ?

Cape. Sometimes.

Poet. Why, sir, my case, in a word, is this ; I, like you, have long been a retainer of the muses, as you may see by their livery.

Cape. They have not discarded you, I hope.

Poet. No, sir, but their upper servants, the booksellers, have.——I printed a collection of jests upon my own account, and they have ever since refused to employ me ; you, sir, I hear, are in their graces : now I have brought you, sir, three imitations of Juvenal in prose ; Tully's oration for Milo, in blank verse ; two essays on the British herring fishery, with a large collection of rebusses ; which, if you will dispose of to them, in your own name, we'll divide the profits.

Cape. I am really, sir, sorry for your distress, but I have a larger cargo of my own manufacturing than they chuse to engage in.

Poet. That's pity ; you have nothing in the

compiling or index way, that you wou'd intrust to
the care of another?

Cape. Nothing.

Poet. I'll do it at half price.

Cape. I'm concern'd it is not in my power at
present to be useful to you ; but if this trifle—

Poet. Sir, your servant. Shall I leave you any
of my——

Cape. By no means.

Poet. An essay, or an ode?

Cape. Not a line.

Poet. Your very obedient.—   *(Exit Poet.*

Cape. Poor fellow ! and how far am I removed
from his condition? Virgil had his Pollio ; Horace
his Mecænas ; Martial his Pliny : my protectors
are Title-page, the publisher ; Vamp, the bookseller ; and Index, the printer, a most noble triumvi-
rate ; and the rascals are as proscriptive and ar-
bitary, as the famous Roman one, into the bargain.

Enter Sprightly.

Spri. What ! in soliloquy, George ? reciting
some of the pleasantries, I suppose, in your new
piece.

Cape. My disposition has, at present, very little
of the *vis comica.*

Spri. What's the matter?

Cape. Survey that mass of wealth upon the
table ; all my own, and earn'd in little more than
a week.

Spri. Why, 'tis an inexhaustible mine !

Cape. Ay, and delivered to me, too, with all
the soft civility of Billingsgate, by a printer's prime
minister, call'd a Devil.

Spri. I met the imp upon the stairs ; but I
thought these midwives to the muses were the
idolizers of you, their favourite sons.

Cape. Our tyrants, Tom. Had I indeed a post-
humous piece of infidelity, or an amourous novel,

decorated with luscious copper-plates, the slaves would be civil enough.

Spri.   Why don't you publish your own works?

Cape.   What! and paper my room with 'em? no . no, that will never do; there are secrets in all trades; ours is one great mystery, but the explanation wou'd be too tedious at present.

Spri.   Then why don't you divert your attention to some other object?

Cape.   That subject was employing my thoughts.

Spri.   How have you resolved?

Cape.   I have, I think, at present, two strings to my bow; if my comedy succeeds, it buys me a commission; if my mistress, my Laura, proves kind, I am settled for life; but if both my cords snap, adieu to the quill, and welcome the musket.

Spri.   Heroically determined!—But *à propos*—how proceeds your honourable passion?

Cape.   But slowly—I believe I have a friend in her heart, but a most potent enemy in her head: you know, I am poor, and she is prudent. With regard to her fortune too, I believe her brother's consent essentially necessary——But you promised to make me acquainted with him.

Spri.   I expect him here every instant. He may, George, be useful to you in more than one capacity; if your comedy is not crouded, he is a character, I can tell you, that will make no contemptible figure in it.

Cape.   His sister gave me a sketch of him last summer.

Spri.   A sketch can never convey him. His peculiarities require infinite labour and high finishing.

Cape.   Give me the out-lines.

Spri.   He is a compound of contrarieties; pride and meanness; folly and archness: at the same time that he wou'd take the wall of a prince of the blood, he would not scruple eating a fry'd sausage at the Mews-Gate. There is a minuteness, now and then, in his descriptions; and some whimsical, unaccountable turns in his conversation, that are entertaining enough : but the extravagance and oddity of his manner, and the boast of his birth, compleat his character.

Cape. But how will a person of his pride and pedigree relish the humility of this apartment?

Spri. Oh, he is prepar'd—You are, George, tho' prodigiously learn'd and ingenious, an abstracted being, odd and whimsical; the case with all you great geniuses: You love the snug, the chimney-corner of life; and retire to this obscure nook, merely to avoid the importunity of the great.

Cape. Your servant——But what attraction can a character of this kind have for Mr. Cadwallader?

Spri. Infinite! next to a peer, he honours a poet : and modestly imputes his not making a figure in the learned world himself to the neglect of his education—hush! he's on the stairs——on with your cap, and open your book. Remember great dignity and absence.

Enter Vamp.

Cape. Oh, no; 'tis Mr. Vamp: your commands, good sir?

Vamp. I have a word, master Cape, for your private ear.

Cape. You may communicate; this gentleman is a friend.

Vamp. An author?

Cape. Voluminous.

Vamp. In what way?

Cape. Universal.

Vamp. Bless me! he's very young, and exceedingly well rigg'd; what, a good subscription, I reckon.

Cape. Not a month from Leyden; an admirable theologist; he study'd it in Germany; if you should want such a thing now, as ten or a dozen manuscript sermons, by a deceas'd clergyman, I believe he can supply you.

Vamp. No.

Cape. Warranted Originals.

Vamp. No, no, I don't deal in the sermon way, now; I lost money by the last I printed, for all 'twas wrote by a methodist; but, I believe, sir, if they be'nt long, and have a good deal of Latin in 'em, I can get you a chap.

Spri. For what, sir?

Vamp. The manuscript sermons you have wrote, and want to dispose of.

Spri. Sermons that I have wrote?

Vamp. Ay, ay; master Cape has been telling me—

Spri. He has; I am mightily oblig'd to him.

Vamp. Nay, nay, don't be afraid; I'll keep council; old Vamp had not kept a shop so long at the Turnstile, if he did not know how to be secret; why in the year forty-five, when I was in the treasonable way, I never squeak'd; I never gave up but one author in my life, and he was dying of a consumption, so it never came to a trial.

Spri. Indeed!

Vamp. Never——look here (*shews the side of his head*) crop'd close!—bare as a board!—and for nothing in the world but an innocent book of bawdy, as I hope for mercy: Oh! the laws are very hard, very severe upon us.

Spri. You have given me, sir, so positive a proof of your secresy that you may rely upon my communication.

Vamp. You will be safe——but gadso, we must mind business, tho'; here, master Cape, you must provide me with three taking titles for these pamphlets, and if you can think of a pat Latin motto for the largest——

Cape. They shall be done.

Vamp. Do so, do so. Books are like women, master Cape; to strike, they must be well dress'd; fine feathers make fine birds; a good paper, an elegant type, a handsome motto, and a catching title, has drove many a dull treatise thro' three editions——Did you know Harry Handy?

Spri. Not that I recollect.

Vamp. He was a pretty fellow; he had his Latin, *ad anguem*, as they say; he would have turn'd you a fable of Dryden's, or an epistle of Pope's into Latin verse in a twinkling; except Peter Hasty the voyage-writer, he was as great a loss to the trade as any within my memory.

Cape. What carry'd him off?

Vamp. A halter; hang'd for clipping and coining, master Cape; I thought there was something the matter by his not coming to our shop for a month or two: He was a pretty fellow!

Spri. Were you a great loser by his death?

Vamp. I can't say:——as he had taken to another course of living, his execution made a noise; it sold me seven hundred of his translations, besides his last dying speech and confession; I got it; he was mindful of his friends in his last moments: he was a pretty fellow!

Cape. You have no further commands, Mr. Vamp?

Vamp. Not at present; about the spring I'll deal with you, if we can agree for a couple of volumes in octavo.

Spri. Upon what subject?

Vamp. I leave that to him; master Cape knows what will do, tho' novels are a pretty light summer reading, and do very well at Tunbridge, Bristol, and the other watering places: no bad commodity for the West-India trade neither; let 'em be novels, master Cape.

Cape. You shall be certainly supply'd.

Vamp. I doubt not ; pray how does Index go on with your journal?

Cape. He does not complain.

Vamp. Ah, I knew the time——but you have over-stock'd the market. Titlepage and I had once lik'd to have engag'd in a paper. We had got a young Cantab for the essays; a pretty historian from Aberdeen; and an attorney's clerk for the true intelligence ; but I don't know how, it drop'd for want of a politician.

Cape. If in that capacity I can be of any—

Vamp. No, thank you, master Cape ; in half a year's time, I have a grandson of my own that will come in; he's now in training as a waiter at the Cocoa-Tree coffee-house ; I intend giving him the run of Jonathan's for three months to understand trade and the funds; and then I'll start him —— no, no, you have enough on your hands; stick to your business: and d'ye hear, 'ware clipping and coining; remember Harry Handy ; he was a pretty fellow !   *(Exit.*

Spri. And I'm sure thou art a most extraordinary fellow ! But prythee, George, what cou'd provoke thee to make me a writer of sermons?

Cape. You seem'd desirous of being acquainted with our business, and I knew old Vamp wou'd let you more into the secret in five minutes than I cou'd in as many hours.   *(Knocking below, loud.)*

Spri. Cape, to your post ; here they are e'faith, a coachful ! let's see, Mr. and Mrs. Cadwallader, and your flame, the sister, as I live.

(Cadwallader without)

Pray, by the bye, han't you a poet above?

(Without.) Higher up.

Cad. Egad, I wonder what makes your poets have such an aversion to middle floors—they are always to be found in the extremities ; in garrets, or cellars ——

Enter Mr. and Mrs. Cadwallader and Arabella.

Cad. Ah! Sprightly!

Spri. Hush!

Cad. Hey, what's the matter?

Spri. Hard at it; untwisting some knotty point; totally absorb'd!

Cad. Gadso! what, that's he! Beck, Bell, there he is, egad, as great a poet, and as ingenious a——— what's he about?———Hebrew?

Spri. Weaving the whole Æneid into a tragedy: I have been here this half hour, but he has not mark'd me yet.

Cad. Cou'd not I take a peep?

Spri. An earthquake wou'd not rouze him.

Cad. He seems in a damn'd passion.

Cape. The belt of Pallas! nor prayers, nor tears, nor supplicating gods shall save thee now.

Cad. Hey! zounds, what the devil? who?

Cape.

———Pallas! te hoc vulnere, Pallas
Immolat, & pœnam scelerato ex sanguine sumit.

Cad. Damn your palace; I wish I was well out of your garret.

Cape. Sir, I beg ten thousand pardons: ladies, your most devoted. You will excuse me, sir, but being just on the catastrophe of my tragedy, I am afraid the poetic furor may have betray'd me into some indecency.

Spri. Oh, Mr. Cadwallader is too great a genius himself, not to allow for these intemperate sallies of a heated imagination.

Cad. Genius! look ye here, Mr. What's-your-name?

Cape. Cape.

Cad. Cape! true; tho' by the bye here, hey! you live devilish high; but perhaps you may chuse that for exercise, hey! Sprightly! Genius! look'e here, Mr. Cape, I had as pretty natural parts, as fine talents!—but between you and I, I had a damn'd fool of a guardian, an ignorant, illiterate, ecod——he cou'd as soon pay the national debt as write his own name, and so was resolv'd to make his ward no wiser than himself, I think.

Spri. Oh! fye, Mr. Cadwallader, you don't do yourself justice.

Cape. Indeed, sir, we must contradict you, we can't suffer this defamation. I have more than once heard Mr. Cadwallader's literary acquisitions loudly talk'd of.

Cad. Have you?——no, no, it can't be, hey! tho' let me tell you, last winter, before I had the measles, I cou'd have made as good a speech upon any subject, in Italian, French, German——but I am all unhing'd; all —— Oh! Lord, Mr. Cape, this is Becky; my dear Becky, child, this is a great poet —— ah, but she does not know what that is —— a little foolish or so, but of a very good fami-.y—here Becky, child, won't you ask Mr. Cape to come and see you?

Mrs. Cad. As Dicky says, I shall be glad to see you at our house, sir.

Cape. I have too great a regard for my own happiness, ma'am, to miss so certain an opportunity of creating it.

Mrs. Cad. Hey! What?

Cape. My inclinations, as well as my duty, I say, will compel me to obey your kind injunctions.

Mrs. Cad. What does he say, our Bell?

Arab. Oh, that he can have no greater pleasure than waiting on you.

Mrs. Cad. I'm sure that's more his goodness than my desert; but when you be'nt better en-gag'd we shou'd be glad of your company of an evening to make one with our Dicky, sister Bell, and I, at whisk and swabbers.

Cad. Hey, ecod do, Cape, come and look at her grotto and shells, and see what she has got—

well, he'll come, Beck,—ecod do, and she'll come
to the third night of your tragedy, hey! won't you,
Beck?——is'nt she a fine girl? hey, you; humour
her a little, do;——hey, Beck; he says you are as
fine a woman as ever he — ecod who knows but
he may make a copy of verses on you?—there, go,
and have a little chat with her, talk any nonsense
to her, no matter what; she's a damn'd fool, and
won't know the difference—there, go, Beck—well,
Sprightly, hey! what are you and Bell like to
come together? Oh, ecod, they tell me, Mr.
Sprightly, that you have frequently lords and vis-
counts and earls, that take a dinner with you;
now I shou'd look upon it as a very particular favour, if you would invite me at the same time,
hey! will you?

Spri. You may depend on it.

Cad. Will you? Gad, that's kind; for between
you and I, Mr. Sprightly, I am of as antient a family as the best of them, and people of fashion
shou'd know one another, you know.

Spri. By all manner of means.

Cad. Hey! should not they so? When you
have any lord, or baron, nay egad, if it be but a
baronet, or a member of parliament, I shou'd take
it as a favour.

Spri. You will do them honour; they must all
have heard of the antiquity of your house.

Cad. Antiquity! hey! Beck, where's my pedigree?

Mrs. Cad. Why at home, lock'd up in the butler's pantry.

Cad. In the pantry! What the devil, how often
have I bid you never to come out without it?

Mrs. Cad. Lord! What signifies carrying such
a lumb'ring thing about?

Cad. Signifies! you are a fool, Beck, why suppose we should have any disputes when we are
abroad, about precedence? how the devil shall we

be able to settle it? But you shall see it at home. Oh Becky, come hither, we will refer our dispute to ———— *(They go apart.)*

Arab. Well, sir, your friend has prevail'd; you are acquainted with my brother; but what use you propose ————

Cape. The pleasure of a more frequent admission to you.

Arab. That all?

Cape. Who knows but a strict intimacy with Mr. Cadwallader may in time incline him to favour my hopes?

Arab. A sandy foundation! Cou'd he be prevail'd upon to forgive your want of fortune; the obscurity, or at least uncertainty, of your birth, will prove an unsurmountable bar.

Cad. Hold, hold, hold, Beck; zounds! you are so ————

Spri. Well, but hear him out, ma'am.

Cape. Consider we have but an instant. What project? What advice?

Arab. O fye! You would be asham'd to receive succour from a weak woman! Poetry is your profession, you know; so that plots, contrivances, and all the powers of imagination, are more peculiarly your province.

Cape. Is this a season to rally?

Cad. Hold, hold, hold; ask Mr. Cape.

Arab. To be serious then; if you have any point to gain with my brother, your application must be made to his better part.

Cape. I understand you; plough with the heifer.

Arab. A delicate allusion, on my word; but take this hint—amongst her passions, admiration, or rather adoration, is the principal.

Cape. Oh; that is her foible?

Arab. One of them; against that fort you must plant your batteries—But here they are.

Mrs. Cad. I tell you, you are a nonsense man, and I won't agree to any such thing: Why what signifies a parliament man? You make such a rout indeed.

Cad. Hold, Becky, my dear, don't be in a passion now, hold; let us reason the thing a little, my dear.

Mrs. Cad. I tell you I won't; what's the man an oafe? I won't reason, I hate reason, and so there's an end on't.

Cad. Why then you are obstinate ecod, perverse hey! But my dear, now, Becky, that's a good girl: Hey! come, hold, hold——Egad, we'll refer it to Mr. Cape.

Mrs. Cad. Defer it to who you will, it will signify nothing.

Cape. Bless me, what's the matter, madam? Sure, Mr. Cadwallader, you must have been to blame; no inconsiderable matter cou'd have ruffled the natural softness of that tender and delicate mind.

Arab. Pretty well commenced.

Mrs. Cad. Why he's always a fool, I think; he wants to send our little Dicky to school, and make him a parliament man.

Cape. How old is master, ma'am?

Mrs. Cad. Three years and a quarter, come lady-day.

Cape. The intention is rather early.

Cad. Hey! early, hold, hold; but Becky, mistakes the thing, egad I'll tell you the whole affair.

Mrs. Cad. You had better hold your chattering, so you had.

Cad. Nay, prithee, my dear; Mr. Sprightly, do, stop her mouth, hold, hold; the matter, Mr. Cape, is this. Have you ever seen my Dicky?

Cape. Never.

Cad. No? Hold, hold, egad he's a fine, a sensi-

ble child; I tell Becky he's like her, to keep her
in humour; but between you and I he has more
sense already, than all her family put together.
Hey! Becky! is not Dicky the picture of you?
He's a sweet child! Now, Mr. Cape, you must
know, I want to put little Dicky to school; now
between—hey! you, hold, you, hold, the great use
of a school is, hey! egad, for children to make acquaintances, that may hereafter be useful to them;
for between you and I, as to what they learn there,
does not signify two-pence.

Cape.   Not a farthing.

Cad.   Does it, hey? Now this is our dispute,
whether poor little Dicky, he's a sweet boy, shall
go to Mr. Quæ-Genius's at Edgware, and make
an acquaintance with my young lord Knap, the
eldest son of the earl of Frize, or to doctor Ticklepitcher's at Barnet, to form a friendship with young
Stocks, the rich broker's only child.

Cape.   And for which does the lady determine?

Cad.   Why I have told her the case; says I, Becky,
my dear; who knows, if Dicky goes to Quæ-Genius's, but my lord Knap may take such a fancy to
him, that upon the death of his father, and he comes
to be earl of Frize, he may make poor little Dicky
a member of parliament? Hey! Cape?

Mrs. Cad.   Ay, but then if Dicky goes to
Ticklepitcher's who can tell but young Stocks,
when he comes to his fortune, may lend him money
if he wants it?.

Cad.   And if he does not want it, he won't take
after his father, hey! Well, what's your opinion,
master Cape.

Cape.   Why Sir, I can't but join with the lady,
money is the main article; it is that that makes the
mare to go.

Cad.   Hey! egad, and the alderman too, you;
so Dicky may be a member, and a fig for my lord;
Well, Becky, be quiet, he shall stick to Stocks.

Mrs. Cad. Ay let'n; I was sure as how I was right.

Cad. Well, hush Becky. Mr. Cape, will you eat a bit with us to-day, hey! will you?

Cape. You command me.

Cad. That's kind; why then Becky and Bell shall step and order the cook to toss up a little, nice——Hey! will you, Becky? Do, and I'll bring Cape.

Mrs. Cad. Ay, with all my heart. Well, Mr. What-d'ye-call'um, the poet; ecod the man's well enough—Your servant.

Cape. I am a little too much in dishabille, to offer your ladyship my hand to your coach.

Cad. Pshaw! never mind, I'll do it—Here you have company coming.

(*Exeunt Mr. and Mrs. Cad. and Arab.*

Enter Governor and Robin.

Cape. Ah, master Robin!

Robin. Why, you have a great levee this morning, sir.

Cape. Ay Robin, there's no obscuring extraordinary talents.

Rob. True, sir; and this friend of mine begs to claim the benefit of them.

Cape. Any friend of yours: But how can I be serviceable to him?

Rob. Why, sir, he is lately return'd from a profitable government; and as you know the unsatisfied mind of man, no sooner is one object possess'd, but another starts up to ————

Cape. A truce to moralizing, dear Robin, to the matter; I am a little busy.

Rob. In a word then, this gentleman, having a good deal of wealth, is desirous of a little honour.

Cape. How can I confer it?

Rob. Your pen may.

Cape. I don't understand you.

Rob. Why touch him up a hàndsome compli-
mentary address from his colony, by way of praising
the prudence of his administration, his justice, va-
lour, benevolence, and ——

Cape. I am sorry 'tis impossible for me now to
misunderstand you. The obligations I owe you,
Robin, nothing can cancel; otherwise, this wou'd
prove our last interview.——Your friend, sir, has
been a little mistaken, in recommending me as a
person fit for your purpose. Letters have been always my passion, and indeed are now my profession;
but tho' I am the servant of the public, I am not
the prostitute of particulars: As my pen has never
been ting'd with gall, to gratify popular resentment
or private pique, so it shall never sacrifice its integrity to flatter pride, impose falshood, or palliate
guilt. Your merit may be great, but let those,
sir, be the heralds of your worth, who are better
acquainted with it.

Gov. Young man, I like your principles and
spirit; your manly refusal gives me more pleasure,
than any honors your papers cou'd have procured me.

Spri. Now this business is dispatch'd, let us return to our own affairs——You dine at Cadwallader's?

Cape. I do.

Spri. Wou'd it not be convenient to you to
have him out of the way?

Cape. Extremely.

Spri. I have a project that I think will prevail.

Cape. Of what kind?

Spri. Bordering upon the dramatic; but the
time is so pressing, I shall be at a loss to procure
performers. Let's see——Robin is a sure card——
A principal may easily be met with, but where
the duce can I get an interpreter?

Rob. Offer yourself, Sir; it will give you an
opportunity of more closely inspecting the conduct of your son.

Gov. True. Sir, tho' a scheme of this sort may ill suit with my character and time of life, yet from a private interest I take in that gentleman's affairs, if the means are honourable——

Spri. Innocent upon my credit.

Gov. Why then, sir, I have no objection, if you think me equal to the task——

Spri. Most happily fitted for it. I shou'd not have taken the liberty—but hush! He's return'd.

Enter Cadwallader.

Spri. My dear friend! the luckiest circumstance!

Cad. Hey! how? Stay, hey!

Spri. You see that gentleman?

Cad. Well, hey!

Spri. Do you know who he is?

Cad. Not I.

Spri. He is interpreter to prince Potowowsky.

Cad. Wowsky? Who the devil is he?

Spri. Why the Tartarian prince, that's come over ambassador from the Cham of the Calmucks.

Cad. Indeed.

Spri. His highness has just sent me an invitation to dine with him; now every body that dines with a Tartarian lord, has a right to carry with him what the Latins call'd his Umbra; in their language it is Jablanousky.

Cad. Jablanousky! well?

Spri. Now if you will go in that capacity, I shall be glad of the honour.

Cad. Hey! why wou'd you carry me to dine with his royal highness?

Spri. With pleasure.

Cad. My dear friend, I shall take it as the greatest favour, the greatest obligation————I shall never be able to return it.

Spri. Don't mention it.

Cad. Hey! but hold, hold, how the devil shall

I get off with the poet? You know I have ask'd him to dinner.

Spri. Oh! the occasion will be apology sufficient; besides, there will be the ladies to receive him.

Cad. My dear Mr. Cape, I beg ten thousand pardons, but here your friend is invited to dinner with prince —————what the devil is his name?

Spri. Potowowski.

Cad. True; now, sir, ecod he has been so kind as to offer to carry me as his Jablanousky, wou'd you be so good to excuse—

Cape. By all means; not a word, I beg.

Cad. That is exceeding kind; I'll come to you after dinner; hey! stay, but is there any ceremony to be used with his highness?

Spri. You dine upon carpets, cross-legg'd.

Cad. Hey! hold, hold, cross-legg'd, zounds! that's odd, well, well, you shall teach me.

Spri. And his highness is particularly pleased with those amongst his guests that do honour to his country soup.

Cad. Oh! let me alone for that; but should not I dress?

Spri. No, there's no occasion for it.

Cad. Dear friend, forgive me; nothing should take me from you, but being a Hobblin Wiskey. Well, I'll go and study to sit cross-legg'd, 'till you call me.

Spri. Do so.

Cad. His highness Potowowsky! This is the luckiest accident!　　　　　　　　　　(*Exit.*

Cape. Hah! hah! hah! but how will you conduct your enterprize?

Spri. We'll carry him to your friend Robin's; dress up one of the under actors in a ridiculous habit; this gentleman shall talk a little gibberish with him. I'll compose a soup of some nauseous ingredients;

let me alone to manage. But do you chuse, sir
the part we have assign'd?

Gov. As it seems to be but a harmless piece of
mirth, I have no objection.

Spri. Well then let's about it; come, sir.

Cape. Mr. Sprightly!

Spri. What's the matter?

Cape. Wou'd it not be right to be a little spruce,
a little smart upon this occasion?

Spri. No doubt; dress, dress, man; no time is
to be lost.

Cape. Well, but Jack, I cannot say that at
present I ———

Spri. Prythee explain. What would you say?

Cape. Why then, I cannot say, that I have any
other garments at home.

Spri. Oh, I understand you, is that all? Here,
here, take my———

Cape. Dear Sprightly, I am quite ashamed, and
sorry.

Spri. That's not so obliging, George; what,
sorry to give me the greatest pleasure that ——But
I have no time for speeches; I must run to get ready my soup. Come, gentlemen.

Rob. Did you observe, sir?

Gov. Most feelingly! But it will soon be over.

Rob. Courage, sir; times perhaps may change.

Cape. A poor prospect, Robin! But this scheme
of life at least must be changed; for what spirit,
with the least spark of generosity, can support a
life of eternal obligation, and disagreeable drudgery?
Inclination not consulted, genius cramp'd, and talents misapply'd.

What prospect have those authors to be read,
Whose daily writings earn their daily bread?

(Exeunt.

END OF THE FIRST ACT.

A C T II.

Young Cape and Mrs. Cadwallader at Cards.

Mrs. Cad.

YOU want four, and I two, and my deal: now, knave noddy ——— no, hearts be trumps.

Cape. I beg.

Mrs. Cad. Will you stock 'em?

Cape. Go on, if you please, madam.

Mrs. Cad. Hearts again—One, two, three; one, two,—hang 'em, they won't slip, three. Diamonds ——— the two: have you higher than the queen?

Cape. No, madam.

Mrs. Cad. Then there's highest—and lowest, by gosh. Games are even; you are to deal.

Cape. Pshaw, hang cards; there are other amusements better suited to a tête-a tête, than any the four aces can afford us.

Mrs. Cad. What pastimes be they?——We ben't enough for hunt the whistle, nor blind-man's buff: but I'll call our Bell, and Robin the butler. Dicky will be here by-an-bye.

Cape. Hold a minute. I have a game to propose, where the presence of a third person, especially Mr. Cadwallader's, wou'd totally ruin the sport.

Mrs. Cad. Ay, what can that be?

Cape. Can't you guess?

Mrs. Cad. Not I; questions and commands, mayhap.

Cape. Not absolutely that——some little resemblance; for I am to request, and you are to command.

Mrs. Cad. Oh daisy! that's charming, I never play'd at that in all my born days; come, begin then.

Cape.   Can you love me?

Mrs. Cad.   Love you! But is it in jest or earnest?

Cape.   That is as you please to determine.

Mrs. Cad.   But mayn't I ask you questions too?

Cape.   Doubtless.

Mrs. Cad.   Why then do you love me?

Cape.   With all my soul.

Mrs. Cad.   Upon your sayso.

Cape.   Upon my sayso.

Mrs. Cad.   I'm glad on't with all my heart. This is the rarest pastime!

Cape.   But you have not answer'd my question.

Mrs. Cad.   Hey? that's true. Why I believe there's no love lost.

Cape.   So; our game will soon be over; I shall be up at a deal. I wish I mayn't be engaged to play deeper here than I intended tho'.   *(Aside.)*

Mrs. Cad.   Well, now 'tis your turn.

Cape.   True; aye; but zooks you are too hasty; the pleasure of this play, like hunting, does not consist in immediately chopping the prey.

Mrs. Cad.   No! How then?

Cape.   Why first I am to start you, then run you a little in view, then lose you, then unravel all the tricks and doubles you make to escape me.

> You fly o'er hedge and stile,
> I pursue for many a mile,
> You grow tir'd at last and quat
> Then I catch you, and all that.

Mrs. Cad.   Dear me, there's a deal on't! I shall never be able to hold out long; I had rather be taken in view.

Cape.   I believe you.

Mrs. Cad.   Well, come, begin and start me, that I may come the sooner to quatting—Hush! here's sister; what the deuce brought her? Bell will be for learning this game too, but don't you teach her for your life, Mr. Poet.

Enter Arabella.

Arab. Your mantua-maker, with your new sack, sister.

Mrs. Cad. Is that all? She might have stay'd, I think.

Arab. What? You were better engaged? But don't be angry, I am sorry I interrupted you.

Mrs. Cad. Hey! Now will I be hang'd if she be'nt jealous of Mr. Poet; but I'll listen, and see the end on't, I'm resolved.   *(Aside and exit.*

Arab. Are you concern'd at the interruption too?

Cape. It was a very seasonable one, I promise you; had you stay'd a little longer, I don't know what might have been the consequence.

Arab. No danger to your person, I hope.

Cape. Some little attacks upon it.

Arab. Which were as feebly resisted.

Cape. Why, consider, my dear Bell; tho' your sister is a fool, she is a fine woman, and flesh is frail.

Arab. Dear Bell! And flesh is frail! We are grown strangely familiar, I think.

Cape. Heydey! In what corner sits the wind now?

Arab. Where it may possibly blow strong enough to overset your hopes.

Cape. That a breeze of your breath can do.

Arab. Affected!

Cape. You are obliging, madam; but pray, what is the meaning of all this?

Arab. Ask your own guilty conscience.

Cape. Were I inclined to flatter myself, this little passion wou'd be no bad presage.

Arab. You may prove a false prophet.

Cape. Let me die, if I know what to— But to descend to a little common sense; what part of my conduct ——

Arab. Look'e, Mr. Cape, all explanations are unnecessary: I have been lucky enough to discover

your disposition before it is too late ; and so you
know there's no occasion —but however, I'll not be
any impediment to you ; my sister will be back
immediately ; l suppose my presence will only —
But consider, sir, I have a brother's honour ——

Cape. Which is as safe from me, as if it was
lock'd up in your brother's closet : But surely, madam, you are a little capricious, here ; have I done
any thing but obey your directions ?

Arab. That was founded upon a supposition
that ——— but no matter.

Cape. That what ?

Arab. Why, I was weak enough to believe,
what you was wicked enough to protest ———

Cape. That I loved you ; and what reason have I
given you to doubt it ?

Arab. A pretty situation I found you in at my
entrance.

Cape. An assumed warmth, for the better concealing the fraud.

Mrs. Cad. What's that ? *(Aside, listening.*

Cape. Surely if you doubted my constancy, you
must have a better opinion of my understanding.

Mrs. Cad. Mighty well. *(Aside.*

Cape. What an ideot, a driveller ! no consideration upon earth, but my paving the way to the
possession of you, could have prevail'd upon me to
support her folly a minute.

Enter Mrs. Cadwallader.

Mrs. Cad. Soh ! Mr. Poet, you are a pretty
gentleman, indeed ; ecod, I'm glad I have caught
you. I'm not such a fool as you think for, man ;
but here will be Dicky presently, he shall hear of
your tricks, he shall ; I'll let him know what a pretty person he has got in his house.

Cape. There's no parrying this ; had not I better decamp.

Arab. And leave me to the mercy of the enemy :

My brother's temper is so odd, there's no knowing
in what light he'll see this.

Mrs. Cad. Oh, he's below, I hear him. Now
we shall hear what he'll say to you, madam.

Enter Cadwallader, Governor, Sprightly, and Robin.

Cad. No, pray walk in, Mr. Interpreter, between you and I, I like his royal highness mightily ;
he's a polite, pretty, well-bred gentleman——but
damn his soup.

Gov. Why, sir, you eat as if you lik'd it.

Cad. Lik'd it ! hey, egad, I would not eat another mess to be his master's prime minister ; as
bitter as gall, and as black as my hat ; and there
have I been sitting these two hours with my legs
under me 'till they are both as dead as a herring.

Cape. Your dinner displeas'd you ?

Cad. Displeas'd ! hey ! Look'e, Mr. Sprightly,
I'm mightily obliged to you for the honour ; but
hold, hold, you shall never persuade me to be a hob-
blinwisky again, if the great cham of the Calmucks
were to come over himself. Hey ! and what a
damn'd language has he got ? Whce, haw, haw !
but you speak it very fluently.

Gov. I was long resident in the country.

Cad. May be so, but he seems to speak it better ; you have a foreign kind of an accent, you don't
sound it through the nose so well as he. Hey !
well Becky, what, and how have you entertain'd
Mr. Cape.

Mrs. Cad. Oh ! here have been fine doings
since you have been gone.

Cape. So, now comes on the storm.

Cad. Hey ! hold, hold, what has been the matter ?

Mrs. Cad. Matter ! why the devil is in the poet,
I think.

Cad. The devil ! hold.

Mrs. Cad. Why here he has been making love to me like bewitch'd.

Cad. How, which way?

Mrs. Cad. Why some on't was out of his poetry I think.

Cad. Hey! hold, hold, egad I believe he's a little mad; this morning he took me for king Turnus, you; now who can tell, but this afternoon he may take you for queen Dido?

Mrs. Cad. And there he told me I was to run, and to double, and quat, and there he was to catch me, and all that.

Cad. Hold, hold, catch you? Mr. Cape, I take it very unkindly; it was, d'ye see, a very unfriendly thing to make love to Becky in my absence.

Cape. But, sir.

Cad. And it was the more ungenerous, Mr. Cape, to take this advantage, as you know she is but a foolish woman.

Mrs. Cad. Ay, me; who am but a foolish woman.

Cape. But hear me.

Cad. A poor ignorant, illiterate, poor Becky! And for a man of your parts to attack ——

Cape. There's no ——

Cad. Hold, hold, ecod it is just as if the grand signor, at the head of his janisaries, was to kick a chimney-sweeper.

Mrs. Cad. Hey! what's that you say, Dicky; what, be I like a chimney-sweeper?

Cad. Hey! hold, hold. Zounds! no, Beck; hey! no: That's only by way of simile, to let him see I understand your tropes, and figures, as well as himself, egad! and therefore——

Spri. Nay, but Mr. Cadwallader ——

Cad. Don't mention it, Mr. Sprightly; he is the first poet I ever had in my house, except the bellman for a Christmas-box.

Spri. Good sir.

Cad. And hold, hold; I am resolved he shall be the last.

Spri. I have but one way to silence him.

Cad. And let me tell you——

Spri. Nay, sir, if I must tell him; he owes his reception here to my recommendation; any abuse of your goodness, any breach of hospitality here, he is answerable to me for.

Cad. Hey! hold, hold, so he is, ecod; at him; give it him home.

Spri. Ungrateful monster! and is this your return for the open, generous treatment——

Mrs. Cad. As good fry'd cow-heel, with a roast fowl and sausages, as ever came to a table.

Cad. Hush, Beck, hush!——

Spri. And cou'd you find no other object, but Mr. Cadwallader; a man, perhaps, possess'd of a genius superior to your own ——

Cad. If I had had a university education——

Spri. And of a family as old as the creation.

Cad. Older; Beck, fetch the pedigree.

Spri. Thus far relates to this gentleman; but now, sir, what apology can you make me, who was your passport, your security?

Cad. Zounds, none; fight him.

Spri. Fight him?

Cad. Ay, do; I'd fight him myself, if I had not had the measles last winter; but stay till I get out of the room.

Spri. No, he's sure of a protection here, the presence of the ladies.

Cad. Pshaw, pox! they belong to the family, never mind them.

Spri. Well, sir, are you dumb? No excuse? No pallation?

Cad. Ay, no palliation?

Mrs. Cad. Ay, no tribulation? It's a shame, so it is.

Cape. When I have leave to speak——

Cad. Speak! what the devil can you say?

Cape. Nay, sir————

Spri. Let's hear him, Mr. Cadwallader, however.

Cad. Hold, hold; come, begin then.

Cape. And first to you, Mr. Sprightly, as you seem most interested; pray does this charge correspond with any other action of my life, since I have had the honour to know you?——

Spri. Indeed, I can't say that I recollect, but still as the scholiasts say — *Nemo repente fuit turpissimus.*

Cad. Hold, hold, what's that?

Spri. Why, that is as much as to say, this is bad enough.

Mrs. Cad. By gosh! and so it is.

Cad. Ecod, and so it is; speak a little more Latin to him; if I had been bred at the university, you shou'd have it both sides of your ears.

Cape. A little patience, gentlemen; now, to you; you were pleased yourself to drop a few hints of your lady's weakness; might not she take too seriously, what was meant as a mere matter of merriment?

Cad. Hey! hold, hold.

Spri. A paltry excuse; can any woman be such a fool as not to know when a man has a design upon her person?

Cad. Answer that Mr. Cape, hey! answer that.

Cape. I can only answer for the innocency of my own intentions; may not your lady, apprehensive of my becoming too great a favourite, contrive this charge with a view of destroying the connexion————

Spri. Connexion!

Cad. Hey! hold, hold, connexion.

Spri. There's something in that————

Cad. Hey! is there? Hold, hold, hey! egad, he is right——You're right, Mr. Cape; hold, Becky, my dear, how the devil cou'd you be so

wicked, hey! child ; ecod, hold, hold, how could
you have the wickedness to attempt to destroy
the connexion?

Mrs. Cad. I don't know what you say.

Cad. D'ye hear? You are an incendiary, but you
have miss'd your point; the connexion shall only
be the stronger : my dear friend, I beg ten thousand
pardons, I was too hasty; but ecod, Becky's to
blame.

Cape. The return of your favour has effaced every other impression.

Cad. There's a good-natured creature!

Cape. But if you have the least doubts remaining,
this lady, your sister, I believe, will do me the justice to own ——

Mrs. Cad. Ay, ask my fellow, if I be a thief.

Cad. What the devil is Becky at now?

Mrs. Cad. She's as bad as he.

Cad. Bad as he? Hey! how; what the devil,
she did not make love to you too? Stop, hey!
hold, hold, hold.

Mrs. Cad. Why no, foolish, but you are always
running on with your riggmonrowles, and won't
stay to hear a body's story out.

Cad. Well, Beck, come let's have it.

Mrs. Cad. Be quiet then : why, as I was telling you, first he made love to me, and wanted me
to be a hare.

Cad. A hare! hold, ecod, that was whimsical;
a hare! hey! oh ecod, that might be because he
thought you a little hair-brain'd already ; Becky, a
damn'd good story. Well, Beck, go on, let's have
it out.

Mrs. Cad. No, I won't tell you no more, so I
won't.

Cad. Nay, prythee, Beck.

Mrs. Cad. Hold your tongue then : And so
there he was going on with his nonsense, and so in
come our Bell ; and so ——

Cad. Hold, hold, Becky; damn your so's; go on, child, but leave out your so's; its a low —— hold, hold, vulgar —— but go on.

Mrs. Cad. Why how can I go on, when you stop me every minute? Well, and then our Bell came in and interrupted him, and methought she looked very frumpish and jealous.

Cad. Well.

Mrs. Cad. And so I went out and listen'd.

Cad. So, what you staid and listen'd?

Mrs. Cad. No; I tell you upon my staying, she went out; no——upon my going out, she staid.

Cad. This is a damn'd blind story, but go on, Beck.

Mrs. Cad. And then at first she scolded him roundly for making love to me; and then he said as how she advised him to it; and then she said no; and then he said ——

Cad. Hold, hold; we shall never understand all these he's and she's; this may all be very true, Beck, but, hold, hold; as I hope to be saved, thou art the worst teller of a story ——

Mrs. Cad. Well, I have but a word more; and then he said as how I was a great fool.

Cad. Not much mistaken in that. *(Aside.)*

Mrs. Cad. And that he wou'd not have stay'd with me a minute, but to pave the way to the possesion of she.

Cad. Well, Beck, well?

Mrs. Cad. And so————that's all.

Cad. Make love to her, in order to get possession of you?

Mrs. Cad. Love to me, in order to get she.

Cad. Hey! Oh, now I begin to understand. Hey! What's this true, Bell? Hey! Hold, hold, hold; ecod, I begin to smoke, hey! Mr. Cape.

Cape. How shall I act?

Rob. Own it, sir, I have a reason.

Cad. Well, what say you, Mr. Cape? Let's

have it, without equivocation ; or, hold, hold, hold, mental reservation. Guilty, or not?

Cape. Of what, sir?

Cad. Of what? Hold, hold, of making love to Bell.

Cape. Guilty.

Cad. Hey! how? Hold, zounds! No, what not with an intention to marry her?

Cape. With the lady's approbation, and your kind consent.

Cad. Hold, hold, what my consent to marry you?

Cape. Ay, sir.

Cad. Hold, hold, hold, what our Bell? To mix the blood of the Cadwalladers with the puddle of a poet?

Cape. Sir?

Cad. A petty, paltry, ragged, rhiming ——

Spri. But Mr. ——

Cad. A scribbling, hold, hold, hold ——. Garretteer? that has no more cloaths than backs, no more heads than hats, and no shoes to his feet.

Spri. Nay, but ——

Cad. The offspring of a dunghill! Born in a cellar, hold, hold, and living in a garret ; a fungus, a mushroom.

Cape. Sir, my family ——

Cad. Your family! hold, hold, hold, Peter, fetch the pedigree ; I'll shew you —— Your family! a little obscure —— hold, hold, I don't believe you ever had a grandfather.

Enter Peter with the pedigree.

There it is ; there ; Peter, help me to stretch it out : There's seven yards more of lineals, besides three of collaterals, that I expect next Monday from the herald's office ; d'ye see, Mr. Sprightly?

Spri. Prodigious!

Cad. Nay, but look'e, there's Welch princes,

and ambassadors, and kings of Scotland, and members of parliament: Hold, hold, ecod, I no more mind an earl or a lord in my pedigree, hold, hold, than Kouli Khan wou'd a serjeant in the train'd bands.

Spri. An amazing descent!

Cad. Hey, is it not? And for this low, lousy son of a shoe-maker, to talk of families — hold, hold, get out of my house.

Rob. Now is your time, sir.

Cad. Mr. Sprightly, turn him out.

Gov. Stop, sir, I have a secret to disclose, that may make you alter your intentions.

Cad. Hold, hold; how, Mr. Interpreter?

Gov. You are now to regard that young man in a very different light, and consider him as my son.

Cape. Your son, sir?

Gov. In a moment, George, the mysteries shall be explain'd.

Cad. Your son? Hold, hold; and what then?

Gov. Then! Why then he is no longer the scribbler, the mushroom you have described, but of birth and fortune equal to your own.

Cad. What! the son of an interpreter equal to me! A fellow that trudges about, teaching of languages to foreign counts.

Gov. A teacher of languages!

Cad. Stay; ecod, a runner to monsieurs and marquisses!

Spri. You are mistaken, sir.

Cad. A jack-pudding! that takes fillips on the nose for six-pence a piece! Hold, hold, ecod, give me eighteen-pennyworth, and change for half a crown.

Gov. Stop, when you are well.

Cad. A spunger at other men's tables! that has jallop put into his beer, and his face black'd at Christmas for the diversion of children.

Gov. I can hold no longer. 'Sdeath, sir; who is it you dare treat in this manner?

Cad. Hey! zounds, Mr. Sprightly, lay hold of him.

Spri. Calm your choler. Indeed, Mr. Cadwallader, nothing cou'd excuse your behaviour to this gentleman, but your mistaking his person.

Cad. Hold, hold. Is not he interpreter to —

Spri. No.

Cad. Why did not you tell ——

Spri. That was a mistake. This gentleman is the prince's friend; and, by a long residence in the monarch's country, is perfect master of the language.

Cad. But who the devil is he then?

Spri. He is Mr. Cape, sir; a man of unblemish'd honour, capital fortune, and late governor of one of our most considerable settlements.

Cad. Governor! Hold, hold, and how came you father to —— hey!——

Gov. By marrying his mother.

Cape. But how am I to regard this?

Gov. As a solemn truth; that foreign friend, to whom you owe your education, was no other than myself; I had my reasons, perhaps capricious ones, for concealing this; but now they cease, and I am proud to own my son.

Cape. Sir; it is not for me *(kneeling)* but if gratitude, duty filial ————

Gov. Rise, my boy; I have ventured far to fix thy fortune, George; but to find thee worthy of it, more than o'erpays my toil; the rest of my story shall be reserved till we are alone.

Cad. Hey! Hold, hold, hold; ecod, a good sensible old fellow this; but, hark'e, Sprightly, I have made a damn'd blunder here: Hold, hold, Mr. Governor, I ask ten thousand pardons; but who the devil cou'd have thought that the interpreter to prince Potowowsky ——

Gov. Oh, sir, you have in your power sufficient means to atone for the injuries done us both.

Cad. Hold, how?

Gov. By bestowing your sister, with, I flatter myself, no great violence to her inclinations, here.

Cad. What, marry Bell? Hey! Hold, hold; zounds, Bell, take him, do; ecod, he is a good likely —— hey! Will you?

Arab. I shan't disobey you, sir.

Cad. Shan't you? That's right. Who the devil knows but he may come to be a governor himself; hey! Hold, hold; come here then, give me your hands both; *(Joins their hands.)* There, there, the business is done: And now brother governor——

Gov. And now, brother Cadwallader.

Cad. Hey, Beck! here's something new for my pedigree; we'll pop in the governor to-morrow.

Mrs. Cad. Hark'e, Mr. Governor, can you give me a black boy and a monkey?

Cad. Hey! Ay, ay, you shall have a black boy, and a monkey, and a parrot too, Beck.

Spri. Dear George, I am a little late in my congratulations; but ——

Gov. Which if he is in acknowledging your disinterested friendship, I shall be sorry I ever own'd him. Now, Robin, my cares are over, and my wishes full; and if George remains as untainted by affluence, as he has been untempted by distress, I have given the poor a protector, his country an advocate, and the world a friend.

(Exeunt Omnes.

FINIS.

NOVELS

Printed for W. LOWNDES.

ABELARD & ELOISA, with seven Poems
Antigallican, or Harry Cobham
Auction, 2 vols
Beaufort, History of Sir Charles, 2 vols
Birmingham Counterfeit, 2 vols
Boyle's Voyages and Adventures | Brother, 2 vols
Casket, or Double Discovery, 2 vols
Clive, Adventures of Francis, 2 vols
Country Seat, or Evening's Amusement, 2 vols
Delia Stanhope, 2 vols
Evelina, by Miss Burney, 2 vols
Fair Philosopher, 2 vols
Fanny Seymour, by Mr. Shields
Fatal Friendship, 2 vols | Fine Lady, 2 vols
Fortunate Country Maid, 3 vols | French Lady, 2 vols
Henrietta, by Mrs. Lennox, 2 vols
High Life, or Miss Frankland, 2 vols
Indiana Danby, 4 vols
Jack Connor, 2 vols
Joseph Andrews, by Fielding, 2 vols
Ladies Miscellany, 2 vols
Lady Manchester, or Husband's Resentment, 2 vols
Lucilla, or Progress of Virtue
Major Bromley, and Miss Cliffin, 2 vols
Margaretta, by Miss Minifie, 2 vols
Miss Melmoth, or New Clarissa, 3 vols
Modern Fine Gentleman, 2 vols | Modern Wife, 2 vols
Mount Henneth, by Mr. Bage, 2 vols
Novelist, or Tea-Table Miscellany, 2 vols
Pamela Howard, 2 vols
Relapse, 2 vols
Sentimental Spy, 2 vols
Singleton's Voyages and Adventures
Surprises of Love, by Cleland
Telemachus, by Fenelon | Tom Jones, by Fielding, 4 vols
Thoughtless Ward | Trinket
Unfashionable Wife, 2 vols
Vaughan's Voyages and Adventures, 2 vols
Wilhelmina, by Jünger, 2 vols
Woman of Fashion, 2 vols
Woman of Honor, by Cleland, 3 vols
Younger Sister, 2 vols

THE

ENGLISHMAN RETURNED FROM PARIS;

BEING THE SEQUEL TO

THE ENGLISHMAN IN PARIS :

A FARCE,

IN TWO ACTS,

AS PERFORMED AT THE

THEATRES-ROYAL IN DRURY-LANE AND COVENT-GARDEN.

WRITTEN BY

SAMUEL FOOTE, Esq.

———◆———

A NEW EDITION.

———◆———

LONDON :

PRINTED FOR W. LOWNDES, 38, BEDFORD STREET.

———

1808.

PROLOGUE,

SPOKEN BY

Mr. FOOTE.

———

OF all the passions that possess mankind,
The love of novelty rules most the mind ;
In search of this, from realm to realm we roam,
Our fleets come fraught with every folly home ;
From Lybia's deserts hostile brutes advance,
And dancing dogs in droves skip here from France ;
From Latian lands gigantic forms appear,
Striking our British breasts with awe and fear,
As once the Lilliputians———Gulliver.
Not only objects that affect the sight,
In foreign arts and artists we delight :
Near to that spot where Charles bestrides a horse,
In humble prose the place is Charing Cross ;
Close by the margin of a kennel's side,
A dirty dismal entry opens wide,
There with hoarse voice, check shirt, and callous hand,
Duff's Indian English trader takes his stand,
Surveys each passenger with curious eyes,
And rustic Roger falls an easy prize ;
Here's China porcelain that Chelsea yields,
And India handkerchiefs from Spitalfields.
With Turkey carpets that from Wilton came,
And Spanish tucks and blades from Birmingham,
Factors are forced to favour this deceit,
And English goods are smuggled thro' the street.
The rude to polish, and the fair to please,
The hero of to-night has cross'd the seas.

3.

PROLOGUE.

Tho' to be born a Briton be his crime,
He's manufactured in another clime.
'Tis Buck begs leave once more to come before ye,
The little subject of a former story,
How chang'd, how fashion'd, whether brute or beau,
We trust the following scenes will fully shew.
For them and him we your indulgence crave,
'Tis ours still to sin on, and yours to save.

EPILOGUE:

SPOKEN BY

Mrs. BELLAMY.

AMONG the arts to make a piece go down,
And fix the fickle favour of the town,
An Epilogue is deem'd the surest way
To atone for all the errors of the play;
Thus when pathetic strains have made you cry,
In trips the Comic Muse, and wipes your eye,
With equal reason, when she has made you laugh,
Melpomene should send you snivelling off.
But our Bard, unequal to the task,
Rejects the dagger, and retains the mask:
Fain would he send you chearful home to-night,
And harmless mirth by honest means excite;
Scorning with luscious phrase or double sense,
To raise a laughter at the fair's expence.
What method shall we choose your taste to hit?
Will no one lend our Bard a little wit?
Thank ye, kind souls, I'll take it from the pit.

EPILOGUE.

The piece concluded, and the curtain down,
Up starts that fatal phalanx, call'd The Town:
In full assembly weighs our author's fate,
And Surly thus commences the debate:
Pray, among friends, does not this poisoning scene
The sacred rights of Tragedy profane?
If Farce may mimic thus her awful bowl:
Oh fie, all wrong, stark naught, upon my soul!
Then Buck cries, Billy, can it be in nature?
Not the least likeness in a single feature.
My lord, Lord love him, 'tis a precious piece;
Let's come on Friday night and have a hiss.
To this a peruquier assents with joy,
Parcequ'il affronte les François, oui, ma foi.
In such distress what can the poet do?
Where seek for shelter when those foes pursue?
He dares demand protection, sirs, from you.

DRAMATIS PERSONÆ.

AT COVENT GARDEN.

BUCK,	Mr. Foote.
CRAB,	Mr. Sparks.
LORD JOHN,	Mr. White.
MACRUTHEN,	Mr. Shuter.
RACKET,	Mr. Cushing.
TALLYHOE,	Mr. Castallo.
LATITAT,	Mr. Dunstall.
SERGEON,	Mr. Wignel.
LUCINDA,	Mrs. Bellamy.

La Jonquil, La Loire, Bearnois, and Servants.

THE ENGLISHMAN RETURNED
FROM PARIS.

ACT I.

Crab discovered reading.

" AND I do constitute my very good friend, Giles Crab, esq. of St. Martin in the Fields, executor to this my will; and do appoint him guardian to my ward Lucinda; and do submit to his direction, the management of all my affairs, till the return of my son from his travels; whom I do intreat my said executor in consideration of our ancient friendship, to advise, to counsel, &c. &c.—

John Buck."

A good, pretty legacy! Let's see, I find myself heir, by this generous devise of my very good friend, to ten actions at common law, nine suits in chancery, the conduct of a boy, bred a booby at home, and finish'd a fop abroad; together with the direction of a marriageable, and therefore an unmanageable wench; and all this to an old fellow of sixty-six, who heartily hates business, is tired of the world, and despises every thing in it. Why how the devil came I to merit ———

Enter Servant.

Ser. Mr. Latitat, of Staple's Inn.
Crab. So, here begin my plagues. Shew the hound in.

Enter Latitat with a bag, &c.

Lat. I would, Mr. Crab, have attended your summons immediately, but I was obliged to sign judgment in error at the Common Pleas; sue out of the Exchequer a writ of *quæ minus*, and surrender in *banco regis* the defendant, before the return of the *sci fa*, to discharge the bail.

Crab. Prithee, man, none of thy unintelligible law jargon to me; but tell me in the language of common sense, and thy country, what I am to do.

Lat. Why, Mr. Crab, as you are already possessed of a *probat*, and letters of administration *de bonis* are granted, you may sue, or, be sued; I hold it sound doctrine for no executor to discharge debts, without a receipt upon record : this can be obtained by no means but by an action. Now, actions, sir, are of various kinds, there are special actions, actions on the case, or *assumpsit's*, actions of trover, actions of *clausum fregit*, actions of battery, actions of ——

Crab. Hey, the devil, where's the fellow running now ?—But hark'ee, Latitat, why I thought all our law proceedings were directed to be in English.

Lat. True, Mr. Crab.

Crab. And what do you call all this stuff, ha!

Lat. English.

Crab. The devil you do.

Lat. Vernacular, upon my honour, Mr. Crab. For as lord Coke describes the common law, to be the perfection ——

Crab. So, here's a fresh deluge of impertinence. A truce to thy authorities, I beg; and as I find it will be impossible to understand thee without an interpreter, if you will meet me at five, at Mr. Brief's chambers, why, if you have any thing to say, he will translate it for me.

Lat. Mr. Brief, sir, and translate, sir !—Sir, I would have you to know, that no practitioner in Westminster Hall, gives clearer ——

Crab. Sir, I believe it; for which reason I have

referred you to a man who never goes into Westminster Hall.

Lat. A bad proof of his practice, Mr. Crab.

Crab. A good one of his principles, Mr. Latitat.

Lat. Why, sir, do you think that a lawyer ——

Crab. Zounds, sir, I never thought about a
lawyer. The law is an oracular idol, you are the
explanatory ministers; nor should any of my own
private concerns have made me bow to your
beastly Baal. I had rather lose a cause, than con-
test it. And had not this old, doating dunce, sir
John Buck, plagued me with the management of
his money, and the care of his booby boy, Bedlam
should sooner have had me, than the bar.

Lat. Bedlam, the bar! Since, sir, I am provoked, I don't know what your choice may be, or
what your friends may choose for you; I wish I
was your *prochain ami:* but I am under some doubts
as to the sanity of the testator, otherwise he could
not have chosen for his executor, under the sanction of the law, a person who despises the law.
And the law, give me leave to tell you, Mr. Crab,
is the bulwark, the fence, the protection, the *sine
qua non*, the *ne plus ultra* ——

Crab. Mercy, good Six-and-eight-pence.

Lat. The defence and offence, the by which,
and the whereby, the statute common and customary, or as Plowden classically and elegantly ex-
presses it, 'tis

Mos commune vetus mores, consulta senatus,
Hæc tria jus statuunt terra Britanna tibi.

Crab. Zounds, sir, among all your laws, are
there none to protect a man in his own house?

Lat. Sir, a man's house is his castellum, his castle; and so tender is the law of any infringement
of that sacred right, that any attempt to invade it
by force, fraud, or violence, clandestinely, or *vi et
armis*, is not only deemed *felonius* but *burglarius*.

Now, sir, a burglary may be committed either upon the dwelling, or out-house.

Crab. O laud! O laud!

Enter Servant.

Ser. Your clerk, sir——The parties, he says, are all in waiting at your chambers.

Lat. I come. I will but just explain to Mr. Crab, the nature of a burglary, as it has been described by a late statute.

Crab. Zounds, sir, I have not the least curiosity.

Lat. Sir, but every gentleman should know ——

Crab. I won't know. Besides, your clients ——

Lat. O, they may stay. I shan't take up five minutes, sir——A burglary ——

Crab. Not an instant.

Lat. By the common law.——

Crab. I'll not hear a word.

Lat. It was but a *clausum fregit.*

Crab. Dear sir, be gone.

Lat. But by the late acts of par ——

Crab. Help, you dog. Zounds, sir, get out of my house.

Ser. Your clients, sir ———

Crab. Push him out [*the lawyer talking all the while*] So, ho! Hark'ee, rascal, if you suffer that fellow to enter my doors again, I'll strip and discard you the very minute.—[*Exit Servant*]—This is but the beginning of my torments. But that I expect the young whelp from abroad, every instant, I'd fly for it myself and quit the kingdom at once.

Enter Servant.

Serv. My young master's travelling tutor, sir, just arrived.

Crab. Oh, then I suppose, the blockhead of a baronet is close at his heels. Shew him in. This bear-leader, I reckon now, is either the clumsy curate of the knight's own parish church, or some

needy highlander, the out-cast of his country, who,
with the pride of a German baron, the poverty of
a French marquis, the address of a Swiss soldier,
and the learning of an academy usher, is to give
our heir apparent politeness, taste, literature ; a
perfect knowledge of the world, and of himself.

Enter Macruthen.

Mac. Maister Crab, I am your devoted servant.

Crab. Oh, a British child by the mess.—Well,
where's your charge ?

Mac. O, the young baronet is o'the road. I
was mighty afraid he had o'er ta'en me ; for between Canterbury and Rochester, I was stopt, and
robb'd by a highwayman.

Crab. Robb'd ! what the devil could he rob
you of ?

Mac. In gude troth, not a mighty booty. Bu-
chanan's history, Lauder against Melton, and two
pound of high-dried Glasgow.

Crab. A travelling equipage. Well, and what's
become of your cub ? Where have you left him ?

Mac. Main you sir Charles ? I left him at Calais, with another young nobleman, returning from
his travels. But why caw ye him cub, maister
Crab ? In gude troth there's a meeghty alteration.

Crab. Yes, yes, I have a shrewd guess at his
improvements.

Mac. He's quite a phenomenon.

Crab. Oh, a comet, I dare swear, but not an
unusual one at Paris. The Faux-bourg of St. Ger-
mains, swarms with such, to the no small amusement of our very good friends the French.

Mac. Oh ! the French were very fond of him.

Crab. But as to the language, I suppose he's a
perfect master of that.

Mac. He can caw for aught that he need, but
he is na quite maister of the accent.

Crab. A most astonishing progress !

Mac. Suspend your judgment awhile, and you'll find him all you wish, allowing for the sallies of juvenility ; and must take the vanity to myself of being, in a great measure, the author.

Crab. Oh, if he be but a faithful copy of the admirable original, he must be a finished piece.

Mac. You are pleased to compliment.

Crab. Not a whit. Well, and what—I suppose you, and your—what's your name?

Mac. Macruthen, at your service.

Crab. Macruthen! Hum! You and your pupil agreed very well?

Mac. Perfectly. The young gentleman is of an amiable disposition.

Crab. Oh, ay : And it would be wrong to sour his temper. You knew your duty better, I hope, than to contradict him.

Mac. It was na for me, Maister Crab.

Crab. Oh, by no means, master Macruthen; all your business was to keep him out of frays ; to take care, for the sake of his health, that his wine was genuine, and his mistresses as they should be. You pimp'd for him I suppose?

Mac. Pimp for him! D'ye mean to affront —

Crab. To suppose the contrary would be the affront, Mr. Tutor. What, man, you know the world. 'Tis not by contradiction, but by compliance, that men make their fortunes. And was it for you to thwart the humour of a lad upon the threshold of ten thousand a year?

Mac. Why, to be sure great allowances must be made.

Crab. No doubt, no doubt.

Mac. I see, maister Crab, you know mankind ; you are sir John Buck's executor.

Crab. True.

Mac. I have a little thought that may be useful to us both.

Crab. As how?

Mac. Could na we contrive to make a hond o'the young baronet?

Crab. Explain.

Mac. Why you, by the will, have the care o'the cash : and I caw make a shift to manage the lad.

Crab. Oh, I conceive you.   And so between us both, we may contrive to ease him of that inheritance which he knows not how properly to employ ; and apply it to our own use.   You do know how.

Mac. Ye ha hit it.

Crab. Why what a superlative rascal art thou, thou inhospitable villain ! Under the roof, and in the presence, of thy benefactor's representative, with almost his ill-bestowed bread in your mouth, art thou plotting the perdition of his only child ! And, from what part of my life didst thou derive a hope of my compliance with such a hellish scheme?

Mac. Maister Crab, I am of a nation ——

Crab. Of known honour and integrity ; I allow it.   The kingdom you have quitted, in consigning the care of its monarch, for ages, to your predecessors, in preference to its proper subjects, has given you a brilliant panegyric, that no other people can parallel.

Mac. Why, to be sure ——

Crab. And one happiness it is, that though national glory can beam a brightness on particulars, the crimes of individuals can never reflect a disgrace upon their country.   Thy apology but aggravates thy guilt.

Mac. Why, maister Crab, I ——

Crab. Guilt and confusion choak thy utterance. Avoid my sight.   Vanish !—[*Exit Mac.*]—A fine fellow this, to protect the person, inform the inexperience, direct and moderate the desires of an unbridled boy ! But can it be strange, whilst the

parent negligently accepts a superficial recommendation to so important a trust, that the person
whose wants perhaps, more than his abilities make
desirous of it, should consider the youth as a kind
of property, and not consider what to make him,
but what to make of him; and thus prudently lay
a foundation for his future sordid hopes, by a criminal compliance with the lad's present prevailing
passions? But vice and folly rule the world.—
Without, there!—[*Enter Servant.*]—Rascal, where
d'you run, blockhead? Bid the girl come hither.—
Fresh instances, every moment, fortify my abhor-
rence, my detestation of mankind. This turn may
be term'd misanthropy; and imputed to chagrin
and disappointment. But it can only be by those
fools, who, through softness or ignorance, regard
the faults of others, like their own, through the
wrong end of the perspective.

Enter Lucinda.

So, what I suppose your spirits are all afloat.
You have heard your fellow's coming.

Luc. If you had your usual discernment, sir,
you would distinguish, in my countenance, an expression very different from that of joy.

Crab. Oh, what, I suppose your monkey has
broke his chain, or your parrot died in moulting.

Luc. A person less censorious than Mr. Crab,
might assign a more generous motive for my distress.

Crab. Distress! a pretty, poetical phrase. What
motive canst thou have for distress? Has not sir
John Buck's death assured thy fortune? and art
not thou ——

Luc. By that very means, a helpless unpro-
tected orphan.

Crab. Pho', prithee, wench, none of thy romantic cant to me. What, I know the sex: the objects of every woman's wish are property and
power. The first you have, and the second you

won't be long without ; for here's a puppy riding post to put on your chains.

Luc. It would appear affectation not to understand you. And, to deal freely, it was upon that subject I wish'd to engage you.

Crab. Your information was needless ; I knew it.

Luc. Nay, but why so severe ? I did flatter myself that the very warm recommendation of your deceased friend, would have abated a little of that rigour.

Crab. No wheedling, Lucy. Age and contempt have long shut these gates against flattery and dissimulation. You have no sex for me. Without preface, speak your purpose.

Luc. What then, in a word, is your advice with regard to my marrying sir Charles Buck ?

Crab. And do you seriously want my advice ?

Luc. Most sincerely.

Crab. Then you are a blockhead. Why where could you mend yourself ? Is not he a fool, a fortune, and in love ? —Look'ee, girl.—[*Enter Servant*]— Who sent for you, sir ?

Ser. Sir, my young master's post-chaise is broke down, at the corner of the street, by a coal-cart. His clothes are all dirt, and he swears like a trooper.

Crab. Ay ! Why then carry his chaise to the coach-maker's, his coat to a scowerer's, and him before a justice.——Prithee, why dost trouble me? I suppose you would not meet your gallant.

Luc. Do you think I should ?

Crab. No, retire. And if this application for my advice, is not a copy of your countenance, a mask ; if you are obedient, I may yet set you right.

Luc. I shall, with pleasure, follow your directions. [*Exit.*

Crab. Yes, so long as they correspond with your own inclination. Now we shall see what Paris has done for this puppy.   But here he comes ; light as the cork in his heels, or the feather in his hat.

Enter Buck, Lord John, La Loire, Bearnois, and Ma-cruthen.

Buck.   Not a word, *mi lor*, *jernie*, it is not to be supported !——after being *rompu tout vif*, disjointed by that execrable *pavé*, to be tumbled into a kennel, by a filthy *charbonnier* ; a dirty retailer of sea-coal, *morbleu !*

Ld. J.   An accident that might have happened any where, sir Charles.

Buck.   And then the hideous hootings of that *canaille*, that murtherous mob, with the barbarous— ' Monsieur in the mud, huzza !' Ah, *pais sauvage, barbare, inhospitable !* ah, ah, *qu'est ce que nous avons ?* Who ?

Mac.   That is maister Crab, your father's executor.

Buck.   Ha, ha.   *Serviteur très humble, monsieur. Eh bien !* What ! is he dumb ? Mac, my lor, *mort de ma vie*, the veritable Jack-Roast-beef of the French comedy.   Ha, ha, how do you do, monsieur-Jack-Roast-beef, ha, ha ?

Crab.   Prithee take a turn or two round the room.

Buck.   A turn or two ! *Volontiers.   Eh bien !* Well, have you, in your life, seen any thing so, ha, ha, hey !

Crab.   Never.   I hope you had not many spectators of your tumble.

Buck.   *Pourquoi ?* Why so ?

Crab.   Because I would not have the public curiosity forestalled.   I can't but think, in a country so fond of strange sights, if you were kept up a little, you would bring a great deal of money.

Buck.   I don't know, my dear, what my person would produce in this country, but the counterpart of your very grotesque figure has been extremely beneficial to the comedians from whence I came. *N'est ce pas vrai, mi lor ?* Ha, ha.

Ld. J. The resemblance does not strike me. Perhaps I may seem singular ; but the particular customs of particular countries, I own, never appeared to me, as proper objects of ridicule.

Buck. Why so?

Ld. J. Because in this case it is impossible to have a rule for your judgment. The forms and customs which climate, constitution and government have given to our kingdom can never be transplanted with advantage to another, founded on different principles. And thus, though the habits and manners of different countries may be directly opposite, yet, in my humble conception, they may be strictly, because naturally, right.

Crab. Why there are some glimmerings of common-sense about this young thing. Harkee, child, by what accident did you stumble upon this blockhead ?—[*to Buck*]—I suppose the line of your understanding is too short to fathom the depth of your companion's reasoning.

Buck. My dear. [*gapes.*]

Crab. I say, you can draw no conclusion from the above premises.

Buck. Who I ? Damn your premises, and conclusions too. But this I conclude from what I have seen, my dear, that the French are the first people in the universe; that, in the arts of living, they do or ought to give laws to the whole world, and that whosoever would either eat, drink, dress, dance, fight, sing, or even sneeze, *avec elegance,* must go to Paris, to learn it. This is my creed.

Crab. And these precious principles you are come here to propagate.

Buck. *C'est vrai, monsieur Crab:* and with the aid of these brother missionaries, I have no doubt of making a great many proselytes. And now for a detail of their qualities. *Bearnois, avancez.*

This is an officer of my household, unknown to this country.

Crab. And what may he be?—I'll humour the puppy.

Buck. This is my Swiss porter. *Tenez vous droit, Bearnois.* There's a fierce figure to guard the gate of an hotel.

Crab. What, do you suppose we have no porters?

Buck. Yes, you have dunces that open the doors; a drudgery that this fellow does by deputy. But for intrepidity in denying a disagreeable visitor; for politeness in introducing a mistress, acuteness in discerning, and constancy in excluding a dun, a greater genius never came from the Cantons.

Crab. Astonishing qualities!

Buck. *Retirez, Bearnois.* But here's a *bijou*, here's a jewel indeed! *Venez ici, mon cher La Loire. Comment trouvez vous ce Paris ici?*

La L. *Très bien.*

Buck. Very well. Civil creature! This, monsieur Crab, is my cook *La Loire*, and for *hors d'oeuvres, entre rotis, ragoûts, entremets,* and the disposition of a desert, Paris never saw his parallel.

Crab. His wages, I suppose, are proportioned to his merit,

Buck. A bagatelle, a trifle. Abroad but a bare two hundred. Upon his cheerful compliance, in coming hither into exile with me, I have indeed doubled his stipend.

Crab. You could do no less.

Buck. And now, sir, to compleat my equipage, *regardez monsieur La Jonquil,* my first *valet de chambre,* excellent in every thing: but *pour l'accommodage,* for decorating the head, inimitable. In one word, La Jonquil shall, for fifty to five, knot, twist, tye, frize, cut, curl, or comb with any *garçon perruquier,* from the land's end, to the Orkneys.

Crab. Why, what an infinite fund of public spirit must you have, to drain your purse, mortify your inclination, and expose your person, for the mere improvement of your countrymen ?

Buck. Oh, I am a very Roman for that. But at present I had another reason for returning.

Crab. Ay, what can that be ?

Buck. Why I find there is a likelihood of some little fracas between us. But, upon my soul, we must be very brutal to quarrel with the dear, agreeable creatures, for a trifle.

Crab. They have your affections then.

Buck. *De tout mon cœur.* From the infinite civility shewn to us, in France, and their friendly professions in favour of our country, they can never intend us an injury.

Crab. Oh, you have hit their humour to a hair. But I can have no longer patience with the puppy. Civility and friendship, you booby ! Yes, their civility at Paris, has not left you a guinea in your pocket, nor would their friendship to your nation leave it a foot of land in the universe.

Buck. Lord John, this is a strange old fellow. Take my word for it, my dear, you mistake this thing egregiously. But all you English are constitutionally sullen.—November fogs, with salt boil'd beef, are most cursed recipes for good humour, or a quick apprehension. Paris is the place. 'Tis there men laugh, love, and live ! *Vive l'amour ! Sans amour, et sans ses desirs, un cœur est bien moins heureux qu'il ne pense.*

Crab. Now would not any soul suppose that this yelping hound had a real relish for the country he has quitted ?

Buck. A mighty unnatural supposition, truly.

Crab. Foppery and affectation all.

Buck. And you really think Paris a kind of purgatory, ha, my dear ?

Crab. To thee the most solitary spot upon earth, my dear.—Familiar puppy !

Buck. Whimsical enough. But come, *pour passer le tems*, let us, old Diogenes, enter into a little debate. Mi lor, and you, Macruthen, determine the dispute between that source of delights, *ce paradis de plaisir*, and this cave of care, this seat of scurvy and the spleen.

Mac. Let us heed them weel, my lord. Maister Crab has met with his match.

Buck. And first for the great pleasure of life, the pleasure of the table ; ah, *quelle différence !* The ease, the wit, the wine, the *badinage*, the *perciflage*, the *double entendre*, the *chansons à boire.* Oh, what delicious moments have I pass'd *chez madame la duchesse de Barbouliac.*

Crab. Your mistress, I suppose.

Buck. Who, I ! *Fi donc !* How is it possible for a woman of her rank, to have a *penchant* for me? Hey, Mac.

Mac. Sir Charles is too much a man of honour to blab. But, to say truth, the whole city of Paris thought as much.

Crab. A precious fellow this !

Buck. *Taisez vous, Mac.* But we lose the point in view. Now, Monsieur Crab, let me conduct you to what you call an entertainment. And first, the melancholy mistress is fixed in her chair, where, by the bye, she is condemned to do more drudgery than a dray-horse. Next proceeds the master, to marshal the guests, in which as much caution is necessary, as at a coronation, with, " my lady, sit here," and, " sir Thomas, sit there," till the length of the ceremony, with the length of the grace, have destroyed all apprehensions of the meat burning your mouths.

Mac. Bravo, bravo ! Did I na' say sir Charles was a phœnomenon ?

Crab. Peace, puppy.

Buck. Then, in solemn silence, they proceed to demolish the substantials, with, perhaps, an occa-

sional interruption, of, " Here's to you, friends,"
" Hob or nob," " Your love and mine." Pork
succeeds to beef, pies to puddings: the cloth is
removed: madam, drenched with a bumper, drops
a curtesy, and departs; leaving the jovial host,
with his sprightly companions, to tobacco, port, and
politics. *Voilà un repas à la mode d'Angleterre*, monsieur Crab.

Crab. It is a thousand pities that your father
is not a living witness of these prodigious improvements.

Buck. *C'est vrai.* But *à propos*, he is dead, as
you say, and you are ———

Crab. Against my inclination, his executor.

Buck. *Peut être:* well, and ———

Crab. Oh, my task will soon determine. One
article, indeed, I am strictly enjoined to see performed; your marriage with your old acquaintance
Lucinda.

Buck. *Ha, ha, la petite Lucinde! & comment* —

Crab. Prithee, peace, and hear me. She is
bequeathed conditionally, that if you refuse to
marry her, twenty thousand pounds; and if she
rejects you, which I suppose she will have the
wisdom to do, only five.

Buck. Reject me! Very probable, hey, Mac!
But could we not have an *entrevüe?*

Crab. Who's there? Let Lucinda know we
expect her.

Mac. Had na' ye better, sir Charles, equip
yourself in a more suitable garb, upon a first visit
to your mistress?

Crab. Oh, such a figure and address can derive
no advantage from dress.

Buck. *Serviteur.* But, however, Mac's hint
may not be so *mal à propos.* *Allons, Jonquil, je m'en
vais m'habiller.* Mi lor, shall I trespass upon your
patience? My toilet is but the work of ten minutes.
Mac, dispose of my domestics *à leur aise*, and then

attend me with my portfeuille, and read, while I dress, those remarks I made in my last voyage from Fontainbleau to Compeigne.

> Serviteur, Messieurs ;
> Car le bon vin
> Du matin
> Sortant du tonneau,
> Vaut bien mieux que
> Le Latin
> De toute la Sorbonne.　　　　[*Exit*.

Crab. This is the most consummate coxcomb! I told the fool of a father, what a puppy Paris would produce him ; but travel is the word, and the consequence, an importation of every foreign folly : and thus the plain persons and principles of old England, are so confounded and jumbled with the excrementitious growth of every climate, that we have lost all our ancient characteristic, and are become a bundle of contradictions ; a piece of patch-work ; a mere harlequin's coat.

Ld. J. Do you suppose then, sir, that no good may be obtained ———

Crab. Why, prithee, what have you gained ?

Ld. J. I should be sorry my acquisitions were to determine the debate. But do you think, sir, the shaking off some native qualities, and the being made more sensible, from comparison, of certain national and constitutional advantages, objects unworthy the attention ?

Crab. You shew the favourable side, young man : but how frequently are substituted for national prepossessions, always harmless, and often happy, guilty and unnatural prejudices !—Unnatural !—For the wretch who is weak and wicked enough to despise his country, sins against the most laudable laws of nature ; he is a traitor to the community, where Providence has placed him ; and should be denied those social benefits he has

rendered himself unworthy to partake. But sen-
tentious lectures are ill calculated for your time of
life.

Ld. J. I differ from you here, Mr. Crab. Principles that call for perpetual practice, cannot be
too soon received. I sincerely thank you, sir, for
this communication, and should be happy to have
always near me so moral a monitor.

Crab. You are indebted to France for her flattery. But I leave you with a lady, where it will
be better employed.

Enter Lucinda.

Crab. This young man waits here, till your
puppy is powdered. You may ask him after your
French acquaintance. I know nothing of him;
but he does not seem to be altogether so great a
fool as your fellow.   [*Exit.*

Luc. I'm afraid, sir, you have had but a disagreeable *tête-à-tête.*

Ld. J. Just the contrary, madam. By good
sense, tinged with singularity, we are entertained
as well as improved. For a lady, indeed, Mr.
Crab's manners are rather too rough.

Luc. Not a jot; I am familiarized to 'em, I
know his integrity, and can never be disobliged by
his sincerity.

Ld. J. This declaration is a little particular,
from a lady who must have received her first im-
pressions in a place remarkable for its delicacy to
the fair-sex. But good sense can conquer even
early habits.

Luc. This compliment I can lay no claim to.
The former part of my life procured me but very
little indulgence. The pittance of knowledge I
possess, was taught me by a very severe mistress,
adversity. But you, sir, are too well acquainted
with sir Charles Buck, not to have known my situation.

Ld. J. I have heard your story, madam, before I had the honour of seeing you. It was affecting ; you'll pardon the declaration ; it now becomes interesting. However, it is impossible I should not congratulate you on the near approach of the happy catastrophe.

Luc. Events that depend upon the will of another, a thousand unforeseen accidents may interrupt.

Ld. J. Could I hope, madam, your present critical condition would acquit me of temerity, I should take the liberty to presume, if the suit of sir Charles be rejected ——

Enter Crab.

Crab. So, Youngster! what I suppose you are already practising one of your foreign lessons. Perverting the affections of a friend's mistress, or debauching his wife, are mere peccadilloes, in modern morality. But at present you are my care. That way conducts you to your fellow-traveller.— [*Exit. Ld. John.*]—I would speak with you in the library.   [*Exit.*

Luc. I shall attend you, sir. Never was so unhappy an interruption. What could my lord mean? But be it what it will, it ought not, it cannot concern me. Gratitude and duty demand my compliance with the dying wish of my benefactor, my friend, my father. But am I then to sacrifice all my future peace? But reason not, rash girl ; obedience is thy province.

Tho' hard the task, be it my part to prove
That sometimes duty can give laws to love.
                                    [*Exit.*

ACT II.

Buck at his toilet, attended by three valets de chambre and Macruthen.

Mac.

NOTWITHSTANDING aw his plain dealing, I doubt whether maister Crab is so honest a man.

Buck. Prithee, Mac, name not the monster. If I may be permitted a quotation from one of their paltry poets,

Who is knight of the shire represents 'em all.

Did ever mortal see such *mirrors*, such looking glass as they have here too! One might as well address oneself, for information, to a bucket of water. *La Jonquil, mettez vous le rouge, assez. Eh bien, Mac, miserable!* Hey!

Mac. It's very becoming.

Buck. Aye, it will do for this place; I really could have forgiven my father's living a year or two longer, rather than be compelled to return to this—[*Enter ld. John.*]—My dear lord, *je demande mille pardons*, but the terrible fracas in my chaise has so *gâtéed* and disordered my hair, that it required an age to adjust it.

Ld. J. No apology, sir Charles, I have been entertained very agreeably.

Buck. Who have you had, my dear lord, to entertain you?

Ld. J. The very individual lady that's soon to make you a happy husband.

Buck. A happy who? husband! What two very opposite ideas confounded *ensemble!* In my conscience, I believe there's contagion in the clime, and my lor is infected. But pray, my dear lor, by what accident have you discovered, that I was upon

the point of becoming that happy—Oh, *un mari !
Diable ?*

Ld. J. The lady's beauty and merit, your inclinations, and your father's injunctions, made me
conjecture that.

Buck. And can't you suppose that the lady's
beauty may be possess'd, her merit rewarded, and
my inclinations gratified, without an absolute obedience to that fatherly injunction ?

Ld. J. It does not occur to me.

Buck. No, I believe not, my lor. Those kind
of talents are not given to every body. *Donnez
moi mon manchon.* And now you shall see me
manage the lady.

Enter Servant.

Ser. Young squire Racket, and sir Toby Tallyhoe, who call themselves your honour's old acquaintances.

Buck. Oh the brutes ! By what accident could
they discover my arrival ! My dear, dear lor, aid
me to escape this *embarras.*

Racket and Tallyhoe without.

Hoic a boy, hoic a boy.

Buck. Let me die if I do not believe the Hot-
tentots have brought a whole hundred of hounds
with them. But they say, forms keep fools at a distance. I'll receive 'em *en cérémonie.*

Enter Racket and Tallyhoe.

Tally. Hey boy, hoix, my little Buck.

Buck. *Monsieur le chevalier, votre très humble
serviteur.*

Tally. Hey.

Buck. *Monsieur Racket, je suis charmé de vous
voir.*

Rack. Anon, what !

Buck. *Ne m'entendez vous?* Don't you understand French?

Rack. Know French! No, nor you neither, I think, sir Toby, foregad I believe the papistes ha bewitch'd him in foreign parts.

Tally. Bewitch'd and transformed him too. Let me perish, Racket, if I don't think he's like one of the folks we used to read of at school, in Ovid's metamorphis; and that they have turned him into a beast.

Rack. A beast! No, a bird, you fool. Lookee, sir Toby, by the lord Harry, here are his wings.

Tally. Hey! ecod and so they are, ha, ha. I reckon, Racket, he came over with the woodcocks.

Buck. *Voilà des véritables Anglois.* The rustic rude ruffians!

Rack. Let us see what the devil he has put upon his pole, sir Toby.

Tally. Aye.

Buck. Do, dear savage, keep your distance.

Tally. Nay, 'fore George we will have a scrutiny.

Rack. Aye, aye, a scrutiny.

Buck. *En grace. La Jonquil,* my lor, protect me from these pirates.

Ld J. A little compassion, I beg, gentlemen. Consider, sir Charles is on a visit to his bride.

Tally. Bride! Zounds he's fitter for a bandbox. Racket, hocks the heels.

Rack. I have 'em, knight. Foregad he is the very reverse of a bantam cock; his comb's on his feet, and his feathers on his head. Who have we got here! What are these fellows, pastry cooks?

Enter Crab.

Crab. And is this one of your newly acquired accomplishments, letting your mistress languish for a ——but you have company, I see.

Buck. O, yes, I have been inexpressibly happy. These gentlemen are kind enough to treat me, upon my arrival, with what I believe they call in this country, a rout.—My dear lor, if you don't favour my flight.   But see if the toads a'n't tumbling my toilet.

Ld. J.   Now's your time, steal off;   I'll cover your retreat.

Buck.   Mac, let La Jonquil follow to re-settle my *cheveux.*—*Je vous remercie mille, mille fois, mon cher* my lor.

Rack.   Hola, sir Toby, stole away!

Buck.   *O mon Dieu.*

Tally.   Poh, rot him, let him alone.   He'll never do for our purpose.   You must know we intend to kick up a riot, to-night, at the play-house, and we wanted him of the party; but that fop would swoon at the sight of a cudgel.

Ld. J.   Pray, sir, what is your cause of contention?

Tally.   Cause of contention, hey, faith, I know nothing of the matter.   Racket, what is it we are angry about?

Rack.   Angry about!   Why you know we are to demolish the dancers.

Tally.   True, true, I had forgot.   Will you make one?

Ld. J.   I beg to be excused.

Rack.   May-hap you are a friend to the French.

Ld. J.   Not I, indeed sir.   But if the occasion will permit me a pun, tho' l am far from being a wellwisher to their arms, I have no objection to the being entertained by their legs.

Tally.   Aye!   Why then if you'll come to night, you'll split your sides with laughing, for I'll be rot if we don't make them caper higher, and run faster, than ever they have done since the battle of Blenheim.   Come, along, Racket.   [*Exit.*

Ld. J.   Was there ever such a contrast?

Crab.   Not so remote as you imagine; they are scions from the same stock, set in different soils. The first shrub, you see, flowers most prodigally, but matures nothing; the last slip, tho' stunted, bears a little fruit; crabbed, 'tis true, but still the growth of the clime. Come, you'll follow your friend.   [*Exeunt.*

Enter Lucinda, with a Servant.

Luc. When Mr. Crab, or sir Charles, enquire for me; you will conduct them hither—[*Exit Serv.*] —How I long for an end to this important interview! Not that I have any great expectations from the issue; but still, in my circumstances, a state of suspence is, of all situations, the most disagreeable. But hush, they come.

Enter sir Charles, Macruthen, Ld. John, and Crab.

Buck. Mac, announce me.

Mac. Madam, sir Charles Buck craves the honour of kissing your hand.

Buck. *Très humble serviteur.* *Et comment se porte mademoiselle.* I am ravished to see thee, *ma chere petite Lucinde.*—*Eh bien, ma reine!* Why you look divinely, child. But, *mon enfant*, they have dress'd you most diabolically. Why, what a *coiffeure* must you have, and, *oh mon Dieu*, a total absence of rouge. But, perhaps, you are out. I had a cargo from Deffreney the day of my departure; shall I have the honour to supply you?

Luc. You are obliging, sir, but I confess myself a convert to the chaste customs of this country, and, with a commercial people, you know, sir Charles, all artifice ——

Buck. Artifice! You mistake the point, *ma chere.* A proper proportion of red, is an indispensible part of your dress; and, in my private opinion, a woman might as well appear, in public, without powder, or a petticoat.

Crab. And, in my private opinion, a woman, who puts on the first, would make very little difficulty in pulling off the last.

Buck. Oh, monsieur Crab's judgment must be decisive in dress. Well, and what amusements, what spectacles, what parties, what contrivances, to conquer father Time, that foe to the fair ? I fancy one must *ennuier considerablement* in your London here.

Luc. Oh, we are in no distress for diversions. We have an opera.

Buck. *Italien,* I suppose, *pitoiable,* shocking, *assommant !* Oh, there is no supporting their *hi, hi, hi, hi. Ah, mon Dieu ! Ah, chassé brillant soleil,*

> *Brillant soleil,*
> *A-t-on jamais veu ton pareil ?*

There's music and melody.

Luc. What a fop !

Buck. But proceed, *ma princesse.*

Luc. Oh, then we have plays.

Buck. That I deny, child.

Luc. No plays !

Buck. No.

Luc. The assertion is a little whimsical.

Buck. Aye that may be ; you have here drama-tic things, farcical in their composition, and ridicu-lous in their representation.

Luc. Sir, I own myself unequal to the contro-versy ; but, surely Shakespeare —My lord, this subject calls upon you for its defence.

Crab. I know from what fountain this fool has drawn his remarks ; the author of the Chinese Orphan, in the preface to which Mr. Voltaire calls the principal works of Shakespeare monstrous farces.

Ld. Y. Mr. Crab is right, madam. Mr. Vol-taire has stigmatized with a very unjust and a very invidious appellation the principal works of that great master of the passions ; and his apparent motive renders him the more inexcusable.

Luc. What could it be, my lord ?

Ld. J. The preventing his countrymen from becoming acquainted with our author; that he might be at liberty to pilfer from him, with the greater security.

Luc. Ungenerous, indeed!

Buck. Palpable defamation.

Luc. And as to the exhibition, I have been taught to believe, that for a natural pathetic, and a spirited expression, no people upon earth —

Buck. You are imposed upon, child: the *Lequesne*, the *Lanoue*, the *Grandval*, the *Dumenil*, the *Gaussen*, what dignity, what action! But, *à propos*, I have myself wrote a tragedy in French.

Luc. Indeed!

Buck. *En verité*, upon Voltaire's plan.

Crab. That must be a precious piece of work.

Buck. It is now in repetition at the French comedy. *Grandval* and *La Gaussen* perform the principal parts. Oh, what an *eclat!* What a burst will it make in the parterre, when the king of Ananamaboe refuses the person of the princess of Cochineal!

Luc. Do you remember the passage?

Buck. Entire; and I believe I can convey it in their manner.

Luc. That will be delightful.

Buck. And first the king;

Ma chere princesse, je vous aime, c'est vrai;
De ma femme vous portez les charmants attraits.
Mais ce n'est pas honnête pour un homme tel que
    moi,
De tromper ma femme, ou de rompre ma foi.

Luc. Inimitable!

Buck. Now the princess; she is, as you may suppose, in extreme distress.

Luc. No doubt.

Buck. Mon grand roy, mon cher adorable,
    Ayez pitie de moi; je suis inconsolable.

[Then he turns his back upon her, at which she in a fury]

 Monstre, ingrat, affreux, horrible, funeste,
 Oh que je vous aime, ah que je vous deteste !

[Then he]

 Pensez vous, madame, à me donner la loi,
 Votre haine, votre amour, sont les mêmes choses
   á moi.

Luc. Bravo!

Ld. J. Bravo, bravo!

Buck. Aye, there's passion and poetry, and reason and rhime. Oh how I detest blood, and blank verse ! There is something so soft, so musical, and so natural, in the rich rhimes of the *theatre François !*

Ld. J. I did not know sir Charles was so totally devoted to the *belles lettres.*

Buck. Oh, entirely. 'Tis the ton, the taste, I am every night at the *Caffé* Procope,* and had not I had the misfortune to be born in this curst country, I make no doubt but you would have seen my name among the foremost of the French academy.

Crab. I should think you might easily get over that difficulty, if you will be but so obliging as publicly to renounce us. I dare engage not one of your countrymen shall contradict, or claim you.

Buck. No!—Impossible. From the barbarity of my education, I must ever be taken for *un Anglois.*

 Crab. Never.

 Buck. En verité ?

 Crab. En verité.

 Buck. You flatter me.

 Crab. But common justice.

 Mac. Nay, maister Crab is in the right, for I

---

* A coffee-house opposite the French comedy, where the wits assemble every evening.

have often heard the French themselves say, Is it possible that gentleman can be British?

Buck. Obliging creatures! And you concur with them.

Crab. Entirely.

Luc. Entirely.

Ld. J. Entirely.

Buck. How happy you make mè!

Crab. Egregious puppy! But we lose time. A truce to this trumpery. You have read your father's will.

Buck. No; I read no English. When Mac has turned it into French, I may run over the items.

Crab. I have told you the part that concerns the girl. And as your declaration upon it will discharge me, I leave you to what you will call an *ecclaircissement.* Come, my lord.

Buck. Nay, but monsieur Crab, my lor, Mac.

Crab. Along with us.   [*Exeunt.*

Buck. A comfortable scrape I am in! What the deuce am I to do? In the language of the place, I am to make love, I suppose. A pretty employment!

Luc. I fancy my hero is a little puzzled with his part. But, now for it.

Buck. A queer creature, that Crab, *ma petite.* But, *à propos*, how d'ye like my lord?

Luc. He seems to have good sense and good breeding.

Buck. *Pas trop.* But don't you think he has something of a foreign kind of air about him?

Luc. Foreign?

Buck. Aye, something so English in his manner.

Luc. Foreign and English! I don't comprehend you.

Buck. Why that is, he has not the ease, the *je ne sçai quoi*, the *bon ton.*—In a word, he does not resemble me now.

Luc. Not in the least.

3.

Buck. Ah, I thought so. He is to be pitied, poor devil, he can't help it. But, *entre nous, ma chere*, the fellow has a fortune.

Luc. How does that concern me, sir Charles?

Buck. Why, *je pense, ma reine*, that your eyes have done execution there.

Luc. My eyes execution!

Buck. Aye, child, is there any thing so extraordinary in that? *Ma foi*, I thought by the vivacity of his praise, that he had already summoned the garrison to surrender.

Luc. To carry on the allusion, I believe my lord is too good a commander, to commence a fruitless siege. He could not but know the condition of the town.

Buck. Condition! Explain, *ma chere.*

Luc. I was in hopes your interview with Mr. Crab had made that unnecessary.

Buck. Oh, aye, I do recollect something of a ridiculous article about marriage, in a will. But what a plot against the peace of two poor people! Well, the malice of some men is amazing! Not contented with doing all the mischief they can in their life, they are for intailing their malevolence, like their estates, to latest posterity.

Luc. Your contempt of me, sir Charles, I receive as a compliment. But the infinite obligations I owe to the man, who had the misfortune to call you son, compel me to insist, that in my presence, at least, no indignity be offered to his memory.

Buck. Heydey! What, in heroics, *ma reine!*

Luc. Ungrateful, unfilial wretch! so soon to trample on his ashes, whose fond heart, the greatest load of his last hours were his fears for thy future welfare.

Buck. *Ma foi, elle est folle*, she is mad, *sans doute.*

Luc. But I am to blame. Can he who breaks through one sacred relation, regard another? Can the monster who is corrupt enough to contemn the place of his birth, reverence those who gave him being?——impossible.

Buck. Ah, a pretty monologue, a fine soliloquy this, child.

Luc. Contemptible. But I am cool.

Buck. I am mighty glad of it. Now we shall understand one another, I hope.

Luc. We do understand one another. You have already been kind enough to refuse me. Nothing is wanting but a formal rejection under your hand, and so concludes our acquaintance.

Buck. *Vous allez trop vite*, you are too quick, *ma chere.* If I recollect, the consequence of this rejection is my paying you twenty thousand pounds.

Luc. True.

Buck. Now that have not I the least inclination to do.

Luc. No, sir? Why you own that marriage —

Buck. Is my aversion. I'll give you that under my hand, if you please; but I have a prodigious love for the *Louis'.*

Luc. Oh, we'll soon settle that dispute; the law ——

Buck. But, hold, *ma reine.* I don't find that my provident father has precisely determined the time of this comfortable conjunction. So, tho' I am condemned, the day of execution is not fixed.

Luc. Sir!

Buck. I say, my soul, there goes no more to your dying a maid, than my living a batchelor.

Luc. O, sir, I shall find a remedy.

Buck. But now suppose, *ma belle,* I have found one to your hand?

Luc. As how? Name one.

Buck. I'll name two. And first, *mon enfant*; tho' I have an irresistable antipathy to the conjugal knot, yet I am by no means blind to your personal

charms ; in the possesion of which, if you please to
place me, not only the aforesaid twenty thousand
pounds, but the whole *terre* of your devoted shall
fall at your ———

Luc. Grant me patience !

Buck. Indeed you want it, my dear.   But if
you flounce, I fly.

Luc. Quick, sir, your other.   For this is—

Buck. I grant, not quite so fashionable as my
other.   It is then, in a word, that you would let
this lubberly lord make you a lady, and appoint
me his assistant, his private friend, his *cicisbei.*
And as we are to be joint partakers of your person, let us be equal sharers in your fortune, *ma
belle.*

Luc. Thou mean, abject, mercenary thing.
Thy mistress ! Gracious heaven ! Universal empire
should not bribe me to be thy bride.   And what
apology, what excuse could a woman of the least
sense or spirit make, for so unnatural a connexion !

Buck. *Fort bien !*

Luc. Where are thy attractions ? Canst thou
be weak enough to suppose thy frippery dress, thy
affectation, thy grimace, could influence beyond
the borders of a brothel ?

Buck. *Très bien !*

Luc. And what are thy improvements ? Thy
air is a copy from thy barber : For thy dress, thou
art indebted to thy taylor.   Thou hast lost thy
native language, and brought home none in exchange for it.

Buck. *Extrêmement bien !*

Luc. Had not thy vanity so soon exposed thy
villainy, I might, in reverence to that name, to
which thou art a disgrace, have taken a wretched
chance with thee for life.

Buck. . I am obliged to you for that.   And a
pretty pacific partner I should have had.   Why,
look'ee child, you have been, to be sure, very

eloquent, and upon the whole, not unentertaining : tho' by the bye, you have forgot, in your catalogue, one of my foreign acquisitions ; *c'est-à-dire*, that I can, with a most intrepid *sang froid*, without a single emotion, support all this storm of female fury. But, *adieu, ma belle*. And when a cool hour of reflection has made you sensible of the propriety of my proposals, I shall expect the honour of a card.

Luc. Be gone for ever !

Buck. *Pour jamais !* Foregad she would make an admirable actress. If I once get her to Paris, she shall play a part in my piece. [*Exit.*

Luc. I am ashamed, this thing has had the power to move me thus. Who waits there ? Dear Mr. Crab ——

Enter Lord John and Crab.

Ld. J. We have been unwillingly, madam, silent witnesses to this shameful scene. I blush that a creature, who wears the outward mark of humanity, should be in his morals so much below——

Crab. Prithee why didst thou not call thy maids, and toss the booby in a blanket ?

Ld. J. If I might be permitted, madam, to conclude what I intended saying, when interrupted by Mr. Crab——

Luc. My lord, don't think me guilty of affectation. I believe, I guess at your generous design ; but my temper is really so ruffled—besides I am meditating a piece of female revenge on this coxcomb.

Ld. J. Dear madam, can I assist ?

Luc. Only by desiring my maid to bring hither the tea.—My lord, I am confounded at the liberty, but——

Ld. J. No apology. You honour me, madam.

Crab. And prithee, wench, what is thy scheme ?

Luc. Oh, a very harmless one, I promise you.

Crab. Zounds, I am sorry for it. I long to see the puppy severely punished, methinks.

Luc. Sir Charles, I fancy, can't be yet got out of the house. Will you desire him to step hither?

Crab. I'll bring him.

Luc. No, I wish to have him alone.

Crab. Why then I'll send him.   [*Exit.*

Enter Lettice.

Luc. Place these things on the table, a chair on each side : very well. Do you keep within call. But hark, he is here. Leave me, Lettice.

[*Exit Lettice.*

Enter Buck.

Buck. So, so, I thought she would come to; but, I confess not altogether so soon. *Eh bien, ma belle,* see me ready to receive your commands.

Luc. Pray be seated, sir Charles. I am afraid the natural warmth of my temper might have hurried me into some expressions not altogether so suitable.

Buck. Ah *bagatelle.* Name it not.

Luc. Voulez-vous du thé, monsieur ?

Buck. Volontiers. This tea is a pretty innocent kind of *beverage* ; I wonder the French don't take it. I have some thoughts of giving it a fashion next winter.

Luc. That will be very obliging. It is of extreme service to the ladies this side the water you know.

Buck. True, it promotes parties, and infuses a kind of spirit of conversation, and that ——

Luc. En voulez-vous encore ?

Buck. Je vous rends mille graces.——But what has occasioned' me, *ma reine,* the honour of your message by Mr. Crab?

Luc. The favours I have received from your family, sir Charles, I thought, demanded from me,

at my quitting your house, a more decent, and ce-
remonious adieu, than our last interview would
admit of.

Buck. Is that all, *ma chere?* I thought your
flinty heart had, at last relented. Well, *ma reine,*
adieu.

Luc. Can you then leave me?

Buck. The fates will have it so.

Luc. Go then, perfidious traitor, be gone; I
have this consolation, however, that if I cannot
legally possess you, no other woman shall.

Buck. Hey, how, what?

Luc. And tho' the pleasure of living with you
is denied me, in our deaths at least, we shall soon
be united.

Buck. Soon be united in death? When, child?

Luc. Within this hour.

Buck. Which way?

Luc. The fatal draught's already at my heart.
I feel it here; it runs thro' every pore. Pangs,
pangs unutterable! The tea we drank, urged by
despair and love—Oh!

Buck. Well!

Luc. I poison'd.

Buck. The devil!

Luc. And as my generous heart would have
shared all with you, I gave you half.

Buck. Oh, curse your generosity!

Luc. Indulge me in the cold comfort of a last
embrace.

Buck. Embrace! O confound you! But it
mayn't be too late. Macruthen, Jonquil! physicians, apothecaries, oils and antidotes. Oh, *je
meurs, je meurs. Ah, la diablesse!* [*Exit.*

Enter Lord John and Crab.

Crab. A brave wench. I could kiss thee for
this contrivance.

Ld. J. He really deserves it all.

Crab. Deserves it ! Hang him. But the sensible resentment of this girl has almost reconciled me to the world again. But stay, let us see—Can't we make a further use of the puppy's punishment? I suppose, we may very safely depend on your contempt of him ?

Luc. Most securely.

Crab. And this young thing here, has been breathing passions and protestations. But I'll take care, my girl sha'nt go a beggar to any man's bed. We must have this twenty thousand pound, Lucy.

Ld. J. I regard it not. Let me be happy, and let him be ——

Crab. Psha, don't scorch me with thy flames. Reserve your raptures; or, if they must have vent, retire into that room, whilst I go and plague the puppy. [*Exeunt.*

Enter Buck, Macruthen, Jonquil, Bearnois, La Loire, Physician, Surgeon. Buck in a cap and night gown.

Surg. This copious phlebotomy will abate the inflammation, and if the six blisters on your head and back rise, why there may be hopes.

Buck. Cold comfort. I burn, I burn, I burn— Ah, there's a shoot. And now, again, I freeze.

Mac. Aye, they are symptoms of a strong poison.

Buck. Oh, I am on the rack.

Mac. Oh, if it be got to the vitals, a fig for aw antidotes.

Enter Crab.

Crab. Where is this miserable devil? What's he alive still?

Mac. In gude troth, and that's aw.

Buck. Oh!

Crab. So you have made a pretty piece of work on't, young man !

Buck. O what could provoke me to return from Paris?

Crab. Had you never been there, this could not have happened.

Enter Racket and Tallyhoe.

Rack. Where is he?—He's dead man, his eyes are fix'd already.

Buck. Oh!

Tally. Who poison'd him, Racket?

Rack. Gad I don't know. His French cook, I reckon.

Crab. Were there a possibility of thy reformation, I have yet a secret to restore thee.

Buck. Oh give it, give it.

Crab. Not so fast. It must be on good conditions.

Buck. Name 'em. Take my estate, my — save but my life, take all.

Crab. First then renounce thy right to that lady, whose just resentment has drawn this punishment upon thee; and, in which she is an unhappy partaker.

Buck. I renounce her from my soul.

Crab. To this declaration you are witnesses. Next, your tawdry trappings, your foreign foppery, your washes, paints, pomades, must blaze before your door.

Buck. What, all?

Crab. All; not a rag shall be reserved. The execution of this part of your sentence shall be assigned to your old friends here.

Buck. Well, take 'em.

Tally. Huzza, come Racket, let's rummage.

[*Exeunt Racket and Tallyhoe.*

Crab. And, lastly, I'll have these exotic attendants, these instruments of your luxury, these panders to your pride, pack'd in the first cart, and sent post to the place from whence they came.

Buck. Spare me but La Jonquil.

Crab. Not an instant. The importation of these puppies makes a part of the politics of your old friends, the French; unable to resist you, whilst you retain your ancient roughness, they have recourse to these minions, who would first, by unmanly means, sap and soften all your native spirit, and then deliver you an easy prey to their employers.

Buck. Since then it must be so, *adieu La Jonquil.*   [*Exeunt Jonquil and Bearnois.*

Crab. And now to the remedy. Come forth, Lucinda.

Enter Lucinda and Lord John.

Buck. Hey, why did not she swallow the poison ?

Crab. No ; nor you neither, you blockhead.

Buck. Why, did not I leave you in pangs ?

Luc. Aye, put on. The tea was innocent, upon my honour, sir Charles. But you allow me to be an excellent actress.

Buck. Oh, curse your talents !

Crab. This fellow's public renunciation, has put your person and fortune in your own power : and if you were sincere in your declaration of being directed by me, bestow it there.

Luc. As a proof of my sincerity, my lord, receive it.

Ld. J. With more transport, than sir Charles the news of his safety.

Luc. to Buck. You are not, at present, in a condition to take possession of your post.

Buck. What ?

Luc. Oh, you recollect ; my lord's private friend ; his assistant you know.

Buck. Oh, ho !

Mac. But, sir Charles, as I find the affair of

the poison was but a joke, had na' ye better withdraw, and tack off your blisters?

Crab. No, let 'em stick. He wants 'em.—And
now concludes my care. But before we close the
scene, receive, young man, this last advice from
the old friend of your father: As it is your
happiness to be born a Briton, let it be your boast;
know that the blessings of liberty are your birth-
right, which while you preserve, other nations may
envy or fear, but can never conquer or contemn
you. Believe, that French fashions are as ill-suited
to the genius, as their politics are pernicious to the
peace of your native land.

A convert to these sacred truths, you'll find,
That poison for your punishment design'd
Will prove a wholesome medicine to your mind.

[*Exeunt omnes.*

FINIS.

COMEDIES, TRAGEDIES, FARCES, 12mo.

PRINTED FOR

W. LOWNDES.

☞ The Plays marked thus *, are each embellished with an elegant plate, and those with †, have inferior frontispieces.

†ABRAMULE—Trapp
†Accomplish'd Maid—Toms
Adventures of Half an Hour —Bullock
Agis—Home
†Albion & Albanius—Dryd.
†Alchemist—Jonson
†Alcibiades—Otway
*All for Love—Dryden
†Ambitious Step-mother — Rowe
†Amphitryon—Dryden
*Amphitryon—Hawkesw.
†Anatomist—Ravenscroft
Antony & Cleopatra—Capel
Arden of Feversham—Lillo
*Artaxerxes—Arne
*Arthur and Emmeline — Kemble
*As you like It—Shakesp.
†Aurengzebe—Dryden
†Bartholomew Fair—Jonson
†Basset Table—Centlivre
*Beaux Stratagem—Farq.
*Beggar's Opera—Gay
†Biter—Rowe
British Enchanters—Lansd.
*Busy Body—Centlivre
Captives—Gay
*Careless Husband—Cibber
*Cato—Addison
†Chaplet, Mendez
†Cleomenes—Dryden

Cobler of Preston—Bullock
Comical Lovers—Cibber
*Committee—Howard
*Comus—Colman
*Confederacy—Vanbrugh
*Conscious Lovers—Steele
*Constant Couple—Farq.
Contre Temps, or Rival Queans
†Contrivances—Carey
*Coriolanus—Shakspeare
*Coriolanus—Sheridan
*Country Girl—Garrick
Country Wife—Wycherley
†Creusa—Whitehead
*Cymbeline—Garrick
Damon & Phillida—Cibber
Damon & Phillida—Dibdin
†Devil to Pay—Coffey
*Distrest Mother—Philips
*Double Dealer—Congreve
*Double Gallant—Cibber
†Dragon of Wantley—Carey
Duke and no Duke—Cokain
†Duke of Guise—Dryden
Edward the Black Prince— Shirley
Esop—Vanbrugh
*Every Man in his Humour —Garrick
*Fair Penitent—Rowe
†False Friend—Vanbrugh
*Foundling—Moore

THE

KNIGHTS;

A

COMEDY,

IN TWO ACTS.

PERFORMED AT THE

THEATRE-ROYAL, IN DRURY-LANE.

WRITTEN BY THE LATE

SAMUEL FOOTE, Esq.

———

—————— *sed habet comœdia tanto*
Plus oneris, quanto veniœ minus. HOR.

———

LONDON:

PRINTED FOR W. LOWNDES, No. 38, BEDFORD-STREET,

1807.

Price One Shilling.

PREFACE.

*AS this is the last opportunity I shall have of
addressing the public this year, I think it my
duty to return them my warmest acknowledge-
ments for their favourable reception of the following little piece.*

*The three principal characters I met with in a
summer's expedition; they are neither vamped
from antiquated plays, pilfered from the French
farces, nor the baseless beings of the poet's brain.
I have given them in their plain natural habit;
they wanted no dramatic finishing; nor can I
claim any other merit than grouping them together and throwing them into action. The justice
done them there by the performers, has been too
strongly distinguished by the town to render any
thing from me necessary, I could only wish that
the managers of the theatres would employ Mr.
Castallo, whose peculiar naïveté and strict propriety would greatly become many characters on
our stage.*

S. FOOTE.

PROLOGUE

Written and Spoken by Mr. FOOTE.

HAPPY my muse, had she first turn'd her art,
From humour's dangerous path, to touch the heart;
They, who in all the bluster of blank verse
The mournful tales of love and war rehearse,
Are sure the critics censure to escape ;
You hiss not heroes now, you only —— gape ;
Nor (strangers quite to heroes, kings, and queens)
Dare you intrude your judgment on their scenes.
A different lot the comic muse attends,
She is obliged to treat you with your friends ;
Must search the court, the forum, and the city,
Mark out the dull, the gallant, and the witty,
Youth's wild profusion, th' avarice of age,
Nay, bring the pit itself upon the stage.
First to the bar she turns her various face ;
Hem ! my lord, I am council in this case,
And if so be your lordship should think fit,
Why, to be sure, my client must submit ;
For why ? because —— Then off she trips again,
And, to the sons of commerce, shifts her scene :
There, whilst the griping sire, with moping care,
Defrauds the world himself t'enrich his heir,
The pious boy, his father's toil rewarding,
For thousands throws a main at Covent-garden !
These are the portraits we're oblig'd to shew ;
You are all judges if they're like or no :
Here should we fail, some other shape we'll try,
And grace our future scenes with novelty.
I have a plan to treat you with burletta,
That cannot miss your taste, mia spiletta :
But, should the following piece your mirth excite,
From Nature's volume we'll persist to write ;
Your partial favour bade us first proceed,
Then spare th' offender since you urg'd the deed.

DRAMATIS PERSONÆ.

HARTOP	—— ——	*Mr. Foote.*
SIR GREGORY GAZETTE	——	*Mr. Yates.*
JENKINS	— —	*Mr. Blakes.*
TIMOTHY	— —	*Mr. Castalle.*
ROBIN	— —	*Mr. Clough.*
JENNY	— — —	*Miss Minors.*
MISS PENELOPE TRIFLE	—	*Mrs. Cross.*
MISS SUKEY TRIFLE	—	*Miss Mills.*

ACT I.

SCENE, *a Room.*

HARTOP *and* JENKINS *discovered.*

Jenk. I SHOULD not choose to marry into such a family.

Hart. Choice, dear Dick, is very little concerned in the matter; and, to convince you that love is not the minister of my counsels, know that I never saw but once the object of my present purpose, and that too at a time, and in a circumstance, not very likely to stamp a favourable impression. What think you of a raw boarding-school-girl at Lincoln-Minster, with a mind unpolished, a figure uninformed, and a set of features tainted with the colours of her unwholesome food?

Jenk. No very engaging object indeed, Hartop.

Hart. Your thoughts now were mine then; but some connections I have since had with her father have

have given birth to my present design upon her.
You are no stranger to the situation of my circumstances: my neighbourhood to Sir Penurious
Trifle was a sufficient motive for his advancing
what money I wanted by way of mortgage; the
hard terms he imposed upon me, and the little
regard I have paid to œconomy, has made it necessary for me to attempt by some scheme the re-
establishment of my fortune: this young lady's
simplicity, not to call it ignorance, presented her
at once as a proper subject for my purpose.

Jenk. Success to you, Jack, with all my soul! a
fellow of your spirit and vivacity mankind ought
to support for the sake of themselves; for, whatever Seneca and the other moral writers may have
suggested in contempt of riches, it is plain their
maxims were not calculated for the world as it
now stands; in days of yore indeed, when virtue
was called wisdom, and vice folly, such principles
might have been encouraged; but, as the present
subjects of our enquiry are, not what man is, but
what he has, as to be rich is to be wise and virtu-
ous, and to be poor ignorant and vicious, I heartily applaud your plan!

Hart. Your observation is but too just! and is
it not, Dick, a little unaccountable, that we, who
condescend so servilely to copy the follies and foppe-
ries of our polite neighbours, should be so totally
averse to an imitation of their virtues? In France,
Has he wealth? is an interrogation never put till they
are disappointed in their inquiries after the birth
and wisdom of a fashionable fellow: but here, How
much a year?—Two thousand.—The devil! In
what country?—Berkshire.—Indeed! God bless
                                    us

us! a happy dog!—How the deuce come I to be interested in a man's fortune unless I am his steward or his tailor? Indeed knowledge and genius are worth examining into; by those my understanding may be improved, or my imagination gratified; but why such a man's being able to eat ortolans, and drink French wine, is to recommend him to my esteem, is what I cannot readily conceive.

Jenk. This complaint may with justice be made of all imitations; the ridiculous side is ever the object imitated. But a truce to moralising and to our business. Prithee, in the first place, how can you gain admittance to your mistress? and, in the second, is the girl independent of her father? his consent, I suppose, you have no thoughts of obtaining.

Hart. Some farther proposals concerning my estate, such as an increase of the mortgage or an absolute sale, is a sufficient pretence for a visit; and, as to cash, twenty to my knowledge! independent too, you rogue! and, besides, an only child, you know! and then, when things are done they can't be undone, and 'tis well its no worse, and a hundred such pretty proverbs, will, its great odds, reconcile the old fellow at last. Besides, my papa in posse has a foible, which, if I condescend to humour, I have his soul, my dear.

Jenk. Prithee, now you are in spirits, give me a portrait of Sir Penurious; though he is my neighbour, yet he is so domestic an animal that I know no more of him than the common country conversation, that he is a thrifty, wary, man.

Hart. The very abstract of penury! Sir John Cutler, with his transmigrated stockings, was but a type

type of him. For instance, the barber has the growth of his and his daughter's head once a year for shaving the knight once a fortnight ; his shoes are made with the leather of a coach of his grand-father's, built in the year 1 ; his male servant is footman, groom, carter, coachman, and tailor; his maid employs her leisure hours in plain-work for the neighbours, which Sir Penurious takes care, as her labour is for his emolument, shall be as many as possible, by joining with his daughter in scouring the rooms, making the beds, &c. thus much for his moral character. Then, as to his intellectual, he is a mere carte blanche; the last man he is with must afford him matter for the next he goes to ; but a story is his idol, throw him in that and he swallows it ; no matter what, raw or roast-ed, savory or insipid, down it goes, and up again to the first person he meets ; it is upon this basis I found my favour with the knight, having acquired patience enough to hear his stories, and equipped myself with a quantity sufficient to furnish him ; his manner is indeed peculiar, and for once or twice entertaining enough. I'll give you a speci-men ;———is not that an equipage ?

Jenk. Hey! yes, faith ! and the owner an ac-quaintance of mine ; Sir Gregory Gazette, by Jupiter ! and his son Tim with him. Now I can match your knight. He must come this way to the parlour. We'll have a scene ; but take your cue, he is a country politician.

Sir Gregory, *entering, and waiter.*

Sir Greg. What, neither the Gloucester Journal, nor the Worcester Courant, nor the Northampton
Mercury,

Mercury, nor the Chester ——— ? Mr. Jenkins, I am your humble servant; a strange town this, Mr. Jenkins, no news stirring, no papers taken in! Is that gentleman a stranger, Mr. Jenkins? Pray, sir, not to be too bold, don't you come from London?

Hart. But last night.

Sir Greg. Lack-a-day! that's wonderful!——— Mr. Jenkins, introduce me.

Jenk. Mr. Hartop, Sir Gregory Gazette.

Sir Greg. Sir, I am proud to ——— Well, sir, and what news? You come from ——— Pray, sir, are you a parliament-man?

Hart. Not I indeed, sir.

Sir Greg. Good lack! may be belong to the law?

Hart. Nor that.

Sir Greg. Oh, then in some of the offices; the treasury or the exchequer?

Hart. Neither, sir.

Sir Greg. Lack-a-day! that's wonderful! Well, but, Mr. ——— Pray what name did Mr. Jenkins, Ha——— Ha———

Hart. Hartop.

Sir Greg. Ay, true! what, not of the Hartops of Boston?

Hart. No.

Sir Greg. May be not. There is, Mr. Hartop, one thing that I envy you Londoners in much;— quires of newspapers!—Now I reckon you read a matter of eight sheets every day?

Hart. Not one.

Sir Greg. Wonderful! then, may be, you are about court; and so, being at the fountain-head, know

know what is in the papers before they are printed

Hart. I never trouble my head about them.—
An old fool! [*Aside.*]

Sir Greg. Good lord! Your friend, Mr. Jenkins, is very close.

Jenk. Why, Sir Gregory, Mr. Hartop is much
in the secrets above; and it becomes a man so
trusted to be wary, you know.

Sir Greg. May be so, may ye so. Wonderful,
ay, ay, a great man no doubt.

Jenk. But I'll give him a better insight into
your character, and that will induce him to throw
off his reserve.

Sir Greg. May be so; do, do; ay, ay!

Jenk. Prithee, Jack, don't be so crusty, indulge
the knight's humour a little; besides, if I guess
right, it may be necessary for the conduct of your
design to contract a pretty strict intimacy here.

[*Aside.*

Hart. Well, do as you will. [*Aside.*]

Jenk. Sir Gregory, Mr. Hartop's ignorance of
your character made him a little shy in his replies,
but you will now find him more communicative;
and, in your ear,—he is a treasure; he is in all the
mysteries of government; at the bottom of every
thing.

Sir Greg. Wonderful! a treasure! ay, ay, may
be so.

Jenk. And, that you may have him to yourself, I'll go in search of your son.

Sir Greg. Do so, do so; Tim is without, just
come from his uncle Tregegle's at Mavagezy in
                                        Cornwall;

Cornwall; Tim is an honest lad: so. [*Exit* Jenk.*] Well, Mr. Hartop, and so we have a peace; lack-a-day! long looked for come at last. But pray, Mr. Hartop, how many newspapers may you have printed in a week?

Hart. About a hundred and fifty, Sir Gregory.

Sir Greg. Good now, good now! and all full, I reckon; full as an egg; nothing but news! well, well, I shall go to London one of these days. A hundred and fifty; wonderful! and, pray now, which do you reckon the best?

Hart. Oh, Sir Gregory, they are as various in their excellencies as their uses; if you are inclined to blacken, by a couple of lines, the reputation of a neighbour, whose character neither your nor his whole life can possibly restore, you may do it for two shillings in one paper; if you are displaced, or disappointed of a place, a triplet against the ministry will be always well received at the head of another; and then, as a paper of morning amusement, you have the Fool.

Sir Greg. The Fool! good lack! and pray who and what may that same Fool be?

Hart. Why, Sir Gregory, the author has artfully assumed that habit, like the royal jesters of old, to level his satire with more security to himself and severity to others.

Sir Greg. May be so, may be so! the Fool! ha, ha, ha! well enough! a queer dog, and no fool, I warrant you! Killigrew, ah, I have heard my grandfather talk much of that same Killigrew, and no fool! But what is all this to news, Mr. Hartop? Who gives us the best account of the king of Spain, and the queen of Hungary, and those great? folks?

folks? Come now, you could give us a little news if you would; come now!—snug!—nobody by!—good now do; come, ever so little!

Hart. Why, as you so largely contribute to the support of the government, it is but fair you should know what they are about.—We are at present in a treaty with the pope!

Sir Greg. With the pope! Wonderful! Good now, good now! how, how?

Hart. We are to yield him up a large tract of the Terra Incognita, together with both the Needles, Scilly Rocks, and the Lizard-point, on condition that the pretender has the government of Laputa, and the bishop of Greenland succeeds to St. Peter's chair; he being, you know, a protestant, when possessed of the pontificals, issues out a bull, commanding all catholics to be of his religion; they, deeming the pope infallible, follow his directions, and then, Sir Gregory, we are all of one mind.

Sir Greg. Good lack, good lack! rare news, rare news, rare news! ten millions of thanks, Mr. Hartop! But might not I just hint this to Mr. Soakum, our vicar? 'twould rejoice his heart.

Hart. O fie, by no means.

Sir Greg. Only a line!—a little hint!—do now.

Hart. Well, sir, it is difficult for me to refuse you any thing.

Sir Greg. Ten thousand thanks! Now the pope! Wonderful! I'll minute it down;——both the Needles?

Hart. Ay, both.

Sir Greg. Good now, I'll minute it;——the Lizard-point,——both the Needles,——Scilly-rocks,——— bishop

—— bishop of Greenland,——St. Peter's Chair.
—— Why then, when this is finished, we may
chance to attack the great Turk, and have holy
wars again, Mr. Hartop?

Hart. That's part of the scheme.

Sir Greg. Ah! good now! you see I have a
head! politics have been my study many a day.
Ah, if I had been in London to improve by the
news-papers!——They tell me Doctor Drybones is
to succeed to the bishopric of ——   [*Whispers*]

Hart. No; Doctor ——   [*Whispers*]

Sir Greg. Indeed! I was told by my landlord at
Ross, that it was between him and the dean of —
    [*Whispers.*]

Hart. To my knowledge ——

Sir Greg. Nay, you know best, to be sure. If
it should —— Hush! here's Mr. Jenkins and son
Tim. Mum!—Mr. Jenkins does not know any
thing about the treaty with the pope?

Hart. Not a word.

Sir Greg. Mum!

Enter TIMOTHY *and* JENKINS.

Jenk. Master Timothy is almost grown out of
knowledge, Sir Gregory.

Sir Greg. Good now, Good now! ay, ay, ill
weeds grow apace. Son Tim, Mr. Hartop: a great
man, child! Mr. Hartop, son Tim.

Hart. Sir, I shall be always glad to know every
branch that springs from so valuable a trunk as
Sir Gregory Gazette.

Sir Greg. May be so! Wonderful! Ay, ay!
Hart,

Hart. Sir, I am glad to see you in Hereford-shire : have you been long from Cornwall ?

Tim. Ay, sir ; a matter of four weeks or a month, more or less.

Sir Greg. Well said, Tim! ay, ay ask Tim any questions, he can answer for himself. Tim, tell Mr. Hartop all the news about the elections, and the tides, the tinners, and the roads, and the pil-chers: I want a few words with my master Jenkins.

Hart. You have been so long absent from your native country that you have almost forgot it.

Tim. Yes, sure; I ha' been at uncle Tregegle's a matter of twelve or a dozen year, more or less.

Hart. Then I reckon you were quite impatient to see your papa and mamma ?

Tim. No sure, not I. Father sent for me to un-cle; sure Mavagezy is a choice place! and I could a'stay'd there all my born day, smore or less.

Hart. Pray, Sir, what were your amusements.

Tim. Nan ? what do you say ?

Hart. How did you divert yourself ?

Tim. Oh, we ha' pastimes enow there ; we ha-bull-baiting, and cock-fighting, and fishing, and hunting, and hurling, and wrestling.

Hart. The two last are sports for which that country is very remarkable : in those, I presume, you are very expert?

Tim. Nan ? what ?

Hart. I say you are a good wrestler ?

Tim. Oh ! yes sure, I can wrestle well enow : but we don't wrestle after your fashion ; we ha'no tripping ; fath and soul ? we all go upon close hugs

or

or the flying mare. Will you try a fall, master ? I wan't hurt you, fath and soul.

Hart. We had as good not venture though. ——— But have you left in Cornwall nothing that you regret the loss of more than hurling and wrestling?

Tim. Nan? what?

Hart. No favourite she?

Tim. Arra, I coupled Favourite and Jowler together, and sure they tugg'd it all the way up. Part with Favourite! no I thank you for nothing : you must know I nursed Favourite myself; uncle's huntsman was going to mill-pond to drown all Music's puppies ; so I saved she : but, fath, I'll tell you a comical story ; at Lanston they both broke loose and eat a whole loin-a'-veal and a leg of beef : Crist ! how landlord swear'd ! fath, the poor fellow was almost mazed ; it made me die wi' laughing : but how came you to know about our Favourite?

Hart. A circumstance, so material to his son, could not escape the knowledge of Sir Gregory Gazette's friends. But here you mistook me a little, 'Squire Tim ; I meant whether your affections were not settled upon some pretty girl; has not some Cornish lass caught your heart?

Tim. Hush ! 'god, the old man will hear ; jog a tiny bit this way ;—won't a' tell father?

Hart. Upon my honour !

Tim. Why then I'll tell you the whole story, more or less. Do you know Mally Pengrouse?

Hart. I am not so happy.

Tim. She's uncle's milkmaid ; she's as handsome, lord ! her face all red and white, like the inside of a shoulder of mutton : so I made love to our Mally;
and

and just, fath, as I had got her good will to run a-
way to Exeter and be married, uncle found it out
and sent word to father, and father sent for me
home ; but I don't love her a bit the worser for
that : but, 'icod, if you tell father he'll knock my
brains out, for he says I'll disparage the family, and
mother's as mad as a March hare about it ; so father and mother ha' brought me to be married to
some young body in these parts.

Hart. What, is my lady here ?

Tim. No sure, Dame Winifred, as father calls
her, could not come along.

Hart. I am sorry for that ; I have the honour to
be a distant relation of her ladyship.

Tim. Like enough, fath ! she's a-kin to half the
world, I think. But don't you say a word to father
about Mally Pengrouse.   Hush !

Jenk. Mr. Hartop, Sir Gregory will be amongst
us some time; he is going with his son to Sir Penurious Trifle's ; there is a kind of a treaty of marriage on foot between Miss Sukey Trifle and Mr.
Timothy.

Hart. The devil ! I shall be glad of every circumstance that can make me better acquainted
with Sir Gregory.

Sir Greg. Good now, good now ! may be so,
may be so.

Tim. Father, sure the gentleman says as how
mother and he are a-kin.

Sir Greg. Wonderful ! lack-a-day ! lack-a-day !
how, how ?   I am proud to ——— But how, Mr.
Hartop, how ?

Hart. Why, sir, a cousin-german of my aunt's
first husband inter-married with a distant relation of

a

a collateral branch by the mother's side, the Apprices of Lantrindon; and we have ever since quartered in an escutcheon of pretence the three goats tails rampant, divided by a chevron, field argent, with a leek pendant in the dexter point, to distinguish the second house.

Sir Greg. Wonderful! wonderful! nearly, nearly, related! good now, good now! if Dame Winifred were here she'd make them all out with a wet finger; but they are above me. Prithee, Tim, good now! see after the horses; —and, d'ye hear! try if you can get any news-papers.

Tim. Yes, father. — But, cousin What-d'ye-call-um, not a word about Mally Pengrouse!

Hart. Mum!

[*Exit Timothy.*

Sir Greg. Good now, that boy will make some mistake about the horses now! I'll go myself. Good now, no farther cousin! if you please, no ceremony! —— A hundred and fifty a week! the Fool! ha, ha, ha! wonderful! an odd dog.

[*Exit Sir Gregory.*

Jenk. So, Jack, here's a fresh spoke in your wheel.

Hart. This is a cursed cross incident!

Jenk. Well, but something must be done to frustrate the scheme of your new cousin. Can you think of nothing?

Hart. I have been hammering: — pray, are the two knights intimate? are they well acquainted with each other's person?

Jenk. Faith, I can't tell; but we may soon know.

Hart.

Hart. Could you recommend me a good spirited girl, who has humour and compliance to follow a few directions, and understanding enough to barter a little inclination for 3000l. a year and a fool?

Jenk. In part I guess your design: the man's daughter of the house is a good lively lass, has a fortune to make, and no reputation to lose. I'll call her.—Jenny! —But the enemy is at hand; — I'll withdraw and prepare Jenny. When the worshipful family are retired I'll introduce the wench.

[*Exit Jenkins.*

Enter Sir Gregory and Timothy.

Sir Greg. Pray now, cousin, are you in friendship with Sir Penurious Trifle?

Hart. I have the honour, sir, of that gentleman's acquaintance.

Sir Greg. May be so, may be so! but, lack-a-day, cousin, is he such a miser as folks say? Good now, they tell me we shall hardly have necessaries for ourselves and horses at Gripe-Hall: but, as you are a relation, you should, good now, know the affairs of the family. Here is Sir Penurious's letter; here, cousin.

Hart. " Your overture I receive with pleasure, and should be glad to meet you in Shropshire."—I fancy, from a thorough knowledge of Sir Penurious's disposition, and by what I can collect from the contents of that letter, he would be much
better

better pleased to meet you here than at his own house.

Sir Greg. Lack-a-day! may be so! a strange man! wonderful! But, good now, cousin, what must we do?

Hart. I will this morning pay Sir Penurious a visit; and, if you will honour me with your commands, I'll ————

Sir Greg. Wonderful! to-day! good now, that's lucky! cousin, you are very kind: good now! I'll send a letter, Tim, by cousin Hartop.

Hart. A letter from so old an acquaintance, and upon so happy an occasion, will secure me a favourable reception.

Sir Greg. Good lack, good lack! an old acquaintance indeed, cousin Hartop! we were at Herefordshire 'size together——let's see, wonderful! how long ago? 'twas while I was courting Dame Winny; the year before I married; good now, how long? let's see, —that year the hackney-stable was built, and Peter Ugly, the blind pad, fell into a saw-pit.

Tim. Mother says, father and she was married, the 1st of April, in the year 10; and I knows 'tis there about, for I am two-and-thirty; and brother Jeremy, and Roger, and Gregory, and sister Nelly, were born'd before I.

Sir Greg. Good now, good now! how time wears away! wonderful! thirty-eight years ago, Tim; I could not have thought it. But come in, let's set about the letter. But pray, cousin, what diversions, good now! are going forward in London?

Hart.

Hart. Oh, sir, we are in no distress for amusement ; we have plays, balls, puppet-shows, mas-
querades, bull-baitings, boxings, burlettas, routs,
drums, and a thousand others. But I am in haste
for your epistle, Sir Gregory.

Sir Greg. Cousin your servant.

[*Exit Sir Greg. and Tim.*

Hart. I am your most obedient. —— Thus far
our scheme succeeds ; and, if Jenkins's girl can assume the aukward pertness of the daughter with as
much success as I can imitate the spirited folly of
Sir Penurious, the father, I don't despair of a happy catastrophe.

Enter Jenny.

Jenny. Sir, Mr. Jenkins ————

Hart. Oh, child, your instructions shall be ad-
ministered within.

Jenny. Mr. Jenkins has opened your design, and
I am ready and able to execute my part.

Hart. My dear, I have not the least doubt of
either your inclination or ability.— But, pox take
this old fellow! what in the devil's name can bring
him back? — Scour, Jenny.

Exit Jenny.

Enter Sir Gregory.

Sir Greg. Cousin, I beg pardon, but I have a favour to beg ;—good now, could not you make interest at some coffee house in London to buy, for a
small

small matter, the old books of news-papers, and send them into the country to me? They would pass away the time rarely in a rainy day!

Hart. Sir, I'll send you a cart-load.

Sir Greg. Good now, good now! ten thousand thanks! you are a cousin indeed! But pray, cousin, let us, good now! see some of the works of that same Fool.

Hart. I'll send them you all; but a ——

Sir Greg. What all? lack-a-day, that's kind, cousin? The Terra Incognita,—both the Needles, —a great deal of that!—But what bishop is to be pope?

Hart. Zounds, sir, I am in haste for your letter; when I return ask as many questions ——

Sir Greg. Good now, good now! that's true!— I'll in, and about it. — But, cousin, the pope is not to have Gibraltar?

Hart. No, no; damn it, no! as none but the Fool could say it, so none but ideots would believe him! Pray, Sir Gregory, ——

Sir Greg. Well, well, cousin! Lack-a-day, you are so —— But, pray ——

Hart. Damn your praying! if you don't finish your letter immediately you may carry it your-self!

Sir Greg. Well, well, cousin! Lack-a-day, you are in such a —— Good now, I go, I go!

Hart. But, If the truth should be discovered, I shall be inevitably disappointed.

Sir Greg. But, cousin, are Scilly-rocks ——

Hart. I wish they were in your guts with all my heart! I must quit the field, I find.

[*Exit.*
Sir Greg.

Sir Greg. Wonderful! good now, good now! a
passionate man! Lack-a-day! I am glad the pope
is not to have Gibraltar though!

[*Exit.*

END OF ACT I.

ACT

A C T   II.

Sir Gregory, and Timothy reading a News-paper to him.

Tim. COnstantinople, N. S. Nov. 15. The Grand Seignour ————

Sir Greg. Lack-a-day! good now, Tim, the politics, child; and read the stars, and the dashes, and the blanks, as I taught you, Tim.

Tim. Yes, father.——We can assure our readers that the D——dash is to go to F blank; and that a certain noble L——is to resign his p——e in the T——y, in order to make r—m for the two three-stars.

Sir Greg. Wonderful! good now, good now! great news, Tim! ah, I knew the two three-stars would come in play one time or other! this London Evening knows more than any of them. Well, child, well!

Tim. From the D. J.

Sir Greg. Ay, that's the Dublin Journal. Go on, Tim.

Tim. Last Saturday a gang of highwaymen broke into an empty house on Ormond-Quay, and stripped it of all the furniture.

Sir Greg.

Sir Greg. Lack-a-day! wonderful! to what a height these rogues are grown!

Tim. The way to Mr. Keith's chapel is, turn of your ——

Sir Greg. Pshaw! skip that, Tim; I know that road as well as the doctor! 'tis in every time.

Tim. I. Ward, at the Cat and Gridiron, Petticoat-lane, makes tabby all over for people inclined to be crooked; and, if he was to have the universal world for making a pair of stays, he could not put better stuff in them.

Sir Greg. Good now! where's that, Tim?

Tim. At the Cat and Gridiron, father.

Sir Greg. I'll minute that: all my lady Izard's children, good now! are inclined to be crooked.

Enter a Waiter.

Wait. Sir, Mr. Jenkins begs to speak with you.

Sir Greg. Good now! desire him to walk in.

[*Exit Waiter.*

Enter Jenkins.

Jenk. I thought it might not be improper to prepare you for a visit from Sir Penurious Trifle: I saw him and his daughter alight at the apothecary's above.

Sir Greg. What, they are come? Wonderful! Very kind, very kind, very kind, indeed! Mr.—— Come, Tim, settle my cravat; good now! let's be

a

a little decent :—remember your best bow to your mistress, Tim.

Tim. Yes, father : but must not I kiss Miss Suck?

Sir Greg. Lack-a-day ! ay, ay ! pray, is cousin Hartop come along?

Jenk. I have not seen him : — but I fancy I had better introduce my neighbours.

Sir Greg. Good now ! would you be so kind ! [*Exit Jenkins.*] Stand behind me, Tim ! Pull down your ruffles, child !

Tim. But, father, won't Miss Suck think me bold if I kiss her chaps the first time ?

Sir Greg. Lack-a-day ! no, Tim, no ! faint heart never won fair lady ! ha ! Tim, had you but seen me attack Dame Winny !—but times ar'n't as they were ; good now ! we were another kind of folks in those days ; stout hearty smacks that would have made your mouth water again, and the mark stood upon the pouting lip like the print upon a pound of butter : but the master-misses of the present age go, lack-a-day ! as gingerly about it, as if they were afraid to fill their mouths with the paint upon their mistress's cheeks. Ah, the days I have seen !

Tim. Nay, father, I warrant, if that's all, I kiss her hearty enow, fath and soul !

Sir Greg. Hush ! Tim, hush ! stand behind me, child.

Enter

*Enter Hartop as Sir Penurious Trifle, and Jenny as
Miss Sukey, and Jenkins.*

Sir Greg. Sir Penurious, I am overjoyed! —
Good now!

Hart. Sir Gregory, I kiss your hand! My
daughter Suck.

Sir Greg. Wonderful! Miss, I am proud to——
Son Tim, Sir Penurious; best bow, child!——
Miss Suck ——

Tim. An't that right, father?   [*Kisses her*]

Sir Greg. Good now, good now! I am glad to
see you look so well! you keep your own, Sir
Penurious.

Hart. Ay, ay! stout enough, Sir Gregory, stout
enough, brother knight! hearty as an oak! hey,
Dick? Gad, now I talk of an oak, I'll tell you a
story of an oak; it will make you die with laughing; hey, you Dick, you have heard it; shall I
tell it Sir Gregory?

Jenk. Though I have heard it so often, yet there
is something so engaging in your manner of telling
a story that it always appears new.

Sir Greg. Wonderful! good now, good now! I
love a comical story. Pray, Sir Penurious, let's
have it: mind, Tim, mind, child.

Tim. Yes, father; fath and soul, I love a choice
story to my heart's blood!

Hart. You knight, I was at Bath last summer;—
a water that people drink when they are ill: you
have heard of the Bath. Dick? Hey, you?

                                        Tim

Tim. Yes, fath, I know Bath; I was there in way up.

Sir Greg. Hush, Tim! good now, hush!

Hart. There's a coffee-house, you; — a place where people drink coffee and tea, and read the news.

Sir Greg. Pray, Sir Penurious, how many papers may they take in?

Hart. Pshaw! damn the news! mind the story.

Sir Greg. Good now, good now! a hasty man, Tim!

Hart. Pox take you both! I have lost the story. —where did I leave off, hey, you Dick?

Tim. About coffee and tea.

Hart. Right, you, right! true, true!—so, God, you knight, I used to breakfast at this coffee-house every morning; it cost me eight-pence though, and I had always a breakfast at home——no matter for that, though there I breakfasted, you Dick, God, at the same table with Lord Tom Truewit:—— you have heard of Truewit, you knight; a droll dog! you Dick, he told us the story and made us die with laughing:—you have heard of Charles the Second, you knight; he was son of Charles the First, king here in England, that was beheaded by Oliver Cromwell: so what does Charles the Second, you knight, do; but he fights Noll at Worcester; a town you have heard of, not far off; but all would not do, you; God, Noll made him scamper, made him run, take to his heels, you knight;—Truewit told us the story, made us die with laughing; I always breakfasted at the coffee house; it cost me eight-pence, though I had a breakfast at home—— so what does Charles do, but hid himself in an oak,

an

an oak-tree, you, in a wood called Boscobel, from two Italian words, bosco bello, a fine wood, you, and off he marches: but old Noll would not let him come home ; no, says he, you don't come here !——Lord Tom told us the story ; made us die with laughing; it cost me eight-pence, though I had a breakfast at home——so, you knight, when Noll died, Monk there, you, afterwards Albermarle, in the North, brought him back; so, you, the cavaliers; you have heard of them? they were friends to the Stuarts ; what did they do, God, you Dick, but they put up Charles in a sign, the royal oak ; you have seen such signs at country alehouses ; so, God, you, what does a puritan do— the Puritans were friends to Noll—but he puts up the sign of an owl in an ivy-bush, and underneath he writes "This is not the royal oak!" you have seen writings under signs, you knight : upon this, say the royalists, God, this must not be ; so, you, what do they do, but, God, they prosecuted the poor Puritan ; but they made him change his sign though ; and, you Dick, how d'ye think they changed? God, he puts up the royal oak, and underneath he writes "This is not the owl in the ivy-bush!"—It made us all die with laughing! Lord Tom told the story; I always breakfasted at the coffee-house, though it cost me eight-pence, and I had a breakfast at home —— hey, you knight! what, Dick, hey !

Sir Greg. Good now, good now ! wonderful !

Tim. A choice tale, fath !

Jenk. Oh, Sir Penurious is a most entertaining companion, that must be allowed.

Sir Greg. Good now ! ay, ay, a merry man ! but, lack-a-day, would not the young lady choose

a

a little refreshment after her ride? some tea, or some ——

Hart. Hey, you knight! no, no! we intend to dine with thee, man. Well, you Tim, what dost think of thy father-in-law that is to be, hey? a jolly cock, you Tim; hey, Dick! But prithee, boy, what dost do with all this tawdry tinsel on? that hat and waistcoat? trash, knight, trash! more in thy pocket and less in thy clothes; hey, you Dick! God, you knight, I'll make you laugh: I went to London, you Dick, last year to call in a mortgage; and what does me I, Dick, but take a trip to a coffee-house in St. Martin's Lane; in comes a French fellow forty times as fine as Tim, with his muff and parlevous, and his Francés, and his head, you knight, as white with powder, God, you, as a twelfth-cake: and who the devil d'ye think, Dick, this might be? hey, you knight?

Sir Greg. Good now! an ambassador to be sure!

Hart. God, you knight, nor better nor worser than Mynheer Vancaper, a Dutch figure-dancer at the opera-house in the Haymarket.

Sir Greg. Wonderful! good now, good now!

Hart. Pshaw! pox! prithee, Tim, nobody dresses now; all plain; look at me, knight, I am in the tip of the mode; now am I in full dress; hey, Dick!

Jenk. You, sir, don't want the aids of dress; but, in Mr. Gazette, a little regard to that particular is but a necessary compliment to his mistress.

Hart. Stuff, Dick, stuff! my daughter, knight, has had other guise breeding; hey, you! Suck, come forward. Plain as a pike-staff, knight; all as nature made her; hey, Tim, no flams! prithee,

Tim

Tim, off with thy lace and burn it; 'twill help to buy the licence; she'll not like thee a bit the better for that; hey, Suck! But, you knight, God, Dick, a toast and tankard would not be amiss after our walk; hey, you?

Sir Greg. Good now, good now! what you will, Sir Penurious.

Hart. God, that's hearty, you! but we won't part the young couple, hey! I'll send Suck some bread and cheese in; hey, knight! At her, Tim! Come, Dick; come, you knight. Did I ever tell you my courtship; hey, Dick? 'twill make you laugh.

Jenk. Not as I remember.

Sir Greg. Lack-a-day! let's have it.

Hart. You know my wife was blind, you knight?

Sir Greg. Good now! wonderful! not I.

Hart. Blind as a beetle when I married her, knight; hey, Dick! she was drowned in our orchard: maid Bess, knight, went to market, you Dick; and wife rambled into the orchard, and, souse, dropped into the fish-pond: we found her out next day, but she was as dead as a herring: no help for that, Dick; buried her though; hey, you! she was only daughter to Sir Tristram Muckworm, you; rich enough, you, hey! God, you, what does she do, you, but she falls in love with young Sleek, her father's chaplain; hey, you! upon that what does me I, but slips on domine's robes, you; passed myself upon her for him, and we were tacked together, you knight, hey! God, though I believe she never liked me; but what signifies that? hey, Dick! she was rich, you! But, come, let's leave the children together.

Sir Greg.

Sir Greg. Sir, I wait on you.

Hart. Nay, pray————

Sir Greg. Good now, good now! 'tis impossible! ——

Hart. Pox of ceremony, you Dick! hey! God, knight, I'll tell you a story: one of our ambassadors in France, you, a devilish polite fellow reckoned, Dick; God, you, what does the king of France do, but, says he, I'll try the manners of this fine gentleman: so, knight, going into a coach together, the king would have my lord go first: oh! an't please your majesty, I can't indeed; you, hey, Dick! upon which, what does me the king, but he takes his arm thus, you, Dick: am I the king of France or you? is it my coach or yours? and so pushes him in thus. Hey, Dick!

Sir Greg. Good now, good now! he, he, he!

Hart. God, Dick, I believe I have made a mistake here; I should have gone in first; hey, Dick! knight, God, you, beg pardon. Yes, your coach, not mine; your house, not mine; hey, knight!

Sir Greg. Wonderful! a merry man, Mr. Jenkins.

[*Exeunt the two Knights and Jenk.*]

Tim. Father and cousin are gone, fath and soul!

Jenny. I fancy my lover is a little puzzled how to begin. [*Aside.*]

Tim. How————Fath and soul I don't know what to say! [*Aside.*] How d'ye do, Miss Suck?

Jenny. Pretty well, thank you.

Tim. You have had a choice walk.—'Tis a rare day, fath and soul!

Jenny. Yes, the day's well enough.

Tim. Is your house a good way off here?

Jenny.

Jenny. Dree or four mile.

Tim. That's a long walk, fath!

Jenny. I make nothing of it, and back again.

Tim. Like enow.   [*Whistles*]

Jenny.   [*Sings*]

Tim. You have a rare pipe of your own, .miss.

Jenny. I can sing loud enough if I have a mind: but father don't love singing.

Tim. Like enow.   [*Whistles*]

Jenny. And I an't over fond of whistling.

Tim. Hey! ay, like enow: and I am a bitter bad singer.

Jenny. Hey! ay, like enough.

Tim. Pray, Miss Suck, did ever any body make love to you before?

Jenny. Before when?

Tim. Before now.

Jenny. What if I won't tell you?

Tim. Why then you must let it alone, fath and soul!

Jenny. Like enough!

Tim. Pray, Miss Suck, did your father tell you any thing?

Jenny. About what?

Tim. About I.

Jenny. What should 'a tell?

Tim. Tell! why, as how I and father was come a wooing.

Jenny. Who?

Tim. Why you! Could you like me for a sweet-heart, Miss Suck?

Jenny. I don't know.

Tim. Mayhap somebody may ha' got your good will already?

                                        Jenny.

Jenny. And what then?

Tim. Then? hey! I don't know: but, if you could fancy me————

Jenny. For what?

Tim. For·your true lover.

Jenny. Well, what then?

Tim. Then! hey! why, fath, we may chance to be married if the old folks agree together.

Jenny. And suppose I won't be married to you?

Tim· Nay, Miss Suck, I can't help it fath and soul! But father and mother bid me come a court- ing; and, if you won't ha' me, I'll tell father so.

Jenny. You are in a woundy hurry, methinks.

Tim. Not I, fath! you may stay as long as————

Enter a Waiter.

Wait. There is a woman without wants to speak with Mr. Timothy Gazette.

[*Exit.*]

Tim. That's I.—I am glad on't! [*Aside.*] Well, Miss Suck, your servant. You'll think about it, and let's know your mind when I come back! —— God I don't care whether she likes me or no; I don't like her half so well as Mally Pengrouse! —— [*Aside.*] Nell, your servant, Miss Suck!

[*Exit.*]

Jenny. Was there ever such an unlicked cub;—— I don't think his fortune a sufficient reward for sa- crificing my person to such a booby: but, as he has money enough, it shall go hard but I please myself! I fear I was a little too backward with my gentleman: but, however a favourable answer to his last question will soon settle matters.

Enter

Enter Jenkins.

Jenk. Now, Jenny! what news child? are things fixed? are you ready for the nuptial knot?

Jenny. We are in a fair way: I thought to have quickened my swain's advances by a little affected coyness; but the trap would not take: I expect him back in a minute, and then leave it to my management.

Jenk. Where is he gone?

Jenny. The waiter called him to some woman.

Jenk. Woman! he neither knows or is known by any body here. What can this mean? no counter-plot! but, pox, that's impossible! you have not blabbed, Jenny?

Jenny. My interest would prevent me.

Jenk. Upon that security any woman may, I think, be trusted. I must after him though.

[*Exit.*]

Jenny. I knew the time when Mr. Jenkins would not have left me so hastily: 'tis odd, that the same cause that increases the passion in one sex should destroy it in the other; the reason is above my reach, but the fact I am a severe witness of : heigh-ho!

Enter Hartop (still as Sir Penurious Trifle,) and Sir Gregory Gazette.

Hart. And so, you knight, says he; you know, knight, what low dogs the ministers were then; how does your pot; a pot, you, that they put over the
fire

fire to boil broth and meat in: you have seen a pot,
you knight? how does your pot boil these trouble-
some times? hey, you! God, my lord, says he, I
don't know, I seldom go into my kitchen; a kitch-
en, you knight, is a place where they dress victu-
als! roast and boil, and so forth; God, says he, I
seldom go into the kitchen; but, I suppose, the
scum is uppermost still; hey, you knight!— hat,
God, hey! but where's your son, Sir Gregory?

Sir Greg. Good, now, good now! where's Tim,
Miss Sukey? lack-a day! what's become of Tim?

Jenny. Gone out a tiny bit; he'll be here presently.

Sir Greg. Wonderful! good now, good now!
well, and how, Miss Sukey, has Tim ——Has
he——Well, and what, you have———Wonderful!

Enter a Servant with a Letter.

Serv. Sir, I was commanded to deliver this into
your own hands by Mr. Jenkins.

Hart. Hey, you! what, a letter? God so! any
answer, you? hey!

Serv. None, sir.   [*Exit*]

Sir Greg. Lack-a-day, Sir Penurious is busy!
Well, Miss, and did Tim do the thing?—did he
please you?—come now, tell us the whole story!
wonderful!—rare news for Dame Winny!—ay!
Tim's father's own son! but come, whisper!—ha!

Hart. [*Reads.*] " I have only time to tell you
that your scheme is blasted: this instant I encounter-
ed

ed Mrs. Penelope Trifle with her niece; they will
soon be with you."——So then all's over! but
let's see what expedition will do!————Well, you
knight, hey! what, have they settled? Is the girl
willing?

Sir Greg. Good now, good now! right as my
leg! ah! Tim, little did I think——But, lack-a-
day! I wonder where the boy is! let's seek him.

Hart. Agreed, you knight! hey! come.

Enter Jenkins.

Sir Greg. Lack-a-day! here's Mr. Jenkins. Good
now! have you seen Tim?

Jenk. Your curiosity shall be immediately satisfied; but I must first have a word with Sir Penurious.

Hart. Well, you! what hey! any news, Dick?

Jenk. Better than you could hope! your rival is
disposed of!

Hart. Disposed of! how?

Jenk. Married by this time, you rogue! the woman that wanted him was no other than Mally
Pengrouse, she trudged it up all the way after
him, as Tim, says: I have recommended them to
my chaplain, and before this the business is done.

Hart. Bravissimo! you rogue! but how shall I
get off with the knight?

Jenk. Nay, that must be your contrivance.

Hart. I have it! Suppose I was to own the whole
design to Sir Gregory as our plan has not succeeded
with his son, and, as he seems to have a tolerable
                                                regard

regard for me, it is possible he may assist my scheme on Sir Penurious.

Jenk. 'Tis worth trying, however:——but he comes.

Sir Greg. Well, good now! Mr. Jenkins, have you seen Tim? I can't think where the boy——

Hart. 'Tis now time, Sir Gregory, to set you clear with respect to some particulars; I am now no longer Sir Penurious Trifle, but your friend and relation, Jack Hartop.

Sir Greg. Wonderful! good now, good now! cousin Hartop as I am a living man!——Hey!—— well but, good now! how, Mr Jenkins, hey?

Jenk. The story, Sir Gregory, is rather too long to tell you now; but in two words, my friend Hartop has very long had a passion for Miss Trifle, and was apprehensive your son's application would destroy his views, which, in order to defeat, he assumed the character of Sir Penurious; but he is so captivated with your integrity and friendship, that he rather chooses to forego his own interest than interrupt the happiness of your son.

Sir Greg. Wonderful! good now, good now! that's kind! who could have thought it, cousin Hartop? lack-a-day! well, but where's Tim? hey! good now! and who are you?

Jenk. This, sir, is Jenny, the handmaid of the house.

Sir Greg. Wonderful! a pestilent hussey! Ah, Hartop, you are a wag! a pize of your pots and your royal oaks! lack-a-day! who could have thought——ah! Jenny, you're a—[*Exit* Jenny.] But where's Tim?

Enter

Enter Robin.

Robin. Wounds, master! never stir alive if master Tim has na gone and married Mally Pengrouse?

Sir Greg. Wonderful! how, sirrah, how! good now, good now! cousin Hartop.——Mally Pengrouse! who the dickens is she?

Robin. Master Timothy's sweetheart in Cornwall.

Sir Greg. And how came she here? Lack-a-day, cousin!

Robin. She tramped it up after master: master Timothy is without, and says as how they be married: I wanted him to come in, but he's afraid you'll knock'n down.

Sir Greg. Knock'n down! Good now! let me come at him! I'll——Ah, rogue! lack-a-day! cousin, shew me where he is! I'll——

Hart. Moderate your fury, good Sir Gregory; consider, it is an evil, without a remedy.

Sir Greg. But what will Dame Winny say? Good now! such a disparagement to——and then what will Sir Penurious say?—lack-a-day! I am almost distracted!—and you, you lubberly dog! why did not you—— [*Exit* Robin.] I'll ——ah cousin Hartop, cousin Hartop! good now, good now!

Hart. Dear sir, be calm; this is no such surprising matter; we have such instances in the newspapers every day.

Sir Greg. Good now! no, cousin, no.

Hart.

Hart. Indeed, Sir Gregory, it was but last week that Lord Lofty's son married his mother's maid, and Lady Betty Forward run away not a month ago her with uncle's butler.

Sir Greg. Wonderful! what in the news? Good now! that's some comfort however; but what will Sir Penurious——

Hart. As to that, leave him to me, I have a project to prevent his laughing at you I'll warrant.

Sir Greg. But how, how, cousin Hartop, how?

Hart. Sir Gregory, do you think me your friend?

Sir Greg. Lack-a-day! ay, cousin, ay!

Hart. And would you in return serve me in a circumstance, that can't injure yourself?

Sir Greg. Good now! to be sure, cousin.

Hart. Will you then permit me to assume the figure of your son, and so pay my addresses to Miss Trifle? I was pretty happy in the imitation of her father, and, if I could impose upon your sagacity, I shall find less difficulty with your brother knight.

Sir Greg. Good now? Tim! ah, you could not touch Tim!

Hart. I warrant you! But see, the young gentleman.

Enter Timothy.

Sir Greg. Ah, Tim, Tim! little did I—— Good now, good now!

Tim. I could not help it now, fath and soul! but, if you'll forgive me this time, I'll never do so no more.

Sir Greg. Well, well, if thee canst forgive thyself, I can forgive thee; but thank thy cousin Hartop.

Hart.

Hart. Oh! sir, if you are satisfied, I am rewarded.   I wish you joy! joy to you, child!

Sir Greg. Thanks, cousin Hartop.

Enter a Waiter.

Wait. Sir, Mrs. Penelope Trifle, with her niece,
being come to town, and hearing your worship
was in the house, would be glad to pay you their
compliments.

Sir Greg. Lack-a-day! wonderful! here we are
all topsy-turvey again! what can be done now,
cousin Hartop?

Hart. Dick, shew the ladies in here, but delay
them a little. [*Exit Waiter.*]   The luckiest incident in the world, Sir Gregory! If you will be
kind enough to lend Jenkins your dress, and master Timothy will favour me with his, I'll make up
matters in a moment.

Sir Greg. Ay, ay, cousin!

Tim. Fath and soul! you shall have mine direc—

Hart. No, no! Step into the next room a minute, Sir Gregory.

Sir Greg. Ay, ay; where you will.

Tim. Fath, here will be choice sport!

[*Exeunt.*]

Enter Miss Penelope Trifle, Miss Sukey Trifle,
and a Waiter.

Wait. The gentlemen will wait on you presently.
Would you choose any refreshment?

Miss Suk.

Miss Suk. A draught of ale, friend, for I'm main dry.   [*Exit Waiter*]

Miss Pen. Fie, fie! niece! Is that liquor for a young lady? Don't disparage your family and breeding! The person is to be born that ever saw me touch any thing stronger than water till I was three-and-twenty!

Miss Suk. Troth! aunt, that's so long ago that I think there's few people alive who can remember what you did then!

Miss. Pen. How gillflirt! none of your fleers! I am glad here's a husband coming that will take you down in your tantrums! you are grown too head-strong and robust for me.

Miss Suk. Gad, I believe you would like to be taken down the same way!

Miss Pen. Oh you are pert!——But, see, your lover approaches. Now, Sukey, be careful, child: none of your——

Enter Jenkins as Sir Gregory Gazette, and Hartop as Timothy.

Jenk. Lack-a-day! lady, I rejoice to see you! wonderful! and your niece.—Tim, the ladies.

Hart. Your servant, mistress; I am glad to see you, Miss Suck. [*Salutes her.*] Fath and soul, Mistress Suck's a fine young woman, more or less!

Miss Suk. Yes, I am well enough, I believe.

Jenk. But, lady, where's my brother Trifle? where is Sir Penurious?

Miss Suk. Father's at home in expectation of you, and aunt and I be come to town to make preparations.

                                                Jenk.

Jenk. Ay! wonderful! pray, lady, shall I, good now! crave a word in private? Tim, will you and your sweetheart draw back a little?

Hart. Yes, father: come, miss, will you jog a tiny bit this way!

Miss Suk. With all my heart!

Jenk. There is, lady a wonderful affair has happened; good now! son Tim has fallen in love with a young woman at his uncle's, and tis 'partly to prevent bad consequences that I am, lack-a-day! so hasty to match him; and one of my men, good now! tells me that he has seen the wench since we have been in town; she has followed us here, sure as a gun, lady! If Tim sees the girl he'll never marry your niece.

Miss Pen. It is indeed, Sir Gregory Gazette, a most critical conjuncture, and requires the most mature deliberation.

Jenk. Deliberation! Lack-a-day! lady, whilst we deliberate the boy will be lost.

Miss Pen. Why, Sir Gregory Gazette, what operations can we determine upon?

Jenk. Lack-a-day! I know but one.

Miss Pen. Administer your propositions, Sir Gregory Gazette; you will have my concurrence, sir, in any thing that does not derogate from the regulations of conduct; for it would be most preposterous in one of my character to deviate from the strictest attention.

Jenk. Lack-a-day! lady, no such matter is wanted. But, good now! could not we tack the young couple together directly? your brother and I have already agreed.

Miss Pen.

Miss Pen. Are the previous preliminaries settled, Sir Gregory Gazette?

Jenk. Good now! as firm as a rock, lady.

Miss Pen. Why then, to preserve your son, and accomplish the union between our families, I have no objections to the acceleration of their nuptials, provided the child is inclined, and a minister may be procured.

Jenk. Wonderful! you are very good: good now! there has been one match already in the house to-day: we may have the same parson. Here, Tim; and young gentlewoman! Well, miss, wonderful! and how has Tim — Hey, boy, is not Miss a fine young lady?

Hart. Fath and soul! father, miss is a charming young woman! all red and white like Mally——Hum!

Jenk. Hush, Tim! Nell, and, miss, how does my boy? he's an honest hearty lad! has he, good now! had the art——How d'ye like him, young gentlewoman?

Miss Suk. Like'n? Well enough, I think.

Jenk. Why then, miss, with your leave, your aunt and I here have agreed, if you are willing to have the wedding over directly.

Miss Suk. Gad! with all my heart. Ask the young man.

Hart. Fath and soul! just as you please, to day, to-morrow, or when you will, more or less!

Jenk. Good now, good now! then get you in there you will find one to do your business [*Exeunt* Hart. *and* Miss Suk.] Wonderful! matters will soon be managed within. Well, lady, this was, good now! so kind! lack-a-day! I verily believe,

if

if Dame Winny was dead that I should be glad to lead up such another dance with you, lady.

Miss Pen. You are, sir, something too precipitate: nor would there, did circumstances concur as you insinuate, be so absolute a certitude, that I, who have rejected so many matches, should instantaneously succumb.

Jenk. Lack-a-day! lady: good now! I——

Miss Pen. No, sir: I would have you instructed, that, had not Penelope Trifle made irrefragable resolutions, she need not so long have preserved her family surname.

Jenk. Wonderful! why, I was only——

Miss Pen. Nor has the title of Lady Gazette such resplendent charms or such bewitching allurements as to throw me at once into the arms of Sir Gregory.

Jenk. Good now! who says——

Miss Pen. Could wealth, beauty, or titles, superior to perhaps——

Enter Sir Gregory and Timothy.

Tim. Yes indeed, father, Mr. Hartop knew on't as well as I; and Mr. Jenkins got us a parson.

Sir Greg. Good now, good now! a rare couple of friends! but I'll be even with them! I'll marr their market! Master Jenkins, you have fobbed me finely!

Jenk. Lack-a-day! what's the matter now!

Sir Greg. Come, come, none of your lack-a-days! none of your gambols nor your tricks to me! good now, good now! give me my clothes! here, take your tawdry trappings! I have found you out at last! I'll be no longer your property!

Jenk.

Jenk. Wonderful! what's all this, lady? Good now, good now! what's here, a stage-play?

Sir Greg. Play me no plays! but give me my wig! and your precious friend, my loving cousin! (pize on the kindred!) let'n——

Jenk. Good now, good now! what are these folks? as sure as a gun they're mad!

Sir Greg. Mad! no, no! we are neither mad nor fools: no thanks to you though!

Miss Pen. What is all this? can you unravel this perplexity, untwine this mystery, Sir Gregory Gazette?

Sir Greg. He Sir Gregory Gazette? Lack-a-day! lady, you are tricked, imposed on, bamboozled! good now, good now! 'tis I am Sir Gregory Gazette!

Miss Pen. How?

Tim. Fath and soul! 'tis true, mistress; and I am his son Tim, and will swear it.

Miss Pen. Why, is not Mr. Timothy Gazette with my niece Susannah Trifle?

Tim. Who, me? Lord! no, 'tis none of I, it is cousin Hartop in my clothes.

Miss Pen. What's this? and pray who——

Enter Hartop and Miss Sukey Trifle.

Jenk. Why, as I see the affair is concluded, you may, madam, call me Jenkins: come, Hartop, you may now throw off your disguise; the knight had like to have embarrassed us.

Miss Pen. How, Mr. Jenkins! and would you sir, participate of a plot too?

Hart.

Hart. Madam, in the issue your family will I
hope, have no great reason to repent; I always had
the greatest veneration for Miss Penelope Trifle's
understanding, the highest esteem for her virtues;
and should think myself highly honoured in being
regarded as her relation.

Miss Pen. Sir, I shall determine on nothing till
I am apprised of my brother's resolution.

Hart. For that we must wait.—Sir Gregory, I
must intreat your and your son's pardon for some
little liberties I have taken with you both.—Mr.
Jenkins, I have the highest obligation to your
friendship.——And, miss, when we become a little better acquainted, I flatter myself the change
will not prove unpleasing.

Miss Suk. I know nothing at all about it.

Hart. Sir Gregory, we shall have your company
at dinner?

Sir Greg. Lack-a-day! no, no: that boy has
spoiled my stomach!—Come, Tim, fetch thy rib,
and let us be jogging towards Wales: but how
thou wilt get off with thy mother————

Tim. Never fear, father!

Since you have been pleas'd our nuptial knot to
    bless.
We shall be happy all our lives—more or less!
                                    [*Exeunt omnes.*]

F I N I S.

THE

MAYOR OF GARRATT;

A

COMEDY

IN TWO ACTS:

AS PERFORMED AT THE

THEATRES ROYAL.

WRITTEN BY THE LATE

SAMUEL FOOTE, Esq.

———————

A NEW EDITION.

═══════════════

LONDON:
PRINTED FOR W. LOWNDES, No. 76, FLEET-STREET,
1797.

Price One Shilling.

DRAMATIS PERSONÆ.

	DRURY-LANE	COVENT-GARDEN.	HAY-MARKET.
Major Sturgeon,	Mr. Palmer.	Mr. Wilson.	Mr. Bannister.
Sir Jacob Jollup,	Mr. Waldron.	Mr. Powel.	Mr. Usher.
Bruin,	Mr. Phillimore.	Mr. Cubitt.	Mr. Maddocks.
Lint,	Mr. Suet.	Mr. Thompson.	Mr. Benson.
Roger,	————	Mr. Farley.	Mr. Waldron, jun.
Mob,	————	————	Mr. Cooke, &c.
Snuffle,	————	————	Mr. Lyons.
Crispin Heel-Tap,	————	————	Mr. Burton.
Jerry Sneak,	Mr. J. Bannister.	Mr. Fawcett.	Mr. J. Bannister.
Mrs. Bruin,	————	Mrs. Crofs.	Miss Tidswell.
Mrs. Sneak,	Mrs. Jordan.	Mrs. Mattocks.	Mrs. Goodall.

THE
MAYOR OF GARRATT.

ACT I.

SCENE *Sir* Jacob's *House at* Garrat.

Enter Sir Jacob.

Sir Jacob.

R OGER—

Enter Roger.

Rog. Anan, Sir—

Sir Jac. Sir, firrah! and why not Sir Jacob, you rafcal? Is that all your manners? Has his Majefty dubb'd me a Knight for you to make me a Mifter? Are the candidates near upon coming?

Rog. Nic Goofe, the taylor, from Putney, they fay, will be here in a crack, Sir Jacob.

Sir Jac. Has Margery fetch'd in the linen?

Rog. Yes, Sir Jacob.

Sir Jac. Are the pigs and the poultry lock'd up in the barn?

Rog. Safe, Sir Jacob.

Sir Jac. And the plate and fpoons in the pantry?

Rog.

Rog. Yes, Sir Jacob.

Sir Jac. Then give me the key; the mob will foon be upon us; and all is fifh that comes to their net. Has Ralph laid the cloth in the hall?

Rog. Yes, Sir Jacob.

Sir Jac. Then let him bring out the turkey and chine, and be fure there is plenty of muftard; and, d'ye hear, Roger, do you ftand yourfelf at the gate, and be careful who you let in.

Rog. I will, Sir Jacob.   [*Exit* Rog.

Sir Jac. So, now I believe things are pretty fecure: But I can't think what makes my daughters fo late ere they—

[*Knocking at the gate.*

Who is that, Roger?

Roger without. Mafter Lint, the potter-carrier, Sir Jacob.

Sir Jac. Let him in. What the deuce can he want?

Enter Lint.

Sir Jac. Well, mafter Lint, your will?

Lint. Why, I come, Sir Jacob, partly to enquire after your health; and partly, as I may fay, to fettle the bufinefs of the day.

Sir Jac. What bufinefs?

Lint. Your worfhip knoweth, this being the day of election, the rabble may be riotous; in which cafe, maims, bruifes, contu-fions,

fions, diflocations, fractures fimple and compound, may likely enfue: now your worfhip need not be told, that I am not only a
pharmacopolift, or vender of drugs, but
likewife chirurgeon, or healer of wounds.

Sir Jac. True, mafter Lint, and equally
fkillful in both.

Lint. It is your worfhip's pleafure to fay
fo, Sir Jacob: Is it your worfhip's will that
I lend a miniftring hand to the maim'd?

Sir Jac. By all means.

Lint. And to whom muft I bring in my
bill?

Sir Jac. Doubtlefs, the veftry.

Lint. Your worfhip knows, that, kill or
cure, I have contracted to phyfic the parifh
poor by the great: but this muft be a feparate charge.

Sir Jac. No, no; all under one: come,
mafter Lint, don't be unreafonable.

Lint. Indeed, Sir Jacob, I can hardly afford it. What with the dearnefs of drugs,
and the number of patients the peace has procured me, I can't get falt to my porridge.

Sir Jac. Bad this year, the better the
next—We muft take things rough and
fmooth as they run.

Lint. Indeed I have a very hard bargain.

Sir Jac. No fuch matter; we are, neighbour Lint, a little better inftructed. Formerly, indeed, a fit of illnefs was very expensive;

penfive; but now, phyfic is cheaper than food.

Lint. Marry, heaven forbid!

Sir Jac. No, no; your effences, elixirs, emetics, fweats,drops, and your paftes, and your pills, have filenced your peftles and mortars. Why a fever, that would former-ly have coft you a fortune, you may now cure for twelve penn'orth of powder.

Lint. Or kill, Sir Jacob.

Sir Jac. And then as to your fcurvies, and gouts, rheumatifms, confumptions, coughs, and catarrhs, tar-water and tur-pentine will make you as found as a roach.

Lint. Noftrums!

Sir Jac. Specifics, fpecifics, mafter Lint.

Lint. I am very forry to find a man of your worfhip's——Sir Jacob, a promoter of puffs; and encourager of quacks, Sir Jacob.

Sir Jac. Regulars, Lint, regulars; look at their names—Roger, bring me the news —not a foul of them but is either P. L. or M. D.

Lint. Plaguy liars! Murderous dogs!

Roger brings the News.

Sir Jac. Liars! Here, look at the lift of their cures. The oath of Margery Squab, of Ratcliff-Highway, fpinfter.

Lint. Perjuries.

Sir

Sir Jac. And fee here, the churchwardens have figned it.

Lint. Fictitious, Sir Jacob.

Sir Jac. Sworn before the worfhipful Mr. Juftice Drowfy, this thirteenth day of ——

Lint. Forgery.

Sir Jac. Why, harkye, firrah, do you think Mr. Juftice Drowfy would fet his hand to a forgery?

Lint. I know, Sir Jacob, that woman; fhe has been cured of fifty difeafes in a fortnight, and every one of 'em mortal.

Sir Jac. You impudent——

Lint. Of a dropfy, by Weft——

Sir Jac. Audacious——

Lint. A cancer, by Cleland——

Sir Jac. Arrogant——

Lint. A palfy, by Walker——

Sir Jac. Impertinent——

Lint. Gout and fciatic, by Rock.

Sir Jac. Infolent——

Lint. Confumption, by Stevens's drops.

Sir Jac. Paltry——

Lint. And fquinting, by the Chevalier Taylor——

Sir Jac. Pill-gilding puppy!

Lint. And as to the Juftice, fo the affidavit brings him a fhilling——

Sir Jac. Why, harkye, rafcal, how dare you abufe the commiffion?——You blood-

letting,

ting, tooth-drawing, corn-cutting, worm-killing, bliftering, gliftering—

Lint. Blefs me, Sir Jacob, I did not think to—

Sir Jac. What firrah, do you infult me in my office? Here, Roger, out with him —turn him out.

Lint. Sir, as I hope to be—

Sir Jac. Away with him. You fcoundrel, if my clerk was within, I'd fend you this inftant to Bridewell. Things are come to a pretty pafs, indeed, if after all my reading in Wood, and Nelfon, and Burn; if after twenty years attendance at turnpike-meetings, feffions petty and quarter; if after fetting of rates, licencing ale-houfes, and committing of vagrants—but all refpect to authority is loft, and *Unus Quorum* now-a-days is no more regarded than a petty conftable. [*Knocking.*] Roger, fee who is at the gate? Why the fellow is deaf.

Rog. Juftice Sturgeon, the fifhmonger, from Brentford.

Sir Jac. Gad's my life! and Major to the Middlefex militia. Ufher him in, Roger.

Enter Major Sturgeon.

Sir Jac. I could have wifh'd you had come a little fooner, Major Sturgeon.

Major.

Major. Why, what has been the matter, Sir Jacob?

Sir Jac. There has, Major, been here an impudent pill-monger, who has dar'd to scandalize the whole body of the bench.

Major. Infolent companion! had I been here, I would have mittimus'd the rafcal at once.

Sir Jac. No, no, he wanted the Major more than the Magiftrate; a few fmart ftrokes from your cane would have fully anfwer'd the purpofe—Well, Major, our wars are done; the rattling drum, and fqueaking fife, now wound our ears no more.

Major. True, Sir Jacob, our corps is difembodied, fo the French may fleep in fecurity.

Sir Jac But, Major, was it not rather late in life for you to enter upon the profeffion of arms?

Major. A little aukward in the beginning, Sir Jacob: the great difficulty they had was, to get me to turn out my toes; but ufe, ufe reconciles all them kind of things: why, after my firft campaign, I no more minded the noife of the guns than a flea-bite.

Sir Jac. No!

Major. No. There is more made of thefe matters than they merit. For the general good, indeed, I am glad of the peace;
but

but as to my fingle felf—And yet, we have had fome defperate duty, Sir Jacob.

Sir Jac. No doubt.

Major. Oh! fuch marchings and coun-ter-marchings, from Brentford to Elin, from Elin to Acton, from Acton to Uxbridge; the duft flying, fun fcorching, men fweat-ing—Why, there was our laft expedition to Hounflow, that day's work carried off Major Moloffas. Bunhill-fields never faw a braver commander! He was an irrepa-rable lofs to the fervice.

Sir Jac. How came that about?

Major. Why, it was partly the Major's own fault; I advifed him to pull off his fpurs before he went upon action; but he was refolute, and would not be rul'd.

Sir Jac. Spirit; zeal for the fervice.

Major. Doubtlefs—But to proceed: In order to get our men in good fpirits, we were quartered at Thiftleworth the even-ing before; at day-break, our regiment formed at Hounflow town's end, as it might be about here. The Major made a fine difpofition: on we march'd, the men all in high fpirits, to attack the gibbet where Gardel is hanging; but turning down a narrow lane to the left, as it might be about there, in order to poffefs a pig's ftye, that we might take the gallows in flank, and, at all events, fecure a re-treat, who fhould come by but a drove of fat at oxen for Smithfield. The drums beat in the front, the dogs bark'd in the rear, the oxen set up a gallop; on they came thundering upon us, broke through our ranks in an instant, and threw the whole corps in confusion.

Sir Jac. Terrible!

Major. The Major's horse took to his heels; away he scour d over the heath. That gallant commander stuck both his spurs into the flank, and for some time held by his mane; but in crossing a ditch, the horse threw up his head, gave the Major a dowse in the chops, and plump'd him into a gravel-pit, just by the powder-mills.

Sir Jac. Dreadful!

Major. Whether from the fall or the fright, the Major mov'd off in a month— Indeed it was an unfortunate day for us all.

Sir Jac. As how?

Major. Why, as Captain Cucumber, Lieutenant Patty-Pan, Ensign Tripe, and myself, were returning to town in the Turnham-Green stage, we were stopp'd near the Hammersmith turnpike, and robb'd and stripp'd by a foot-pad.

Sir Jac. An unfortunate day, indeed!

Major. But in some measure to make me amends, I got the Major's commission.

Sir Jac. You did.

Major.

Major. O yes. I was the only one of the corps that could ride; otherwise, we always fucceeded of courfe: no jumping over heads, no underhand work among us; all men of honour; and I muft do the regiment the juftice to fay, there never was a fet of more amiable officers.

Sir Jac. Quiet and peaceable.

Major. As lambs, Sir Jacob. Excepting one boxing-bout at the Three Compaffes in Acton, between Captain Sheers and the Colonel, concerning a game at All-fours, I don't remember a fingle difpute.

Sir Jac. Why, that was mere mutiny; the Captain ought to have been broke.

Major. He was; for the Colonel not only took away his cockade, but his cuftom; and I don't think poor Captain Sheers has done a ftitch for him fince.

Sir Jac. But you foon fupplied the lofs of Moloffas?

Major. In part only: no, Sir Jacob, he had great experience; he was train'd up to arms from his youth; at fixteen he trail'd a pike in the Artillery-ground; at eighteen got a company in the Smithfield pioneers; and by the time he was twenty, was made aid-de-camp to Sir Jeffery Grub, Knight, Alderman, and Colonel of the Yellow.

Sir Jac. A rapid rife!

Major,

Major. Yes, he had a genius for war; but what I wanted in practice, I made up by doubling my diligence. Our porter at home had been a serjeant of marines ; so after shop was shut up at night, he us'd to teach me my exercise ; and he had not to deal with a dunce, Sir Jacob.

Sir Jac. Your progress was great.

Major. Amazing. In a week I could shoulder, and rest, and poize, and turn to the right, and wheel to the left; and in less than a month I could fire without winking or blinking.

Sir Jac. A perfect Hannibal!

Major. Ah, and then I learnt to form lines, and hollows, and squares, and evolutions, and revolutions : let me tell you, Sir Jacob, it was lucky that Monsieur kept his myrmidons at home, or we should have pepper'd his flat-bottom'd boats.

Sir Jac. Ay, marry, he had a marvellous escape.

Major. We would a taught him what a Briton can do, who is fighting *pro arvis* and *focus.*

Sir Jac. Pray now, Major, which do you look upon as the best disciplin'd troops, the London regiments, or the Middlesex militia?

Major. Why, Sir Jacob, it does not become me to say ; but lack-a-day, they have never seen any service—Holiday soldiers !
Why,

Why, I don't believe, unlefs indeed upon a
lord-mayor's day, and that mere matter of
accident, that they were ever wet to the
fkin in their lives.

Sir Jac. Indeed!

Major. No! foldiers for fun-fhine, Cockneys; they have not the appearance, the
air, the freedom, the *Jenny fequi* that—Oh
could you but fee me falute! you have
never a fpontoon in the houfe?

Sir Jac. No; but we could get you a
fhove-pike.

Major. No matter. Well, Sir Jacob, and
how are your fair daughters, fweet Mrs.
Sneak, and the lovely Mrs. Bruin; is fhe as
lively and as brilliant as ever?

Sir Jac. Oh, oh, now the murder is out;
this vifit was intended for them: come, own
now, Major, did not you expect to meet
with them here? You officers are men of
fuch gallantry!

Major. Why, we do tickle up the ladies,
Sir Jacob; there is no refifting a red coat.

Sir Jac. True, true, Major.

Major. But that is now all over with me.
" Farewell to the plumed fteeds and neigh-
" ing troops," as the black man fays in the
play; like the Roman cenfurer, I fhall retire to my Savine field, and there cultivate
cabbages.

Sir Jac. Under the fhade of your laurels.

Major.

Major. True; I have done with the Major, and now return to the Magistrate ; *Cedunt Arma Togge.*

Sir Jac. Still in the service of your country.

Major. True; man was not made for himself ; and so, thinking that this would prove a busy day in the justicing way I am come, Sir Jacob, to lend you a hand.

Sir Jac. Done like a neighbour.

Major. I have brought, as I suppose most of our business will be in the battery way, some warrants and mittimuses ready fill'd up, with all but the names of the parties, in order to save time.

Sir Jac. A provident magistrate.

Major. Pray, how shall we manage as to the article of swearing ; for I reckon we shall have oaths as plenty as hops.

Sir Jac. Why, with regard to that branch of our business, to-day, I believe, the law must be suffer'd to sleep.

Major. I should think we might pick up something that's pretty that way.

Sir Jac. No, poor rascals, they would not be able to pay; and as to the stocks, we should never find room for their legs.

Major. Pray, Sir Jacob, is Matthew Marrow-bone, the butcher of your town, living or dead ?

Sir Jac. Living.

Major.

Major. And fwears as much as he ufed?

Sir Jac. An alter'd man, Major; not an oath comes out of his mouth.

Major. You furprife me; why, when he frequented our town of a market-day, he has taken out a guinea in oaths—and quite chang'd?

Sir Jac. Entirely; they fay his wife has made him a Methodift, and that he preaches at Kennington-Common.

Major. What a deal of mifchief thofe rafcals do in the country—Why then we have entirely loft him?

Sir Jac. In that way; but I got a brace of bind-overs from him laft week for a couple of baftards.

Major. Well done, mafter Matthew—but pray now, Sir Jacob——

[*Mob without huzza!*

Sir Jac. What's the matter now, Roger?

Enter Roger.

Rog. The electors defire to know, if your worfhip has any body to recommend?

Sir Jac. By no means; let them be free in their choice: I fhan't interfere.

Rog. And if your worfhip has any ob-jection to Crifpin Heel-Tap the Cobler's being returning officer?

Sir Jac. None, provided the rafcal can keep himfelf fober: Is he there?

Rog.

Rog. Yes, Sir Jacob : make way there; ſtand farther off from the gate: here is Madam Sneak in a chair, along with her huſband.

Major. Gad-ſo, you will permit me to convoy her in ? [*Exit* Major.

Sir Jac. Now here is one of the evils of war. This Sturgeon was as pains taking a Billingſgate-broker as any in the bills of mortality. But the fiſh is got out of his element; the ſoldier has quite demoliſh'd the citizen.

Enter Mrs. Sneak *handed by the* Major.

Mrs. Sneak. Dear Major, I demand a million of pardons. I have given you a profuſion of trouble ; but my huſband is ſuch a gooſe-cap, that I can't get no good out of him at home or abroad—Jerry, Jerry Sneak! —Your bleſſing, Sir Jacob.

Sir Jac. Daughter, you are welcome to Garratt.

Mrs. Sneak. Why, Jerry Sneak ! I ſay: *Enter* Sneak, *with a band-box, a hoop-petticoat under his arm, and cardinal,* &c. &c. &c. &c.

Sneak. Here, lovy.
Mrs. Sneak. Here, looby: there, lay theſe things in the hall ; and then go and look after the horſe : are you ſure you have got all the things out of the chaiſe ?

Sneak:

Sneak. Yes, chuck.

Mrs. Sneak. Then give me my fan.

[Jerry *drops the things in searching his pocket for the fan.*

Mrs Sneak. Did ever mortal see such a—I declare, I am quite asham'd to be seen with him abroad: go, get you gone out of my sight.

Sneak. I go, lovy: Good-day to my father-in-law.

Sir Jac. I am glad to see you, son Sneak: But where is your brother Bruin and his wife.

Sneak. He will be here anon, father Sir Jacob; he did but just step into the Alley to gather how tickets were sold.

Sir Jac. Very well, son Sneak.

[*Exit Sneak.*

Mrs Sneak. Son! yes, and a pretty son you have provided.

Sir Jac. I hope all for the best: why, what terrible work there would have been, had you married such a one as your sister? one house could never have contain'd you —Now, I thought this meek mate—

Mrs Sneak. Meek! a mushroom! a milksop!

Sir Jac. Lookye, Molly, I have married you to a man; take care you don't make him a monster.   [*Exit Sir* Jac.

Mrs Sneak. Monster! Why, Major, the fellow has no more heart than a mouse: Had my my kind ftars indeed allotted me a military man, I fhould, doubtlefs, have deported myfelf in a befeemingly manner.

Major. Unqueftionably, madam.

Mrs Sneak. Nor would the Major have found, had it been my fortune to intermarry with him, that Molly Jollup would have difhonoured his cloth.

Major. I fhould have been too happy.

Mrs. Sneak. Indeed, Sir, I reverence the army ; they are all fo brave ; fo polite ; fo every thing a woman can wifh—

Major. Oh! madam—

Mrs. Sneak. So elegant ; fo genteel ; fo obliging : and then the rank ; why, who would dare to affront the wife of a Major?

Major. No man with impunity ; that I take the freedom to fay, madam.

Mrs. Sneak. I know it, good Sir : Oh! I am no ftranger to what I have mifs'd.

Major. Oh, madam!—Let me die, but fhe has infinite merit.   [*Afide.*

Mrs. Sneak. Then to be join'd to a fneaking flovenly cit; a paltry, praying, pitiful pin-maker!

Major. Melancholy!

Mrs. Sneak. To be joftled and cramm'd with the crowd ; no refpe&t, no place, no precedence ; to be choak'd with the fmoak of the city; no country jaunts but to Ifling-ton ; no balls but at Pewterers-hall.

Major.

Major. Intolerable!

Mrs. Sneak. I fee, Sir, you have a proper fenfe of my fufferings.

Major. And would fhed my beft blood to relieve them.

Mrs. Sneak. Gallant gentleman!

Major. The brave muft favour the fair.

Mrs. Sneak. Intrepid Major!

Mjor. Divine Mrs. Sneak!

Mrs. Sneak. Obliging commander!

Major. Might I be permitted the honor—

Mrs. Sneak. Sir—

Major. Juft to ravifh a kifs from your hand.

Mrs. Sneak. You have a right to all we can grant.

Major. Courteous, condefcending, complying—Hum—Ha!

Enter Sneak.

Sneak. Chuck, my brother and fifter Bruin are juft turning the corner; the Clapham ftage was quite full, and fo they came by water.

Mrs. Sneak. I wifh they had all been fous'd in the Thames—A praying, impertinent puppy!

Major. Next time I will clap a centinel to fecure the door.

Mrs. Sneak. Major Sturgeon, permit me to withdraw for a moment; my drefs demands a little repair.

Major. Your ladyfhip's moft entirely devoted.

Mrs.

Mrs. Sneak. Ladyſhip! he is the very Broglio and Belleiſle of the army!

Sneak. Shall I wait upon you, dove?

Mrs. Sneak. No, dolt; what, would you leave the Major alone? is that your manners, you mongrel?

Major. Oh, madam, I can never be alone; your ſweet idera will be my conſtant companion.

Mrs. Sneak. Mark that: I am ſorry, Sir, I am obligated to leave you.

Major. Madam—

Mrs. Sneak. Eſpecially with ſuch a wretched companion.

Major. Oh, madam—

Mrs. Sneak. But as ſoon as my dreſs is reſtored, I ſhall fly to relieve your diſtreſs.

Major. For that moment I ſhall wait with the greateſt impatience.

Mrs. Sneak. Courteous commander.

Major. Barragon of women!

Mrs Sneak. Adieu!

Major. Adieu!   [*Exit Mrs.* Sneak.

Sneak. Notwithſtanding, Sir, all my chicken has ſaid, I am ſpecial company when ſhe is not by.

Major. I doubt not, maſter Sneak.

Sneak. If you would but come one Thurſday-night to our club, at the Nag's-Head, in the Poultry, you would meet ſome roaring, rare boys, i'faith; There's Jemmy Perkins,

kins, the packer; little Tom Simkins, the grocer; honeſt Maſter Muzzle, the midwife—

Major. A goodly company!

Sneak. Ay, and then ſometimes we have the Choice Spirits from Comus's Court, and we crack jokes, and are ſo jolly and funny; I have learnt myſelf to ſing "An old woman clothed in grey." But I durſt not ſing out loud, becauſe my wife would overhear me; and ſhe ſays as how I bawl worſer than the broom-man.

Major. And you muſt not think of diſobliging your lady.

Sneak. I never does: I never contradicts her, not I.

Major. That's right: ſhe is a woman of infinite merit.

Sneak. O, a power: and don't you think ſhe is very pretty withal?

Major. A Venus!

Sneak. Yes, werry like Wenus—Mayhap you have known her ſome time?

Major. Long.

Sneak. Belike, before ſhe was married?

Major. I did, Maſter Sneak.

Sneek. Ay, when ſhe was a wirgin. I thought you was an old acquaintance, by your kiſſing her hand; for we ben't quite ſo familiar as that---But then, indeed, we han't been married a year.

Major.

Major. The meer honey-moon.

Sneak. Ay, ay, I fuppofe we fhall come to it by degrees.

Bruin [*within*] Come along Jane; why you are as purfy and lazy, you jade—

Enter Bruin *and* Wife; Bruin *with a cotton cap on; his Wife with his wig, great-coat, and fifhing-rod.*

Bruin. Come, Jane, give me my wig; you flut, how you have toufled the curls? Mafter Sneak, a good morning to you. Sir, I am your humble fervant, unknown.

Enter Roger.

Rog. Mrs. Sneak begs to fpeak with the Major.

Major. I will wait on the lady immediately.

Sneak. Don't tarry an inftant; you can't think how impatient fhe is. [*Exit* Major.

Sneak. A good morrow to you, brother Bruin; you have had a warm walk acrofs the fields.

Mrs. Bruin. Good lord, I am all in a muck.—

Bruin. And who may you thank for it, huffy? If you had got up time enough, you might have fecur'd the ftage; but you are a lazy lie-a-bed.

Mrs. Bruin. There's Mr. Sneak keeps my fifter a chay.

Bruin.

Bruin. And so he may; but I know better what to do with my money : indeed, if the war had but continued awhile, I don't know what mought ha' been done; but this plaguy peace, with a pox to't, has knock'd up all the trade of the Alley.

Mrs. Bruin. For the matter of that, we can afford it well enough as it is.

Bruin. And how do you know that? Who told you as much, Mrs. Mixen? I hope I know the world better than to trust my concerns with a wife : no, no, thank you for that, Mrs. Jane.

Mrs. Bruin. And pray who is more fitterer to be trusted?

Bruin. Hey-day! Why, the wench is bewitch'd : come, come, let's have none of your palaver here—Take twelve-pence and pay the waterman.—But first see if he has broke none of the pipes—And, d'ye hear Jane, be sure to lay the fishing-rod safe.   [*Exit* Mrs. Bruin.

Sneak. Ods me, how finely she's manag'd! what would I give to have my wife as much under!

Bruin. It is all your own fault, brother Sneak.

Sneak. D'ye think so? she is a sweet pretty creature.

Bruin. A vixen.

Sneak.

Sneak. Why, to fay the truth, fhe does now and then hector a little ; and, between ourfelves, domineers like the devil: O Lord, I lead the life of a dog: why, fhe allows me but two fhillings a week for my pocket.

Bruin. No!

Sneak. No, man ; 'tis fhe that receives and pays all : and then I am forc'd to trot after her to church, with her cardinal, pattens, and prayer-book, for all the world as if I was ftill a'prentice.

Bruin. Zounds! I would foufe them all in the kennel.

Sneak. I durft not—And then at table, I never gets what I loves.

Bruin. The devil !

Sneak. No ; fhe always helps me herfelf to the tough drumfticks of turkies, and the damn'd fat flaps of fhoulders of mutton; I don't think I have eat a bit of under-cruft fince we have been married : you fee brother Bruin, I am almoft as thin as a lath.

Bruin. An abfolute fkeleton !

Sneak. Now, if you think I could carry my point, I would fo fwinge and leather my lambkin ; God, I would fo curry and claw her.

Bruin. By the lord Harry, fhe richly deferves it.

Sneak. Will you, brother, lend me a lift.

Bruin. Command me at all times.

Sneak.

Sneak. Why then, I will verily pluck up a spirit; and the first time she offers to—

Mrs. Sneak [*within*] Jerry, Jerry Sneak!

Sneak. Gad's my life, sure as a gun that's her voice: look-ye, brother, I don't chuse to breed a disturbance in another body's house; but as soon as ever I get home—

Bruin. Now is your time.

Sneak. No, no; it would not be decent.

Mrs. Sneak. [*within.*] Jerry! Jerry!——

Sneak. I come, lovy. But you will be sure to stand by me?

Bruin. Trot, nincompoop.

Sneak. Well, if I don't—I wish—

Mrs. Sneak. [*within.*] Where is this lazy puppy a-loitering?

Sneak. I come, chuck, as fast as I can—Good Lord, what a sad life do I lead!

[*Exit* Sneak.

Bruin. Ex quovis linguo: who can make a silk purse of a sow's ear?

Enter Sir Jacob.

Sir Jac. Come, son Bruin, we are all seated at table, man; we have but just time for a snack: the candidates are near upon coming.

Bruin. A poor, paltry, mean-spirited—Damn it, before I would submit to such a—

Sir Jac. Come, come, man; don't be so crusty.

Bruin

Bruin. I follow, Sir Jacob: Damme'
when once a man gives up his prerogative'
he might as well give up—But, however, it
is no bread and butter of mine—Jerry,
Jerry!——Zounds, I would Jerry and jerk
her too.   [*Exit.*

End of the First Act.

ACT II. SCENE continues.

Sir JACOB, *Major* STURGEON, *Mr. and
Mrs.* BRUIN, *Mr. and Mrs.* SNEAK,
discovered.

Mrs. Sneak.

INDEED, Major, not a grain of curiosity.
Can it be thought that we, who have a
Lord-Mayor's show every year, can take
any pleasure in this?

Major. In time of war, madam, these
meetings are not amiss: I fancy a man
might pick up a good many recruits: but in
these piping times of peace, I wonder Sir
Jacob permits it.

Sir Jac. It would, Major, cost me my
popularity to quash it: the common people
are as fond of their customs as the barons
were of their *Magna Charta*: besides, my
tenants make some little advantage.

                                     Enter

Enter Roger.

Rog. Crifpin Heel-Tap, with the electors, are fet out from the Adam and Eve.

Sir Jac. Gad-fo, then they will foon be upon us: come, good folks, the balcony will give us the beft view of the whole. Major, you will take the ladies under protection.

Major. Sir Jacob, I am upon guard.

Sir Jac. I can tell you, this Heel-Tap is an arch rafcal.—

Sneak. And plays the beft game at cribbage in the whole corporation of Garratt.

Mrs. Sneak. That puppy will always be a-chattering.

Sneak. Nay, I did but—

Mrs. Sneak. Hold your tongue, or I'll fend you home in an inftant—

Sir Jac. Pr'ythee, daughter!—You may to-day, Major, meet with fomething that will put you in mind of more important tranfactions.

Major. Perhaps fo.

Sir Jac. Lack-a-day, all men are alike; their principles exactly the fame: for tho' art and education may difguife or polifh the manners, the fame motives and fprings are univerfally planted.

Major. Indeed!

Sir Jac. Why, in this mob, this group of plebeians, you will meet with materials to make a Sylla, a Cicero, a Solon, or a Cæfar;

let

et them but change conditions, and the world's great lord had been but the beft wreftler on the green.

Major. Ay, ay, I could have told thefe things formerly; but fince I have been in the army, I have entirely neglected the claffes.   *Mob without huzza.*

Sir Jac. But the heroes are at hand, Major.

Sneak. Father Sir Jacob, might not we have a tankard of ftingo above?

Sir Jac. By all means.

Sneak. D'ye hear, Roger.

[*Exeunt into the balcony.*

SCENE, a STREET.

Enter Mob, *with* Heel-Tap *at their head*; *fome crying a* Goofe; *others a* Mug; *others a* Primmer.

Heel-Tap. Silence, there; filence!

1*ft. Mob.* Hear neighbour Heel-Tap.

2*d Mob.* Ay, ay, hear Crifpin.

3*d Mob.* Ay, ay, hear him, hear Crifpin: He will put us into the model of the thing at once.

Heel-Tap. Why then, filence! I fay.

All. Silence.

Heel-Tap. Silence, and let us proceed, neighbours, with all the decency and con-fufion ufual upon thefe occafions.

1*ft Mob.* Ay, ay, there is no doing with-out that.

All.

All. No, no, no.

Heel-Tap. Silence then, and keep the peace : what, is there no refpect paid to authority ? am not I the returning officer ?

All. Ay, ay, ay.

Heel-Tap. Chofen by yourfelves, and approved of by Sir Jacob ?

All. True, true.

Heel-Tap. Well then, be filent and civil; ftand back there, that gentleman without a fhirt, and make room for your betters : where's Simon Snuffle the Sexton ?

Snuffle. Here.

Heel-Tap. Let him come forward; we appoint him our fecretary : for Simon is a fcolard, and can read written hand ; and fo let him be refpected accordingly.

3d Mob. Room for Mafter Snuffle.

Heel-Tap. Here, ftand by me : and let us neighbours, proceed to open the premunire of the thing : but firft, your reverence to the lord of the manor : a long life and a merry one to our landlord Sir Jacob ! Huzza !

Mob. Huzza !

Sneak. How fares it, honeft Crifpin ?

Heel-Tap. Servant, Mafter Sneak.—Let us now open the premunire of the thing, which I fhall do briefly, with all the loquacity poffible ; that is, in a medium way ; which, that we may the better do it, let the fecretary read the names of the candidates, and

and what they fay for themfelves; and then we fhall know what to fay of them: Mafter Snuffle, begin.

Snuffle. " To the worthy inhabitants of " the ancient corporation of Garratt: Gen- " tlemen, your votes and intereft are hum- " bly requefted in favour of Timothy " Goofe, to fucceed your late worthy may- " or, Mr. Richard Dripping, in the faid " office, he being" ———

Heel-Tap. This Goofe is but a kind of Gofling, a fort of fneaking fcoundrel: who is he?

Snuffle. A journeyman taylor, from Put-ney.

Heel-Tap. A journeyman taylor! A raf-cal, has he the impudence to tranfpire to be mayor? D'ye confider, neighbours, the weight of this office? Why, it is a burthen for the back of a porter; and can you think that this crofs-legg'd cabbage-eating fon of a cucumber, this whey-fac'd ninny, who is but the ninth part of a man, has ftrength to fupport it?

1ft Mob. No Goofe! no Goofe!

2d Mob. A Goofe!

Heel-Tap. Hold your hiffing, and pro-ceed to the next.

Snuffle. " Your votes are defired for " Matthew Mug."

1ft Mob. A Mug! A Mug!

Heel-

Heel-Tap. Oh, oh, what you are all ready to have a touch of the tankard : but, fair and foft, good neighbours, let us tafte this Mafter Mug, before we fwallow him ; and unlefs I am miftaken, you will find him a damn'd bitter draught.

1ft Mob. A Mug! a Mug!

2d Mob. Hear him; hear Mafter Heel-Tap.

1ft Mob. A Mug! a Mug!

Heel-Tap. Harkye, you fellow, with your mouth full of Mug, let me afk you a queftion : bring him forward : pray is not this Matthew Mug a victualler?

3d Mob. I believe he may.

Heel-Tap. And lives at the fign of the Adam and Eve?

3d Mob. I believe he may.

Heel-Tap. Now anfwer upon your honour, and as you are a gentleman, what is the prefent price of a quart of home-brew'd at the Adam and Eve?

3d Mob. I don't know.

Heel-Tap. You lie, firrah: an't it a groat;

3d Mob. I believe it may.

Heel-Tap. Oh, may be fo: now, neighbours, here's a pretty rafcal; this fame Mug, becaufe, d'ye fee, ftate-affairs would not jog glibly without laying a farthing a quart upon ale; this fcoundrel, not contented

ed to take things in a medium way, has had the impudence to raife it a penny.

Mob. No Mug! no Mug!

Heel-Tap. So, I thought I fhould crack Mr. Mug. Come, proceed to the next, Simon.

Snuffle. The next upon the lift is Peter Primmer, the fchoolmafter.

Heel-Tap. Ay, neighbours, and a fufficient man: let me tell you, Mafter Primmer is the man for my money; a man of learning; that can lay down the law: why, adzooks, he is wife enough to puzzle the parfon: and then, how you have heard him oration at the Adam and Eve of a Saturday night, about Ruffia and Pruffia: Ecod, George Gage the excifeman is nothing at all to un.

4th Mob. A Primmer!

Heel-Tap. Ay, if the folks above did but know him; why, lads, he will make us all ftatefmen in time.

2d Mob. Indeed!

Heel-Tap. Why, he fwears as how all the mifcarriages are owing to the great people's not learning to read.

3d Mob. Indeed!

Heel-Tap. For, fays Peter, fays he, if they would but once fubmit to be learned by me, there is no knowing to what a pitch the nation might rife.

1ft Mob.

1ſt Mob. Ay, I wiſh they would.

Sneak. Criſpin, what is Peter Primmer a candidate ?

Heel-Tap. He is, Maſter Sneak.

Sneak. Lord, I know him, mun, as well as my mother : why, I uſed to go to his lectures to Pewterers-hall 'long with deputy Firkin.

Heel-Tap. Like enough.

Sneak. Odds-me, brother Bruin, can you tell me what is become of my vife ?

Bruin. She is gone off with the Major.

Sneak. Mayhap to take a walk in the garden; I will go and take a peep at what they are doing. *(Exit* Sneak.

Mob without huzza.

Heel-Tap. Gad-ſo! the candidates are coming. Come, neighbours, range yourſelves to the right and left, that you may be canvaſs'd in order : let us ſee who comes firſt ?

1ſt Mob. Maſter Mug.

Heel-Tap. Now, neighbours, have a good caution that this Maſter Mug does not cajole you ; he is a damn'd palavering fellow.

Enter Matthew Mug.

Mug. Gentlemen, I am the loweſt of your ſlaves : Mr. Heel-Tap, have the honour of kiſſing your hand.

Heel-Tap. There, did not I tell you ?

Mug.

Mug. Ah, my very good friend, I hope your father is well?

1*st Mob.* He is dead.

Mug. So he is. Mr. Grub, if my wishes prevail, your very good wife is in health.

2*d Mob.* Wife! I never was married.

Mug. No more you were. Well, neighbours and friends—Ah! what honest Dick Bennet.

3*d Mob.* My name is Gregory Gubbins.

Mug. You are right, it is so; and how fares it with good Master Gubbins?

3*d Mob.* Pretty tight, Master Mug.

Mug. I am exceedingly happy to hear it.

4*th Mob.* Harkye, Master Mug.

Mug. Your pleasure my very dear friend?

4*th Mob.* Why as how, and concerning our young one at home.

Mug. Right; she is a prodigious promising girl.

4*th Mob.* Girl! Zooks, why 'tis a boy.

Mug. True; a fine boy! I love and honour the child.

4*th Mob.* Nay, 'tis none such a child; but you promis'd to get un a place.

Mug. A place! what place?

4*th Mob.* Why, a gentleman's service, you know.

Mug. It is done; it is fixed; it is settled.

4*th Mob.* And when is the lad to take on!

Mug. He must go in a fortnight at farthest.

4*th Mob.*

4th Mob. And is it a pretty goodifh birth Mafter Mug?

Mug. The beft in the world; head butler to lady Barbara Bounce.

4th Mob. A lady!

Mug. The wages are not much, but the nails are amazing.

4th Mob. Barbara Bunch?

Mug. Yes; fhe has routs on Tuefdays and Sundays, and he gathers the tables; only he finds candles, cards, coffee, and tea.

4th Mob. Is Lady Barbara's work pretty tight?

Mug. As good as a fine-cure; he only writes cards to her company, and dreffes his miftrefs's hair.

4th Mob. Hair! Zounds, why Jack was bred to dreffing of horfes.

Mug. True; but he is fuffered to do that by deputy.

4th Mob. May be fo.

Mug. It is fo. Harkye, dear Heel-Tap, who is this fellow? I fhould remember his face.

Heel-Tap. And don't you?

Mug. Not I, I profefs.

Heel-Tap. No!

Mug. No.

Heel-Tap. Well faid, Mafter Mug; but come, time wears: have you any thing more to fay to the Corporation?

Mug.

Mug. Gentlemen of the Corporation of Garratt.

Heel-Tap. Now, twig him; now, mind him: mark how he hauls his mufcles about.

Mug. The honour I this day folicit, will be to me the moſt honourable honour that can be conferr'd; and, ſhould I fucceed, you, gentlemen, may depend on my uſing my utmoſt endeavours to promote the good of the borough; for which purpoſe, the encouragement of your trade and manufaſtories will moſt principally tend. Garratt it muſt be own'd, is an inland town and has not, like Wandſworth and Fulham and Putney, the glorious advantage of a port; but what nature has denied, induſtry may fupply; cabbage, carrots, and colly-flowr's, may be deemed at preſent, your ſtaple commodities; but why ſhould not your commerce be extended? Were I, gentlemen, worthy to adviſe, I ſhould recommend the opening a new branch of trade ; fparagrafs, gentlemen, the manufaſturing of fparagrafs: Batterſea, I own, gentlemen, bears, at preſent, the belle ; but where lies the fault? In ourſelves, gentlemen : let us, gentlemen, but exert our natural ſtrength, and I will take upon me to fay, that a hundred of grafs from the Corporation of Garratt, will in a ſhort time, at the London market, be held, at leaſt as an equivalent to a Batterſea bundle.

Mob. A Mug! a Mug!

Heel-

Heel-Tap. Damn the fellow what a tongue he has! God, I muft ftep in, or he will carry the day. Harkee, Mafter Mug!

Mug. Your pleafure my very good friend:

Heel-Tap. No flummering me: I tell thee, Matthew, 'twon't do: why, as to this article of ale here, how comes it about that you have raifed it a penny a quart?

Mug. A word in your ear, Crifpin; you and your friends fhall have it at threepence.

Heel-Tap. What, firrah, d'ye offer a bribe! D'ye dare to corrupt me, you fcoundrel!

Mug. Gentlemen—

Heel-Tap. Here, neighbours; the fellow has offer'd to bate a penny a quart, if fo be as how I would be confenting to impofe upon you.

Mob. No Mug! no Mug!

Mug. Neighbours, friends——

Mob. No Mug!

Mug. I believe this is the firft borough that ever was loft by the returning officer's refufing a bribe. [*Exit* Mug.

2d Mob. Let us go and pull down his fign.

Heel-Tap. Hold, hold, no riot: but that we may not give Mug time to pervert the votes and carry the day, let us proceed to the election.

Mob. Agreed! agreed!

[*Exit* Heel-Tap, *and* Mob.

Sir

Sir Jacob, Bruin, *and Wife, come from the balcony.*

Sir Jac. Well, fon Bruin, how d'ye re-
'lifh the Corporation of Garratt?

Bruin. Why, lookye, Sir Jacob, my
way is always to fpeak what I think: I
don't approve on't at all.

Mrs. Bruin. No!

Sir Jac. And what's your objection?

Bruin. Why, I was never over-fond of
your May-games: befides, corporations are
too ferious things; they are edge-tools, Sir
Jacob.

Sir Jac. That they are frequently tools,
I can readily grant; but I never heard much
of their edge.

Mrs. Bruin. Well now, I proteft, I am
pleas'd with it mightily.

Bruin. And who the devil doubts it?—
You women folks are eafily pleas'd.

Mrs. Bruin. Well, I like it fo well, that
I hope to fee one every year.

Bruin. Do you? Why then you will be
damnably bit; you may take your leave I
can tell you, for this is the laft you fhall fee.

Sir Jac. Fye, Mr. Bruin, how can you
be fuch a bear: is that a manner of treating
your wife?

Bruin. What, I fuppofe you would have
me fuch a fniveling fot as your fon-in-law

C 4   Sneak,

Sneak, to truckle and cringe, to fetch and to—

Enter Sneak, *in a violent hurry.*

Sneak. Where's brother Bruin? O Lord! brother, I have fuch a difmal ftory to tell you—

Bruin. What's the matter?

Sneak. Why, you know I went into the garden to look for my vife and the Major, and there I hunted and hunted as fharp as if it had been for one of my own minikens; but the deuce a Major or Madam could I fee: at laft a thought came into my head to look for them up in the fummer houfe.

Bruin. And there you found them?

Sneak. I'll tell you, the door was lock'd; and then I look'd thro' the key-hole: and, there, Lord a mercy upon us! ⌊*Whifpers*⌋ as fure as a gun.

Bruin. Indeed! Zounds, why did not you break open the door?

Sneak. I durft not: what, would you have me fet my wit to a foldier? I warrant the Major would have knock'd me down with one of his boots; for I could fee they were both of them off.

Bruin. Very well! Pretty doings? You fee, Sir Jacob, thefe are the fruits of indulgence: you may call me a bear, but your daughter fhall never make me a beaft.

Mob.

Mob huzzas.

Sir Jac. Hey day! What is the election over already.

Enter Crifpin, &c.

Heel-Tap. Where is mafter Sneak?

Sneak. Here, Crifpin.

Heel-Tap. The ancient Corporation of Garratt, in confideration of your great parts and abilities, and out of refpect to their landlord, Sir Jacob, have unanimoufly chofen you mayor.

Sneak. Me! huzza! good Lord, who would have thought it: but how came Mafter Primmer to lofe it?

Heel-Tap. Why, Phill Fleam had told the electors, that Mafter Primmer was an Irifhman; and fo they would none of them give their vote for a foreigner.

Sneak. So then, I have it for certain: Huzza! Now, brother Bruin, you fhall fee how I'll manage my Madam: Gad, I'll make her know I am a man of authority; fhe fhan't think to bullock and domineer over me.

Bruin. Now for it, Sneak; the enemy's at hand.

Sneak. You promife to ftand by me, brother Bruin.

Bruin. Tooth and nail.

Sneak. Then now for it; I am ready, let her come when fhe will.

Enter

Enter Mrs. Sneak.

Mrs. Sneak. Where is the puppy?

Sneak. Yes, yes, fhe is axing for me.

Mrs. Sneak. So, fot; what, is this true that I hear?

Sneak. May be 'tis, may be 'tan't: I don't chufe to truft my affairs with a vo-man. Is that right, brother Bruin?

Bruin. Fine! don't bate her an inch.

Sneak. Stand by me.

Mrs. Sneak. Hey-day! I am amaz'd! Why, what is the meaning of this?

Sneak. The meaning is plain, that I am grown a man, and vil do what I pleafe, without being accountable to nobody.

Mrs. Sneak. Why, the fellow is furely bewitch'd.

Sneak. No, I am unwitch'd, and that you fhall know to your coft; and fince you provoke me, I will tell you a bit of my mind: what, I am the hufband, I hope?

Bruin. That's right: at her again.

Sneak. Yes; and you fhan't think to hector and domineer over me as you have done; for I'll go to the club when I pleafe, and ftay out as late as I lift, and row in a boat to Putney on Sundays, and wifit my friends at Vitfontide, and keep the key of the till, and help myfelf at table to vhat vittles I like, and I'll have a bit of the brown.

Bruin

Bruin. Bravo, brother! Sneak, the day's your own.

Sneak. An't it? vhy, I did not think it vas in me : fhall I tell her all I know?

Bruin. Every thing; you fee fhe is ftruck dumb.

Sneak. As an oyfter : befides madam, I have fomething furder to tell you : ecod, if fome folks go into gardens with Majors, mayhap other people may go into garrets with maids.—There, I gave it her home, brother Bruin.

Mrs. Sneak. Why doodle! jackanapes! harkee, who am I?

Sneak. Come, don't go to call names: am I? vhy my vife, and I am your mafter.

Mrs. Sneak. My mafter! you paltry, puddling puppy; you fneaking fhabby, fcrubby, fniveling-whelp!

Sneak. Brother Bruin, don't let her come near me.

Mrs. Sneak. Have I, firrah, demean'd myfelf to wed fuch a thing, fuch a reptile as thee! Have I not made myfelf a bye-word to all my acquaintance! Don't all the world cry, Lord, who would have thought it! Mifs Molly Jollup to be married to Sneak ; to take up at laft with fuch a noodle as he!

Sneak. Ay, and glad enough you could catch me : you know, you was pretty near your laft legs.

Mrs. Sneak.

Mrs. Sneak. Was there ever fuch a con-
fident cur? My laft legs ! Why, all the
country knows, I could have pick'd and
chus'd where I would : did not I refufe
'Squire Ap-Griffith from Wales? did not
Counfellor Crab come a courting a twelve-
month? did not Mr. Wort, the great
brewer of Brentford, make an offer that I
fhould keep my poft-chay ?

Sneak. Nay, brother Bruin, fhe has had
werry good proffers, that is certain.

Mrs. Sneak. My laft legs !—but I can
rein my paffion no longer ; let me get at
the villain.

Bruin. O fye, fifter Sneak.

Sneak. Hold her faft.

Mrs. Sneak. Mr. Bruin, unhand me :
what, is it you that have ftirred up thefe
coals then; he is fet on by you to abufe me.

Bruin. Not I; I would only have a man
behave like a man.

Mrs. Sneak. What, and are you to teach
him, I warrant—But here comes the Major.

Enter Major Sturgeon.

Oh Major! fuch a riot and rumpus! Like
a man indeed! I wifh people would mind
their own affairs, and not meddle with matters that does not concern them : but all in
good time; I fhall one day catch him alone
when he has not his bullies to back him.

Sneak.

Sneak. Adod, that's true, brother Bruin; what shall I do when she has me at home, and nobody by but ourselves?

Bruin. If you get her once under, you may do with her whatever you will.

Major. Look ye, Master Bruin, I don't know how this behaviour may suit with a citizen; but, were you an officer, and Major Sturgeon upon your court-martial—

Bruin. What then?

Major. Then! why then you would be broke.

Bruin. Broke! and for what?

Major. What! read the articles of war: but these things are out of your spear; points of honour are for the sons of the sword.

Sneak. Honour! if you come to that, where was your honour when you got my vife in the garden?

Major. Now, Sir Jacob, this is the curse of our cloth: all suspected for the faults of a few.

Sneak. Ay, and not without reason; I heard of your tricks at the king of Bohemy, when you was campaining about, I did: father Sir Jacob, he is as wicious as an old ram.

Major. Stop whilst you are safe, Master Sneak; for the sake of your amiable lady, I pardon what is past—But for you—

Bruin. Well.

Major. Dread the whole force of my fury.

Bruin.

Bruin. Why, lookye, Major Sturgeon, I don't much care for your poppers and fharps, becaufe why, they are out of my way; but if you will doff with your boots, and box a couple of bouts——

Major. Box! box! blades! bullets! Bagfhot!

Mrs. Sneak. Nor for the world, my dear Major! oh, rifk not fo precious a life. Ungrateful wretches! and is this the reward for all the great feats he has done? After all his marchings, his foufings, his fweatings, his fwimmings; muft his dear blood be fpilt by a broker!

Major. Be fatisfy'd, fweet Mrs. Sneak; thefe little fracafes we foldiers are fubject to; trifles, bagatailes, Mrs. Sneak: but that matters may be conducted in a military manner, I will get our chaplain to pen me a challenge. Expect to hear from my adjutant.

Mrs. Sneak. Major, Sir Jacob; what, are you all leagu'd againft his dear——A man! yes, a very manly action indeed to fet married people a quarreling, and ferment a difference between hufband and wife : if you were a man, you would not ftand by and fee a poor woman beat and abus'd by a brute, you would not.

Sneak. Oh Lord, I can hold out no longer! why, brother Bruin, you have fet her a veeping: my life, my lovy, don't veep :

veep: did I ever think I fhould have made
my Molly to veep?

Mrs. Sneak. Laft legs! you lubberly—
[*Strikes him.*

Sir Jac. Oh, fye! Molly.

Mrs. Sneak. What, are you leagu'd
againft me, Sir Jacob?

Sir Jac. Prithee, don't expofe yourfelf
before the whole parifh: but what has
been the occafion of this?

Mrs. Sneak. Why has not he gone and
made himfelf the fool of the fair? Mayor
of Garratt indeed! ecod, I could trample
him under my feet.

Sneak. Nay, why fhould you grudge
me my purfarment?

Mrs. Sneak. Did you ever hear fuch an
oaf? why thee wilt be pointed at wherever
thee goeft: lookye, Jerry, mind what I
fay; go get 'em to chufe fomebody elfe,
or never come near me again.

Sneak. What fhall I do, father Sir Jacob?

Sir Jac. Nay, daughter, you take this
thing in too ferious a light; my honeft neighbours thought to compliment me: but
come, we'll fettle the bufinefs at once.
Neighbours, my fon Sneak being feldom
amongft us, the duty will never be done,
fo we will get our honeft friend Heel-Tap
to execute the office; he is, I think every
way qualified.

Mob. A Heel-Tap!

Heel-Tap. What d'ye mean, as Mafter
Jeremy's deputy? *Sir*

Sir Jac. Ay, ay, his *Locum Tenens.*

Sneak. Do, Crifpin : do be my *Locum Tenens.*

Heel-Tap. Give me your hand, Mafter Sneak, and to oblige you I will be the *Locum Tenens.*

Sir Jac. So, that is fettled ; but now to heal the other breich : come, Major, the gentlemen of your cloth feldom bear malice ; let me interpofe between you and my fon.

Major. Your fon-in-law, Sir Jacob, does deferve a caftigation ; but on recollection, a cit would but fully my arms. I forgive him.

Sir Jac. That's right ; as a token of amity, and to celebrate our feaft, let us call in the fiddles. Now if the Major had but his fhoes, he might join in a country-dance.

Major. Sir Jacob, no fhoes, a Major muft be never out of his boots ; always ready for action. Mrs. Sneak will find me lightfome enough.

Sneak. What are all the vomen engaged? why then my *Locum Tenens* and I will jig together. Forget and forgive, Major.

Major. Freely.
Nor be it faid, that, after all my toil,
I ftain'd my regimentals by a broil.
To you I dedicate boots, fword, and fhield,

   Sir Jac. As harmlefs in the chamber as the field.

THE END.

THE

ORATORS

A

COMEDY

IN THREE ACTS,

AS PERFORMED AT THE

THEATRE-ROYAL IN THE HAY-MARKET.

WRITTEN BY

SAMUEL FOOTE, Esq.

―――――――

Where more is meant than meets the ear. IL PENSEROSO.

――◆――

A NEW EDITION.

――◆――

LONDON:

PRINTED FOR W. LOWNDES, 38, BEDFORD STREET.

――

1808.

LECTURER,   Mr. Foote.

PUPILS, &c. .
{
Mr. Weston.
Mr. Pynn.
Mr. Quick.
Mr. Bannister.
Mr. Davis.
Mr. Loveman.
Mr. Castle.
Mr. Palmer.
Mr. Strange.
Mr. Smith.
Mr. Pearce.
Mr. Keen.
Mr. Gardiner.
Mr. Newton.
Mr. Shuter.
}

Printed by T. C. Hansard,
Peterborough-Court,
Fleet-Street.

THE

ORATORS.

ACT I.

Enter Will Tirehack, *and* Harry Scamper, *booted,*
with Whips in their Hands, into a Side-Box.

Scamper.

PSHAW! zounds; prithee, Will, let us go; what
signifies our staying here?

Tirehack. Nay, but tarry a little; besides, you
know we promised to give Poll Bayliss and Bett
Skinner the meeting.

Scamper. No matter, we shall be sure to find
them at three at the Shakspeare.

Tirehack. But as we are here, Harry, let us know
a little what it's about?

Scamper. About! Why lectures, you fool! Have
not you read the bills? and we have plenty of them
at Oxford you know!

Tirehack. Well, but for all that, there may be
fun.

Scamper. Why then, stay and enjoy it yourself;
and I'll step to the Bull and Gate, and call upon
Jerry Lack-Latin, and my horse. We shall see you
at three.   [*Rising.*

Tirehack. Nay, but prithee, stay.

Scamper. Rot me if I do.

[*Going out of the Box.*

Tirehack. Halloo, Harry! Harry——

Scamper. Well, what's the matter now?

[*Returniug.*

Tirehack. Here's Poll Bayliss come into the gallery.

Scamper. No.——

Tirehack. She is, by——

Scamper. [*looking.*] Yes, faith! it is she, sure enough.—How goes it, Poll?

Tirehack. Well, now, we shall have you, I hope?

Scamper. Ay, if I thought we should get any fun.

Tirehack. I'll make an enquiry. Halloo! snuffers, snuffers!

Enter Candle-snuffer.

Your pleasure, sir?

Tirehack. What is all this business about here?

Snuffer. Can't say, sir.

Scamper. Well but you could if you would, let us into the secret.

Snuffer. Not I, upon my honour!

Tirehack. Your honour, you son of a whore! D'ye hear, bid your master come hither, we want to ask him a question.

Snuffer. I will——   [*Exit.*

Tirehack. Scamper, will you ask him, or shall I?

Scamper. Let me alone to him——

Enter FOOTE.

Tirehack. O! here he is——

Foote. Your commands with me, gentlemen?

Scamper. Why, you must know Will and I here are upon a scheme from Oxford; and because cash begins to run low——How much have you, Will?

Tirehack. Three and twenty shillings, besides the crown I paid at the door.

Scamper. And I eighteen; now, as this will last us but to-night, we are willing to husband our time; let us see, Will, how are we engaged?

Tirehack. Why at three, with Bett and Poll, there, at the Shakspeare; after that to the Coronation; for you know we have seen it but nine times——

Scamper. And then back to the Shakspeare again ; where we sup, and take horse at the door.

Tirehack. So there's no time to be lost, you see ; we desire, therefore, to know what sort of a thing this affair here of yours is? What, is it damn'd funny and comical ?

Foote. Have you not seen the Bills ?

Scamper. What, about the lectures ? ay, but that's all slang, I suppose ; no, no.   No tricks upon travellers ; no, we know better—What, are there any more of you ; or do you do it all yourself ?

Foote. If I was in want of comedians, you gentlemen, are kind enough to lend me a lift ; but upon my word, my intentions, as the bill will inform you, are serious——

Tirehack. Are they ? then I'll have my money again.   What, do you think we come to London to learn any thing ?—Come, Will.   [*Going.*

Foote. Hold, Gentlemen, I would detain you if possible.   What is it you expect ?

Scamper. To be jolly, and laugh, to be sure—

Foote. At what ?

Tirehack. At what——damme, I don't know— at you, and your frolicks and fancies—

Foote. If that is all you desire, why, perhaps we shan't disappoint you—

Scamper. Shan't you ?—why, that is an honest fellow—come, begin—

Foote. But you'll be so kind as not to interrupt me ?

Scamper. Never fear——

Foote. Ladies and gentlemen—

[Suds *from the opposite box calls to* Foote, *and stops him short.*

Suds. Stop a minute ; may I be permitted to speak ?

Foote. Doubtless, Sir—

Suds. Why the affair is this : My wife Alice— for you must know my name is Ephraim Suds, I am a soap-boiler in the city,—took it into her head, and

nothing would serve her turn, but that I must be a
common-council man this year; for, says Alice, *says
she,* It is the *onliest* way to rise in the world.

Foote. A just observation—you succeeded?

Suds. Oh! there was no danger of that—yes, yes,
I got it all hollow ; but now to come to the marrow
of the business. Well, Alice, says I, now I am
chosen, what's next to be done? " Why now, says
Alice, *says she,* thee must learn to make speeches ;
why dost not see what purferment neighbour Gro-
gram has got ; why man, 'tis all brought about by
his *speechifying.* I tell thee what, Ephraim, if thee
can'st but once learn to lay down the law, there's no
knowing to what thee may'st rise——"

Foote. Your lady had reason.

Suds. Why I thought so too; and, as good luck
would have it, who should come into the city, in the
very nick of time but master professor along with
his lectures—Adod, away, in a hurry, Alice and I
danced to Pewterers-Hall.

Foote. You improved, I hope?

Suds. O Lud ! it is unknown what knowledge
we got ; we can read—Oh ! we never stop to spell
a word now—and then he told us such things about
verbs, and nouns, and adverbs, that never entered
our heads before, and emphasis, and accent ; heaven
bless us, I did not think there had been such things
in the world.

Foote. And have you *speechified* yet ?

Suds. Soft ? soft and fair ; we must walk before
we can run—I think I have laid a pretty foundation.
The Mansion-house was not built in a day, Master
Foote. But to go on with my tale, my dame one day
looking over the papers, came running to me ;
Now, Ephraim, says she, thy business is done ; rare
news, lad ; here is a man at the other end of the
town, that will make thee a *speecher* at once, and
out she pull'd your proposals. Ah, Alice, says I,
thee be'st but a fool, why I know that man, he is all

upon his fun ; he lecture—why 'tis all but a bam—
Well, 'tis but seeing, says she, so, *wolens nolens*, she
would have me come hither; now if so be you be
serious, I shall think my money wisely bestowed;
but if it be only your comical works, I can tell you,
you shall see me no more.

Foote. Sir, I should be extremely sorry to lose
you ; if I knew but what would content you?

Suds. Why, I want to be made an orator *on* ;
and to speak speeches, as I tell you, at our meetings,
about politicks, and peace, and addresses, and the
new bridge, and all *them* kind of things.

Foote. Why, with your happy talents I should
think much might be done.

Suds. I am proud to hear you say so. Indeed I
am. I did *speechify* once at a vestry concerning new
lettering the church buckets, and came off cutely
enough; and, to say the truth, that was the thing
that provoked me to go to Pewterers-Hall.

[*Sits down again.*

Foote. Well, sir, I flatter myself, that in proportion to the difference of abilities in your two instruc-
tors, you will here make a tolerable progress. But
now, sir, with your favour, we will proceed to explain the nature of our design, and I hope in the pro-
cess, you, gentlemen, will find entertainment, and
you, sir, information.

Mr. FOOTE *then proceeded in his lecture.*

My plan, gentlemen, is to be considered as a su-
perstructure on that admirable foundation laid by
the modern professor of English, both our labours
tending to the same general end ; the perfectioning
of our countrymen in a most essential article, the
right use of their native language.

But what he has happily begun, I have the vanity
to think I have as happily finished ; he has, it is true,
introduced you into the body of the church, but I
induct you into the choir of the cathedral : Or, to

explain myself by a more familiar allusion, though he is the Poitier who teaches you the step and the grounds ; yet I am the Gallini who gives you the air, and the grace of the minuet.

His aim is propriety alone ; mine propriety with elegance.

For though reading, so shamefully neglected, not only by those of tender years, but the adult ; not only by children, but even by grown men and women ; not only in our private seminaries, but in our public universities ; is allowed to be a necessary ingredient towards the formation of an orator ; yet, a great many other rules, a great many other precepts are requisite to obtain this perfection.

Nay, perhaps we might, to support an argument without the danger of a defeat, at least if we may trust observation, that of all the professions that require a verbal intercourse with the public, there is no one to which reading is of so little utility as that of oratory.

I need not insist upon this head, as I believe every gentleman's experience will furnish him with instances of men, eminent in oratory, who, from an early vivacity have neglected, or the indulgence of their parents have been emancipated from the attention and application necessary, it is true, to acquire this rugged art, but at the same time so ill-suited to their tender years, and so opposite to those innocent amusements in which children are known universally to delight. *Thwart not a child, for you spoil his temper*—is, or at least ought to be, an English proverb, as it is an universal practice.

I would not here be understood to depreciate the usefulness of reading, or to detract from the exceeding merit of the professor's plan ; no, my meaning is only just to drop a hint that I may occasionally use him as a walking stick ; a kind of an *elegantly clouded Mocoa*, or an *airy Anamaboo :* yet that it is by no means my intention to depend upon him as a *support*, or lean upon him as a *crutch*; in a word, he will be rather ornamental than necessary to me.

But useless as is his plan to me, I sincerely wish it success for the sake of the public; and if my influence was equal to my inclination, I would have a law enacted, upon the plan of the militia bill, that annually, or biennially, draughts should be made from every parish of two, three, or more, as in that act of able-bodied, so in this of intelligent persons, who at the expence of the several counties, should be sent to the capital, and there compelled to go through as many courses of the professor's lectures as he shall deem sufficient; thus, by those periodical rural detachments, the whole nation will, in a few years, be completely served, and a stock of learning laid in, that will last till time shall be no more.

Would our rulers but adopt this scheme! how superior would England be even to the most illustrious periods of Greece and Rome! what an unrivalled happiness for us, what an eternal fund of fame for them! Ye Solons, ye Lycurgus's, ye Numas, hide your diminished heads; see what a revolution two laws in a few years have produced; see a whole people, sunk in more than Gothic ignorance, accustomed to no other iron implements than the pacific plough-share, or the harmless spade, start out at once profound scholars and veteran soldiers: If at this happy period, a Frenchman, thinking any thing out of his own country worthy his attention, should condescend to pay this kingdom a visit, methinks, I anticipate the account he will give us at his return, (like his countryman of old, who, at the taking of Rome, bursting into the capitol, and there finding the senate fixed and immovable in their seats, declared them an assembly of kings,) so will he at once pronounce the whole British nation to be an army of generals,

and one congregation of doctors. Happy country!
where the *Arma & Toga* are so fortunately blended,
as to prevent all contention for the pre-eminence.

I know but one objection that can be made to
this plan, and that merely a temporary one; that
the culture of our lands will sustain an infinite
injury, if such a number of peasants were to
deparochiate, there being already scarce hands
sufficient, from the recruits constantly made for
Germany, &c. &c. &c. to carry on the common
ness of husbandry.

But what are riches, perishable commodities,
glittering, transitory, fallacious goods, when com-
pared to the substantial, incorruptible endowments
of the mind! this truth is indeed, happily inculcated
by an old English adage;

" When lands and goods are gone and spent,
" Then learning is most excellent."

This sensible and poetical distich, I would
recommend to Mr. Professor, as a motto for his
intended treatise; but I suppose he is already well
provided with an apt *Latin*, if not a *Greek* one, to
either of which I must yield the preference.

But to wave this ethical argument; I think I
can easily foil the force of this objection, by a
natural and obvious *Succedaneum.* Suppose a clause
was to be added to the bill for the importation of
tallow, raw hides, and live cattle from Ireland, that,
during this literary emigration, a sufficient number
of inhabitants of that country may be transported
hither to supply the vacancy: but here it must be
observed, that for this purpose an act of parliament
is indispensibly necessary; for though it would be
difficult, if not impossible, for us, in our present
condition, to get in even our harvests, without the
aid of hands annually exported for that purpose
from Ireland; yet this is at the best but an illicit
trade, and the men themselves are to be considered

under the article of smuggled goods; a very heavy
penalty being laid by statute on all masters of
vessels, who shall venture to import any of the
abovecited commodity into this realm, without
special licence; to this purpose I recollect a case
in point, the fifth of William and Mary, Ban. Reg.
The King contra Oflaarty.   Vide V. Rep. vol. iii.
chap. 9. page 4.

But if this should be thought by the people in
power too great an indulgence to the Irish, as we
have never been remarkably profuse in our favours
to our loyal and affectionate sister, I see no other
method of redressing the imaginary evil, than by
exempting from this service all the males till a
general peace, and accepting, in their room, a
suitable number of discreet middle-aged females;
and these when they have been properly perfected in
the mysteries of our language, may be returned to
their several parishes, and there form little infantine
communities of literati, which will be a stock for
the succeeding generation; and, indeed, upon consideration, I don't know whether this won't prove
the best method for the introduction and universal
propagation of the plan.

For the English common people, naturally sullen
and obstinate, and religiously attached to their old
customs, might be shocked and scandalized to see,
at one bold stroke, the fescues and fasces, which
have been, from time immemorial, consigned to one,
or more matron in every village, ravished at once
from their hands, and delivered over to the administration of the opposite sex.

But to return to my own subject, from which my
zeal for Mr. Professor's success has tempted me to
make rather too long a digression.

When I ventured to affirm that the profession
of an Orator might exist independently of an accurate knowledge of the arrangement, and different
combinations of the four and-twenty letters so far

as *(in the words of the Professor)* they relate to their
being the arbitrary marks of meaning upon paper;
yet, I would not be understood to assert this generally, as to every species of oratory, but to confine
myself to those particular branches only, where the
orator's own mind suggests the matter that his own
mouth discharges: For instance, now, as when
affairs of state are weighed at a common council,
religious points militated at the Robin-Hood, the
arts and sciences handled in the Strand, or politics
debated near Westminster-abbey ; here the argu-
ments and words given are supposed to arise from
the immediate impulse of the giver ; but where
they are concurrent agents, as in the oratory
peculiar to the pulpit and the stage, where one
individual furnishes the matter, and another admi-
nisters the manner, the case is widely different.

In the first instance, a tolerable proficiency in
reading is indispensibly requisite, as scarce any
memory but the late Mr. Heydegger's could retain,
to any degree of certainty, the various parts of
the Liturgy, the Old and New Testament, briefs,
faculties, excommunications, &c. &c. &c. and a
lapse on those solemn occasions might be attended
with very aukward circumstances! nor would I
here be supposed to insinuate, that the pieces of
oratory delivered from the pulpit are not the composition of the deliverer ; no—This is so far from
being generally the case, that I have often heard
complaints made against particular agents, that
that they have forced upon their congregations their
own crude and insipid productions, when, at the
same time, their native language would furnish them
with so extensive and noble a collection of admirable materials.   But here the auditor, unless he
be well read in theology, may be led into a mistake;
for there are some men, who, by a particular happi-
piness in their manner, have the address to make
the works of other men so absolutely their own,

that there is no distinguishing the difference;
at this the poet hints in his *male dum recitas*, &c.
For these various reasons, I think a warm application to the art of reading cannot be too strongly
recommended to the professors of this kind of
oratory.

With regard to the professors. of the stage, tho'
reading is undoubtedly useful, yet, as the performer
is to repeat, and not to read, the deficiency may be
supplied by the introduction of a third agent, viz.
a person to read to him till the words are rooted
in his memory. This expedient, tho' tedious, I
have known frequently practised with good success:
little blunders will now and then unavoidably
arise, either from the misapprehension of the
second agent, or the ignorance or waggery of
the third ; but these slips are generally unobserved,
or, through inattention or indulgence, over-looked
by an audience. But to return to the consideration
of my own plan, from which no temptation shall,
for the future seduce me to digress.

We will first, then, consider the utility of oratory.

Secondly, the distinct and various kinds, or
species, of that science, as they are practised at
this day in this kingdom.

Thirdly, we will demonstrate, that every branch
of English oratory is peculiarly our own, owes its
rise, progress, and perfection to this country, and
was not only unknown to the ancients, but is
intirely repugnant to all those principles they have
endeavoured to establish.

Fourthly, that any rhetorical system now existing,
instead of a cross in the hands, with letters to direct
you on your road, will prove only but a Will in the
Wisp, to confound, perplex and bewilder you.

Fifthly, from hence will result a necessity for
the immediate establishment of an academy, for
the promulgation and inculcation of modern oratory.

To which academy, the author of these propo-

sals does hope, sixthly, that he shall be appointed
perpetual professor.

Perhaps it may not be impertinent here to observe
that the author has industriously avoided, and
will, in the course of this treatise, avoid all poetical allusion, all grandeur of expression, all splendor
of diction ; in short, renounce every rhetorical prop,
as knowing that, on didactic subjects, order, simplicity, and perspicuity, are the means to gain his
end, which is not to gratify the imagination, but
to improve and polish the understanding of my
countrymen.

First, then, we are to demonstrate the utility of
oratory : and, this, we flatter ourselves, will, in a
great measure, be evident from the consideration
of its universality, and the distinctions it procures,
both lucrative and honourable, to any man eminent in the art.

There is, by the constitution of this kingdom,
an assembly of many individuals, who, as the seventh
son of a seventh son is born a physician, are orators
by hereditary right ; that is, by birth they are enabled to give their opinions and sentiments on all
subjects, where the interest of their country is
concerned : To this we are to add another assembly,
consisting of 558 individuals, where, tho' the same
privilege is enjoyed as in the first instance, yet this
advantage is not possessed in virtue of any inherent
natural right, but is obtained in consequence of an
annual, triennial, or septennial deputation from
the whole body of the people ; if then we add to
this list the number of all those candidates who
are ambitious of this honour, with the infinite variety of changes that a revolution of twenty years
will produce, we cannot estimate those funds of
national orators in *esse, posse,* and *velle,* to a smaller
quantity than 20,000 ; and, this I believe, by the
disciples of Demoivre, will be thought a very moderate computation.

The two orders of the long robe next demand our attention ; and as the pre-eminence is unquestionably due to the priesthood, let us consider what number of persons is necessary to supply that service? England is divided into nine thousand nine hundred and thirteen parishes: now, if we suppose two pastors for every parish, this learned body will be found to consist of nineteen thousand eight hundred and twenty-six individuals; but as the most sacred characters are no more exempted from that fatal stroke that puts a temporary period to our existence, than the profane, it is necessary that a provision should be made of fit and able persons; so that at all events there be no lack of labourers in this plentiful vineyard: nor has the policy of this nation been so blinded as not to guard against this possible contingency, by erecting schools, seminaries, and universities, in which a convenient quantity of our youth are properly trained, in order to fill up chasms which may be occasionally made by the insatiable scythe of death. If then we estimate this corps de reserve at the half only of the standing force, we shall find the army entire amount to 29,739.

I foresee that an objection will be made to this calculation, viz. That two pastors to every parish is a most exorbitant and improbable charge ; for that many parishes, from impropriations, appropriations, and other accidents, instead of two, are scarce able to support one pastor; and that this complaint is almost general throughout the whole principality of Wales, where many individuals of this respectable order, to the great damage of their dignity, are obliged to have recourse to very unclerical professions for the support of themselves and families.

This objection we will allow its full force ; but then if it be considered that in our original estimate we omitted all deans, canons, prebends, heads and fellows of colleges, chaplains to ships, regiments

and private families, together with the whole body
of dissenting ministers of all denominations, field-
preachers, and parish clerks, I believe we shall be
thought rather to have diminished than exaggerated
the real quantity.

As I have not been able to get admittance to the
archives of the several inns of court in this metropolis, I am afraid we shall not be able to determine,
with the same degree of certainty, the exact number of those who have devoted their lives and labours to the explanation and due execution of our
municipal laws : I am, therefore, obliged to depend
on circumstantial evidence, which, in some cases, is
admitted, even in our courts, to have equal force
with proof positive.

And here the reason of the law (as the law is
the perfection of reason) is extremely clear. To
illustrate this by an instance :

A swears a robbery against B; A may lye, or at
least be mistaken; but if the goods stolen from A,
and previously described by him, are found, with
their mark, in the possession of B, B not being able
to account for such possesion, that circumstance
shall be deemed of at least equal weight against B,
as if A was to swear positively to the personal
identity of B. This being the practice of the
courts, we shall proceed, with all possible expedition (which, indeed, is not the practice of the courts)
to produce our proofs circumstantial. As in the
former instance we have grounded our calculation
on the number of parishes, we shall in this derive
our computation from the number of houses in the
kingdom.

To any man tolerably acquainted with the country of England, it is unnecessary to observe, that
not only in every town, but almost in every hamlet through which he travels, his eyes are constantly
caught by the appearance of a smart house, prefaced
with white rails, and prologued by a red door,

with a brass knocker; when you desire to be acquainted with the name and quality of the owner of this mansion, you are always told that it belongs to lawyer such a one ; now, if a hamlet containing thirty houses, with perhaps an environ of an equal number, where labour and the fruits of the earth are the only sources of wealth, can support one attorney in this rural magnificence, what an infinite number of lawyers can a commercial capital sustain ? But because I would rather retrench than exceed, I will only quarter one attorney upon fifty houses. The number of houses in the reign of George the First (since which time the quantity is considerably encreased,) was computed at 1,175,951. The number of attorneys then will be 23,518; and, if we reckon one barrister to twenty attorneys, the sum total is 24,693.

I know it will be here objected, that but one small part of this numerous body can be benefitted by my plan, the privilege of speaking publickly being permitted to the superior order, the barristers alone : but this criticism is confined to the observation of what passes merely in Westminster-Hall, without considering that, at every quarter and petty session, at all county-courts, courts-leet, courts-baron, &c. &c. &c. full power of pleading is permited to every practitioner of the law.

As the number of those who incorporate themselves to promote, not only with their cash but their counsel, the progress of the arts and sciences, is unlimited, it will be impossible for any fixed period to ascertain their quantity; nor can we, with any certainty, as the Court-Register has been silent to the members of common-council, determine the amount of the city orators; besides, as what has been already offered is more than sufficient to prove the utility of our scheme from its universality, we shall not trouble our readers nor ourselves with any farther calculations; for tho' they are replete with great depth of knowledge, are the result of intense application, and the vehicles of mathematical truths, yet to the million the disquisition is but dry and tedious, and our purpose always was, and is, to mix with our instruction a proper portion of delection.

We will, therefore, for these reasons, hasten to the consideration of the second point proposed, viz. An inquiry into the various kinds of oratory now existing in this country. And we shall not, on this occasion, trouble ourselves with the investigation of all the smaller branches of this art; but, like the professors in anatomy, contenting ourselves with the dissection of the noble parts, remit the examination of the ignoble ones to the care of subaltern artists. Leaving, then, to the minute philosophers of the age all the orators of vestries, clubs, and coffee-houses, *Paulo majora canamus*; and for the better illustration of this head, permit me, reader, to be a little fanciful. We will suppose oratory to be one large tree, of which tree science is the *radix*; eloquence the trunk; from which trunk sprout nine distinct ramifications; from which ramifications depends a fruit peculiar to each. But to make this clearer, we will present thee with the tree itself, not enigmatically hieroglyfied, but plainly and palpably pourtrayed.

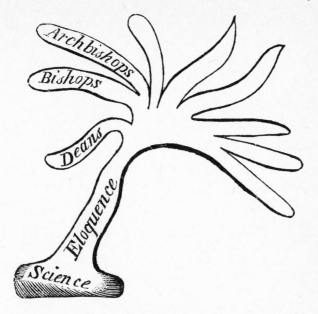

But here, reader, let me not arrogate to myself
the merit of this happy explication ; I own the
hint was first given me with my grammar. The
ingenious, profound Lilly, after he has led his
pupils through the various and almost impervious
provinces of nouns, pronouns, verbs, participles, and
adverbs, conducts them to the foot of that arduous
and stupendous mountain *Qui mihi:* here, dreading
lest their youthful ardour might be damp'd with the
steep ascent, he reanimates their slackened nerves
with the mystic picture of an apple-tree, the access
to whose boughs, though tedious and difficult,
will yet be amply rewarded by leave to revel un-
controuled through the whole region of pepins.
May the luscious fruit sprouting from the apex of
each of my ramifications prove an equal spur to
every beardless orator

I don't know whether the mentioning another
order of orators, as they are not at present existing

in this kingdom, may not be deemed an impropriety. But as I am a sincere lover of my country, I can't help recommending an immediate importation of some of those useful and able artists. Sir William Temple, in his essay on poetry, has recorded their virtues; and as the race was not extinguished in his time, it is to be hoped that it still remains.

In Ireland, says sir William, the great men of their septs, among many officers of their family, had not only a physician, a huntsman, a smith, and such like, but a poet and tale teller.

The first recorded and sung the actions of their ancestors, and entertained the company at feasts; the latter amused them with tales, when they were melancholy and could not sleep : and a very gallant gentleman has told me, of his own experience, that in his wolf-hunting there, when he used to be abroad in the mountains three or four days together, and lye very ill at nights, so as he could not well sleep, they would bring one of those tale-tellers, that when he lay down would begin a story of a king, or a giant, a dwarf and a damsel, and continue all night long in such an even tone that you heard him going on whenever you awakened ; and he believed nothing any physicians could give had so good and so innocent an effect to make men sleep in any pains or distempers of body or mind. These are sir William Temple's words, which contain an amazing instance of the power of those orators over the passions, it requiring full as much art and address to assuage and quell, as to blow up, and excite, a tumult in the mind.

In a bill not long since depending in parliament, for the better regulating the city watch, a clause was recommended, by a late respectable magistrate, that, to prevent the watchmen from sleeping at nights on bulks (the source of many disorders) the said watchmen should be compelled to sleep six hours in the day; an arch member seconded the

the motion, and begged to be included in this clause ; for that, being grievously afflicted with the gout, he could not for many days sleep a single wink ; now if he could be compelled to take a six hours sleep every day, he apprehended that his fits would be of a much shorter duration. Upon this dry comment, the motion was rashly rejected ; but if the house had received the least intimation of the astonishing abilities of the Rockers, (for by that appellation I choose to distinguish this order of orators,) I am convinced that the above clause would not only have been received, but that proper encouragement would have been given, by parliament, for the introduction and establishment of this useful oratorical sect.

Nor, indeed, considering the vast addition to our customary cares, from the unaccountable fluctuation of our funds, the cause of concern to many thousand individuals, do I think a visit from a convenient quantity of those artists would be now out of season ; but how this honour is to be obtained, whether any of these great men are now residing amongst us, under the disguise of chairmen and hackney coachmen ; or whether it would not be more adviseable to employ those gentlemen who have so lately and successfully rummaged the Highlands of Scotland and Ireland for the remains of Runic poetry in search of the ablest professors ; is submitted to the Society for the Encouragement of Arts.

I am aware that, on this occasion, some arch wag, possessed of the same spirit with the above senator, will object to my scheme of importation, by alledging, that we have of our own growth an ample provision of rockers, and refer us for proof to our several churches and chapels, during the hours of eleven and two on a Sunday, where the sleep-compelling power will be experimentally demonstrated to exist in its full force amongst us ; but not to derogate

from the abilities of my countrymen, surely the
shortness of the time, the cause of the nap, rarely
continuing above fifteen or sixteen minutes, will
not admit of a proper experiment : besides, how
can one orator supply a whole parish, unless,
indeed, our churches were to be converted into
dormitories, which I can't think will happen, as
this would be attended with inconveniences to
obvious to need a recital.

Abstracted from this last order, the English
orators are to be divided into four distinct classes,
the pulpit, the senate, the bar, and the stage ; with
the first of these branches, the pulpit, I shan't interfere, and, indeed, so few people now of consequence
and consideration frequent the churches, that the
art is scarce worth cultivation.   The bar —

Scamper.   Pshaw ! there's enough of this dull
prosing ; come, give us a little of something that's
funny ; you talked about pupils.   Could not we
see them ?

Foote.   Rather too precipitate, Sir ; but however
in some measure to satisfy you, and demonstrate
the success of our scheme ; give me leave to introduce to you a most extraordinary instance, in
the person of a young Highlander.   It is not
altogether a year since this astonishing subject spoke nothing but Erse.   Encouraged by the
prodigies of my brother professor's skill, whose
fame, like the Chevalier Taylor's, pierces the remot-
est regions, his relations were tempted to send this
young genius to Edinburgh ; where he went
through a regular course of the professor's lectures,
to finish his studies ; he has been about six weeks
under my care, and, considering the time, I think
you will be amazed at his progress.   Donald !—

Enter Donald.

What's yer wull, sir ?

Foote.   Will you give these ladies and gentlemen
a proof of your skill ?

Donald. Ah, ye wad ha' a specimen of my oratorical art.

Foote. If you please.

Donald. In gude troth on ye sal; wol ye gi' me a topick?

Foote. O! chuse for yourself.

Donald. Its aw one to Donald.

Foote. What think you of a short panegyrick on the science we are treating of?

Donald. On oratory? wi' aw my heart.

Foote. Mind your action; let that accompany your words ——

Donald. Dunna heed, mon —The topick I presum to haundle, is the miraculous gifts of an orator, wha' by the bare power of his words, he leads men, women, and bairns as he lists —

Scamper. And who?

Donald. [*tartly.*] Men, women and bairns.

Scamper. Bairns; who are they?

Foote. Oh! children——his meaning is obvious enough.

Donald. Ay, ay; men, women, and bairns wherever he lists; and first for the antiquity of the art—Ken ye, my lads, wha was the first orator? Mayhap, ye think it was Tully the Latinest; ye are wide o'the mark; or Demosthenes the Greek? in gude troth, ye're as far off as before—Wha was it then? It was e'en that arch-chiel, the Deevil himsel —

Scamper. [*Hastily.*] The devil it was; how do you prove that?

Donald. Guds zounds, mon, ye brake the thrid of my harang; an ye'll but ha'd your tongue, I'se prove it as plain as a pike-staff.

Tirehack. Be quiet, Will, and let him go on.

Donald. I say it was that arch-chiel, the Deevil himsel. Ye ken weel, my lads, how Adam and Eve were planted in Eden, wi' plenty o' bannocks

and cail, and aw that they wished, but were prohibited the eating of pepins ——

Scamper.   Apples ——

Donald.   Weel, weel, and are na pepins and
apples aw the same thing?

Foote.   Nay, pray, gentlemen, hear him out.
Go on with your pepins ——

Donald.   Prohibited the eating of pepins; upon
which what does me the orator Satan, but he whispers a saft speech in her lug; egad our grannum
fell to in an instant, and eat a pepin without
staying to pare it ——(*Addresses himself to the Oxonians.*)
Ken ye lads, wha was the first orator, now?

Tirehack. [*to Scamper.*] What say you to that?

Scamper.   By my soul, the fellow's right—

Donald.   Ay, but ye wan'na ha' patience —ye
wan'na ha' patience, lads —

Tirehack.   Hold your jaw, and go on —

Donald.   Now, we come to the definition of an
orator; and it is from the Latin words *oro, orare,*
to intreat, or perswad; and how, by the means
o' elocution, or argument, which argument consists
o' letters, which letters joined mak syllables, which
syllables compounded mak words, which words
combined mak sentences, or periods, or which aw
together mak an orator, so the first gift of an orator
is words—

Scamper.   Here, Donald, you are out.

Donald.   How so?

Scamper.   Words, the first gift of an orator! No,
Donald, no, at school I learned better than that:
Do'st not remember, Will, what is the first perfec-
tion of an orator? action. The second, action.
The third, action.

Tirehack.   Right, right, Harry, as right as my
nail; there, Donald, I think he has given you a dose—

Donald.   An ye stay me, i' the midst o' my argument ——

Scamper.   Why don't you stick to truth?

Donald. I tell ye, I can *logically.*

Tirehack. Damn your logick —

Donald. Mighty weel—Maister Foote, how ca' ye this usage?

Foote. Oh! never mind them—proceed.

Donald. In gude troth, I'se nat say ane word mare.

Foote. Finish, finish, Donald.———

Donald. Ah! they have jumbled aw my ideas together; but an they will enter into a fair argumentation, I'se convince 'em that Donald Macgregor is mare than a match.———

Scamper. You be ——

Donald. Very weel ——

Foote. Nay, but my dear Donald——

Donald. Hands aff, maister Foote—I ha' finished my tale, the De'el a word mare sal ye get out o' Donald——yer servant, sir.   [*Exit.*

Foote. You see, gentlemen, what your impatience has lost us.

Scamper. Rot him, let him go; but is this fellow one of your *pupils?* why, what a damnable twang he has got, with his men, women and bairns!——

Foote. His pronunciation is, I own, a little irregular; but then consider he is but merely a novice; why, even in his present condition, he makes no bad figure for his five minutes at the Robin-Hood; and in a month or two, we shan't be ashamed to start him in a more *respectable place.*

But now, gentlemen, we are to descend to the peculiar essential qualities of each distinct species of oratory; and first for the bar—but as no didactic rules can so well convey, or words make a proper impression, we will have recourse to more palpable means, and endeavour, by a lively imitation, to demonstrate the extent of our art. We must, for this end, employ the aid of our pupils; but as some preparation is necessary, we hope you will indulge us in a short interruption.

END OF THE FIRST ACT.

A C T II.

SCENE, A Hall of Justice.

Enter FOOTE.

THE first species of Oratory we are to demonstrate our skill in, is that of the bar ; and, in order
to give our lecture an air of reality, you are to
suppose this a court of justice, furnished with
proper ministers to discharge the necessary func-
tions. But, to supply these gentlemen with business,
we must likewise institute an imaginary cause ;
and, that the whole may be ideal, let it be the
prosecution of an imaginary being ; I mean the
phantom of Cock-lane, a phænomenon that has
much puzzled the brains, and terrified the minds,
of many of our fellow subjects.

You are to consider, ladies and gentlemen, that
the language of the bar is a species of oratory distinct from every other. It has been observed, that
the ornaments of this profession have not shone
with equal lustre in an assembly near their own
hall ; the reason assigned, though a pleasant, is not
the true *one*. It has been hinted, that these gentlemen were in want of their briefs ; but was that
the disease, the remedy would be easy enough :
they need only have recourse to the *artifice* successfully practised by some of their colleagues ; instead
of having their briefs in their hands, to hide them
at the bottom of their hats.

    [*Calls to his pupils, who enter dressed as a justice,
    a clerk, a serjeant at law, and a counsellor.*]

You will remember, gentlemen, your proper
pauses, repetitions, hums, ha's, and interjections :
now seat yourselves, and you the counsel remem-

ber to be mighty dull, and you the justice to fall
asleep. I must prepare to appear in this cause as
a witness. [*Exit.*

Justice. Clerk, read the Indictment.

Clerk reads.

Middlesex, to wit.

Fanny Phantom, you are indicted, That on or
before the first day of January, 1762, you the said
Fanny did, in a certain house, in a certain street,
called Cock-lane, in the county of Middlesex, mali-
ciously, treacherously, wickedly, and wilfully, by
certain thumpings, knockings, scratchings, and
flutterings against doors, walls, wainscots, bed-
steads, and bedposts, disturb, annoy, assault, and
terrify divers innocent, inoffensive, harmless, quiet,
simple people, residing in, at, near or about the
said Cock-lane, and elsewhere, in the said county
of Middlesex, to the great prejudice of said people
in said county. How say you, guilty, or ——

(Counsellor stops the Clerk short.)

May it please your worship—hem—I am counsel
in this cause for the ghost—hem—and before I can
permit her to plead, I have an objection to make,
that is—hem—I shall object to her pleading at all.
—Hem—It is the standing law of this country
—hem—and has—hem—always been so allowed,
deemed, and practised, that—hem—all criminals
should be tried *par pares,* by their equals—hem—that
is—hem—by a jury of equal rank with themselves.
Now, if this be the case, as the case it is ; I—hem—
I should be glad to know, how my client can be
tried in this here manner. And first, who is my
client ? She is in the indictment called a phantom,
a ghost ; What is a ghost ? a spirit. What is a
spirit ? a spirit is a thing that exists independently
of, and is superior to, flesh and blood. And can
any man go for to think, that I can advise my client

to submit to be tried by people of an inferior rank to herself? certainly no—I therefore, humbly move to squash this indictment, unless a jury of ghosts be first had, and obtained ; unless a jury of ghosts be first had and obtained.   [*Sits down.*

Serjeant. I am, in this cause, counsel against Fanny Phantom the ghost ;—eh—and notwithstanding the rule laid down by Mr. Prosequi, be —eh—right in the main, yet here it can't avail his client a whit.   We allow—eh—we do allow, please your worship, that Fanny *quoad* Phantom,—eh— had originally a right to a jury of ghosts ; but —eh—if she did, by any act of her own, forfeit this right, her plea cannot be admitted. Now, we can prove, please your worship, prove by a cloud of witnesses, that said Fanny did, as specified in the indictment, scratch, knock, and flutter ;—eh —which said scratchings, knockings, and flutterings —eh—being operations, merely peculiar to flesh, blood, and body—eh—we do humbly apprehend —eh—that by condescending to execute the aforesaid operations, she has waved her privilege as a ghost, and may be tried in the ordinary form, according to the statute so made and provided in the reign of, &c. &c. &c.

Your worship's opinion.

Tirehack. Smoke the justice, he is as fast as a church.

Scamper. I fancy he has touched the tankard too much this morning ; he'll know a good deal of what they have been saying.

Justice. [*Is waked by the Clerk, who tells him they have pleaded.*] Why the objection—oh—brought by Mr. Prosequi, is *(whispers the clerk)* doubtless provisionally a valid objection ; but then, if the culprit has, by an act of her own, defeated her privilege, as asserted in Mr. Serjeant's replication ; we conceive she may be legally tried—oh,—besides—oh, —besides, I, I, I, can't well see how we could impannel a jury of ghosts; or—oh—how twelve spirits, who have no body at all, can be said to take a corporal oath, as required by law—unless, indeed, as in case of the peerage, the prisoner may be tried on their honour.

Counsellor. Your worship's distinction is just; knockings, scratchings, &c. as asserted by Mr. Serjeant.——

Serjeant. Asserted—Sir, do you doubt my instructions?

Counsellor. No interruptions, if you please, Mr. Serjeant; I say as asserted, but can assertions be admitted as proofs? certainly no ——

Serjeant. Our evidence is ready ——

Counsellor. To that we object, to that we object, as it will anticipate the merits—your worship ——

Serjeant. Your worship ——.

Justice. Why, as you impeach the ghost's privilege, you must produce proofs of her scratchings.

Serjeant. Call Shadrach Bodkin.

Clerk. Shadrach Bodkin, come into court.

Enter Bodkin.

Serjeant. Pray, Mr. Bodkin, where do you live?

Bodkin. I sojourn in Lukener's-lane.

Serjeant. What is your profession?

Bodkin. I am a teacher of the word, and a taylor.

Scamper. Zounds, Will, it is a methodist.

Tirehack. No, sure!

Scamper. By the lord Harry, it is.

Clerk. Silence.

Serjeant. Do you know any thing of Fanny the Phantom?

Bodkin. Yea—I do.

Serjeant. Can you give any account of her thumpings, scratchings, and flutterings?

Bodkin. Yea——manifold have been the scratchings and knockings that I have heard.

Serjeant. Name the times.

Bodkin. I have attended the spirit Fanny from the first day of her flutterings, even to the last scratch she gave.

Serjeant. How long may that be?

Bodkin. Five weeks did she flutter, and six weeks did she scratch.

Scamper. Six weeks—Damn it, I wonder she did not wear out her nails.

Clerk. Silence.

Serjeant. I hope the court is convinced.

Counsellor. Hold, master Bodkin, you and I must have a little discourse. A taylor, you say. Do you work at your business?

Bodkin. No —

Counsellor. Look upon me, look upon the court —Then your present trade is your teaching?

Bodkin. It is no trade.

Counsellor. What is it then, a calling?

Bodkin. No, it is no calling—it is rather—as I may say—a forcing—a compelling ——

Counsellor. By whom?

Bodkin. By the spirit that is within me —

Scamper. It is an evil spirit, I believe; and needs must when the devil drives, you know, Will.

Tirehack. Right, Harry—

Counsellor. When did you first feel these spiritual motions?

Bodkin. In the town of Norwich, where I was born;—One day as I was sitting cross-legged on my shop-board, new seating a cloth pair of breeches of Mr. Alderman Crape's—I felt the spirit within me, moving upwards and downwards, and this way and that way, and tumbling and jumbling—at first I thought it was the colic —

Counsellor. And how are you certain it was not?

Bodkin. At last I heard a voice whispering

within me, crying, Shadrach, Shadrach, Shadrach, cast away the things that belong to thee, thy thimble and sheers, and do the things that I bid thee.

Counsellor. And you did?

Bodkin. Yea, verily.

Counsellor. I think I have heard a little of you, master Bodkin ; and so you quitted your business, your wife, and your children ?

Bodkin. I did.

Counsellor. You did—But then you communed with other men's wives?

Bodkin. Yea, and with widows, and with maidens.

Counsellor. How came that about, Shadrach ?

Bodkin. I was moved thereunto by the spirit.

Counsellor. I should rather think by the flesh— I have been told, friend Bodkin, that twelve became pregnant ——

Bodkin. Thou art deceived—They were barely but nine.

Counsellor. Why, this was an active spirit.

Serjeant. But to the point, Mr. Prosequi.

Counsellor. Well, then—you say you have heard those scratchings and knockings?

Bodkin. Yea ——

Counsellor. But why did you think they came from a spirit ?

Bodkin. Because the very same thumps, scratches, and knocks, I have felt on my breast-bone from the spirit within me ——

Counsellor. And these noises you are sure you heard on the first of January ?

Bodkin. Certain ——

Serjeant. But to what do all those interrogatories tend ?

Counsellor. To a most material purpose ; your worship observes, that Bodkin is positive as to the noises made on the first day of January by Fanny the Phantom : now if we can prove an *alibi*, that is, that, on that very day, at that very time, the said

Fanny was scratching and fluttering any where else, we apprehend that we destroy the credit of this witness—Call Peter Paragraph.

Clerk.   Peter Paragraph, come into court.

Counsellor.   This gentleman is an eminent print-er, and has collected, for the public information, every particular relative to this remarkable story ; but as he has the misfortune to have but one leg, your worship will indulge him in the use of a chair.

Clerk.   Peter Paragraph, come into court.

Enter Paragraph.

Counsellor.   Pray, Mr. Paragraph, where was you born ?

Paragraph.   Sir, I am a native of Ireland, and born and bred in the city of Dublin.

Counsellor.   When did you arrive in the city of London ?

Paragraph.   About the last autumnal equinox ; and now I recollect, my Journal makes mention of my departure for England, in the Bessborough Packet, Friday, October the tenth, N. S. or New Stile.

Counsellor   Oh ! then the Journal is yours ?

Paragraph.   Please your worship, it is ; and re-lating thereto I believe I can give you a pleasant conceit—Last week I went to visit a peer, for I know peers, and peers know me.   Quoth his lord-ship to me, Mr. Paragraph, with respect to your Journal, I would wish that your paper was whiter, or your ink blacker.   Quoth I to the peer, by way of reply, I hope you will own there is enough for the money ; his lordship was pleased to laugh.   It was such a pretty repartee, he, he, he, he ——

Justice.   Pray, Mr. Paragraph, what might be your business in England ?

Paragraph.   Hem——a little love affair, please your worship.

Counsellor.   A wife, I suppose——

Paragraph.   Something tending that way ; even

so long ago as January 1739-40, there past some
amorous glances between us; she is the daughter
of old Vamp of the Turnstile; but at that time I
stifled my passion, Mrs. Paragraph being then in
the land of the living.

Counsellor. She is now dead?

Paragraph. Three years and three quarters,
please your worship: we were exceeding happy
together; she was, indeed, a little apt to be jealous.

Counsellor. No wonder——

Paragraph. Yes: they can't help it, poor souls;
but notwithstanding, at her death, I gave her a
prodigious good character in my Journal.

Counsellor. And how proceeds the present affair?

Paragraph. Just now, we are quite at a stand——

Counsellor. How so?

Paragraph. The old scoundrel her father has
played me a slippery trick.

Counsellor. Indeed!

Paragraph. As he could give no money in hand,
I agreed to take her fortune in copies; I was to
have the Wits *Vade Mucum* entire; four hundred
of News from the Invisible World, in sheets; all
that remained of Glanvil upon Witches; Hill's
Bees, Bardana, Brewing, and Balsam of Honey,
and three eights of Robinson Crusoe.

Counsellor. A pretty fortune!

Paragraph. Yes; they are things that stir in
the trade; but you must know that we agreed to
go halves in Fanny the Phantom. But whilst I
and two authors, whom I had hired to ask questions, at nine shillings a night, were taking notice
of the knockings at the house of Mr. Parsons himself, that old rascal Vamp had privately printed off
a thousand eighteenpenny scratchings, purchased
of two methodist preachers, at the public house
over the way ——

Counsellor. Now we come to the point—look
upon this evidence; was he present at Mr. Parsons's knockings?

Paragraph. Never ; this is one of the rascally methodists—Harkee, fellow, how could you be such a scoundrel to sell for genuine your counterfeit scratchings to Vamp ?

Bodkin. My scratchings were the true scratchings ——

Paragraph. Why, you lying son of a whore, did not I buy all my materials from the girl's father himself?

Bodkin. What the spirit commanded, that did I.

Paragraph. What spirit?

Bodkin. The spirit within me ——

Paragraph. If I could but get at you, I would soon try what sort of a spirit it is—stop, you villain. —[*Exit Bodkin.*]—The rogue has made his escape —but I will dog him, to find out his haunts, and then return for a warrant—His scratchings! a scoundrel; I will have justice, or I'll turn his tabernacle into a pigstye.   [*Exit Paragraph.*

Counsellor. I hope, please your worship, we have sufficiently established our *Alibi.*

Justice. You are unquestionably entitled to a jury of ghosts.

Counsellor. Mr. Serjeant, you will provide us a list ?

Serjeant. Let us see—you have no objection to sir George Villars ; the evil genius of Brutus ; the ghost of Banquo ; Mrs. Veal.

Counsellor. We object to a woman—your worship—

Justice. Why, it is not the practice ; this, it must be owned, is an extraordinary case.   But, however, if, on conviction, the Phantom should plead pregnancy, Mrs. Veal will be admitted into the jury of matrons.

Serjeant. I thank your worship ; then the court is adjourned.

[*Terence and Dermot in an upper box.*

Terence. By my shoul, but I will spake

Dermot. Arrah, be quiet, Terence.

Terence. Dibble burn me but I will; hut, hut, not spake, what should ail me? harkee you, Mr. Justice—

Scamper. Halloo, what's the matter now, Will?

Dermot. Leave off, honey Terence, now you are well—

Terence. Dermot, be easy—

Scamper. Hear him—

Tirehack. Hear him—

Terence. Ay, hear him, hear him; why the matter is this, Mr. Justice, that little hopping fellow there, that Dublin journal man, is as great a liar as ever was born—

Tirehack. How so?

Terence. Ay, prithee don't bodder me; what, dy'e learn no more manners at Oxford college, than to stop a gentleman in the midst of his speech before he begins? oh, for shame of yourself— Why the matter is this, Mr. Justice, that there what the debble dy'e call him, Pra-Praragraf, but by my shoul, that is none of his name neither, I know the little bastard as well as myself; as to Fanny the Phantom, long life to the poor gentlewoman, he knows no more of her than the mother that bore her——

Suds. Indeed! good Lord, you surprise me!

Terence. Arrah, now, honey Suds, spake when you are spoke to; you arn't upon the jury, my jewel, now; by my shoul you are a little too fat for a ghost.

Tirehack. Prithee, friend Ephraim, let him go on; let's hear a little what he would be at—

Terence. I say, he knows nothing about the case that is litigated here, dy'e see, at all, at all; because why, I hant ha been from Dublin above four weeks, or a month; and I saw him in his shop every day; so how could he be here and there too? unless, indeed, he used to fly backwards and forwards, and that you see is impossible, because why, he has got a wooden leg.

Scamper.   What the devil is the fellow about?

Tirehack.   I smoke him—harkee, Terence, who do you take that lame man to be?

Terence.   Oh, my jewel, I know him well enough sure by his parson, for all he thought to conceal himself by changing his name——

Scamper.   Why, it is Foote, you fool.

Terence.   Arrah, who?

Tirehack.   Foote.

Terence.   Fot, what the lecture-man? Pa—

Tirehack.   Yes.

Terence.   Arrah, be easy, honey ——

Scamper.   Nay, enquire of Suds.

Suds.   Truly I am minded 'twas he.

Terence.   Your humble servant yourself, Mr. Suds; by my shoul, I'll wager you three thirteens to a rap, that it is no such matter at all, at all.

Scamper.   Done—and be judged by the company.

Terence.   Done—I'll ask the orator himself—— here he comes;

Enter Foote.

harkee, honey Fot, was it yourself that was happing about here but now?

Foote.   I have heard your debate, and must give judgment against you ——

Terence.   What, yourself, yourself!

Foote.   It was ——

Terence.   Then, faith, I have lost my thirteens— Arrah, but Fot, my jewel, why are you after playing such pranks to bring an honest jontleman into company where he is nat ——But what is this selling of lectures a thriving profession?

Foote.   I can't determine as yet; the public have been very indulgent; I have not long opened.

Terence.   By my shoul, if it answers, will you be my pupil and learn me the trade?

Foote. Willingly ——
Terence. That's an honest fellow, long life to you, lad.   [*Sits down.*

Enter M'George.

M'George. Here is doctor Friscano without.
Foote. Friscano—who is he?
M'George. The German physician from James-Street.
Foote. Well; what is his business with me?
M'George. He is in danger of losing his trade.
Foote. How so?
M'George. He says, last summer, things went on glibly enough, for then he had the market all to himself; but this year there is an Italian fellow started up in the Garden, that with his face and grimace has taken all his patients away.
Foote. That's hard.
M'George. Dreadful——if you was to hear the poor man's terrible tale you would really be moved to compassion: he says that his bleeding won't find him in bread; and as to the tooth trade, excepting two stumps, for sixpence a piece, 'tis a month since he looked in a mouth ——
Foote. How can I help him?
M'George. Why he thinks oratory will do all with the English; and if you would but teach him to talk, he should get his custom again——
Foote. Can he read?
M'George. Oh Lord! poor man, no.
Foote. Well let him attend here on—
M'George. He hopes that you will quickly dispatch him, for if he finds he can't do as a doctor, he intends to return to the curing of horses again.
Foote. Well, tell him he may rest assured, he shall either bleed or shoe in a fortnight.
                                   [*Exit M'George.*
Foote. Having thus completed our lecture on the eloquence peculiar to the bar, we shall produce

one great group of orators, in which will be exhi-
bited specimens of every branch of the art.　You
will have, at one view, the choleric, the placid, the
voluble, the frigid, the frothy, the turgid, the calm,
and the clamorous; and as a proof of our exquisite
skill, our subjects are not such as a regular education has prepared for the reception of this sublime
science, but a set of illiterate mechanics, whom you
are to suppose assembled at the Robin-Hood in
the Butcher-row, in order to discuss and adjust the
various systems of Europe; but particularly to determine the separate interest of their own mother
country.

END OF THE SECOND ACT.

ACT III.

SCENE, *The Robin-Hood.*

The PRESIDENT.

Dermot O' Droheda, *a Chairman*; Tim Twist, *a Taylor*; Strap, *a Shoemaker*; Anvil, *a Smith*; Sam Slaughter, *a Butcher*; Catchpole, *a Bailiff. All with pewter pots before them.*

President.

SILENCE, gentlemen; are your pots replenished with porter?

All. Full, Mr. President.

President. We will then proceed to the business of the day; and let me beg, gentlemen, that you will, in your debates, preserve that decency and decorum that is due to the importance of your deliberations, and the dignity of this illustrious assembly—[*Gets up, pulls off his hat, and reads the motion.*— Motion made last Monday to be debated to-day, " That, for the future, instead of that vulgar potation called porter, the honourable members may be supplied with a proper quantity of Irish usquebaugh.   " Dermot O'Droheda † his mark."

O'Droheda.   [*Gets up*] That's I myself.

President.   Mr. O'Droheda.

O'Droheda.   Mr. President, the case is this; it is not becase I am any great lover of that same usquebagh that I have set my mark to the motion; but becase I did not think it was decent for a number of gontlemen that were, dy'e see, met to settle the affairs of the nation, to be guzzling a pot of porter; to be sure the liquor is a pretty sort of a liquor enough when a man is hot with trotting

between a couple of poles ; but this is another guess
matter, becase why, the head is concerned ; and if
it was not for the malt and the haps, dibble burn
me but I would as soon take a drink from the
Thames as your porter. But as to usquebagh ; ah,
long life to the liquor—it is an exhilirator of the
bowels, and a stomatic to the head; I say, Mr.
President, it invigorates, it stimulates, it—in short
it is the onliest liquor of life, and no man alive
will die whilst he drinks it.

> [*Sits down. Twist gets up, having a piece of
> paper, containing the heads of what he says, in
> his hat.*

President. Mr. Timothy Twist.

Tim. Twist. Mr. President, I second Mr. O'Droheda's motion ; and, sir, give me leave—I say, Mr.
President—[*looks in his hat.*]—give me leave to observe, that, sir, tho' it is impossible to add any force
to what has been advanced by my honourable friend
in the straps ; yet, sir,—[*looks in his hat again.*]—it
may, sir, I say, be necessary to obviate some objections that may be made to the motion ; and first, it
may be thought—I say, sir, some gentlemen may
think, that this may prove pernicious to our manufacture—[*looks in his hat,*]—and the duty doubtless
it is of every member of this illustrious assembly to
have a particular eye unto that ; but Mr. President
—sir—[*looks in his hat, is confused, and sits down.*]

President. Mr. Twist, O pray finish, Mr. Twist.

Twist. [*Gets up.*] I say, Mr. President, that, sir,
if, sir, it be considered that—as—I say—[*looks in
his hat.*]—I have nothing farther to say.

> [*Sits down, and Strap gets up.*

President. Mr. Strap.

Strap. Mr. President, it was not my intention to
trouble the assembly upon this occasion, but when
I hear insinuations thrown out by gentlemen, where
the interest of this country is so deeply concerned,
I own I cannot sit silent ; and give me leave to say,

sir, there never came before this assembly a point of more importance than this; it strikes, sir, at the very root of your constitution; for, sir, what does this motion imply? it implies that porter, a wholesome, domestic manufacture, is to be prohibited at once. And for what, sir? for a foreign pernicious commodity. I had, sir, formerly the honour, in conjunction with my learned friend in the leather apron, to expel sherbet from amongst us, as I looked upon lemons as a fatal and foreign fruit; and can it be thought, sir, that I will sit silent to this? No, sir, I will put my shoulders strongly against it ; I will oppose it *manibus totibus.* For should this proposal prevail, it will not end here : fatal, give me leave to say, will, I foresee, be the issue ; and I shan't be surprised, in a few days, to hear from the same quarter, a motion for the expulsion of gin, and a premium for the importation of whisky.

> [*A hum of approbation, with significant nods and winks from the other members. He sits down ; and Anvil and another member get up together ; some cry Anvil, others Jacobs.*

President. Mr. Anvil.

Anvil. Mr. President, sir—

> [*The members all blow their noses, and cough ; Anvil talks all the while, but is not heard.*

President. Silence, gentlemen ; pray, gentlemen. A worthy member is up.

Anvil. I say Mr. President, that if we consider this case in its utmost extent—[*All the members cough and blow their noses again,*]—I say, sir, I will. Nay; I insist on being heard. If any gentleman has any thing to say any where else, I'll hear him.

> [*Members all laugh, and Anvil sits down in a passion, and Slaughter gets up.*

President. Mr. Samuel Slaughter.

Slaughter. Sir, I declare it, at the bare hearing

of this here motion, I am all over in a sweat; for
my part I can't think what gentlemen mean by
talking in that there manner; not but I likes that
every man should deliver his mind; I does mine;
it has been ever my way; and when a member
opposes me I like him the better for it; it's right;
I am pleased; he can't please me more; it is as it
should be; and tho' I differ from the honourable
gentleman in the flannel night-cap, over the way,
yet I am pleased to hear him say what he thinks;
for, sir, as I said, it is always my rule to say what
I think, right or wrong—[*a loud laugh.*]—Ay, ay,
gentlemen may laugh, with all my heart, I am used
to it, I don't mind it a farthing; but, sir, with
regard to that there motion, I entirely agree with
my worthy friend with the pewter-pot at his mouth.
Now, sir, I would fain ask any gentleman this here
question; Can any thing in nature be more natural for an Englishman, than porter? I declare, Mr.
President, I think it the most wholesomest liquor
in the world. But if it must be a change, let us
change it for rum, a wholesome palatable liquor,
a liquor that—in short, Mr. President, I don't
know such a liquor. Ay, gentlemen may stare; I
say, and I say it upon my conscience, I don't know
such a liquor. Besides, I think there is in this here
affair a point of law, which I shall leave to the
consideration of the learned, and for that there reason, I shall take up no more of your time.

[*He sits down, Catchpole gets up.*

President. Mr. Catchpole.

Catchpole. I get up to the point of law. And
though, sir, I am bred to the business, I can't say I
am prepared for this question. But though this
usquebagh, as a dram, may not (by name) be subject to a duty, yet, it is my opinion, or rather belief,
it will be considered, as in the case of horses, to
come under the article of dried goods—But I move
that another day this point be debated.

Slaughter. I second the motion.

[*Catchpole gives a paper to the President, who reads it.*

President. Hear your motion.

" That it be debated next Thursday, whether the dram usquebagh is subject to a particular duty ; or, as in the case of horses, to be considered under the article of dried goods."

All. Agreed, agreed.

Foote. And, now, ladies and gentlemen, having produced to you glaring proofs of our great ability in every species of oratory, having manifested, in the persons of our pupils, our infinite address in conveying our knowledge to others, we shall close our morning's lecture, instituted for public good, with a proposal for the particular improvement of individuals. We are ready to give private instructions to any reverend gentleman in his probationary sermon for a lectureship ; to young barristers who have causes to open, or motions to make ; to all candidates of the sock or buskin ; or to the new members of any of those oratorical societies with which this metropolis is at present so plentifully stocked.

[*Exeunt omnes.*

FINIS.

T. C. Hansard, Printer,
Peterborough-Court,
Fleet-Street.

COMEDIES, TRAGEDIES, FARCES, 12mo.

PRINTED FOR

W. LOWNDES.

☞ The Plays marked thus *, are each embellished with an elegant plate, and those with †, have inferior frontispieces.

Fox—Jonson
†Friendship in Fashion —— Otway
*Funeral— Steele
†Gamester—Centlivre
*Gamester—Moore
Gil Blas—Moore
*Good-natured Man—Goldsmith
*Grecian Daughter — Murphy
Greenwich Park—Mountf.
*Henry IV. part 1 ⎫
†Henry V. ⎪
†Henry VI. part 1 ⎬ Shakesp.
*Henry VIII. ⎪
†Henry V.—Hill ⎭
†Hob in the Well--Hippisley
*Hypocrite—Bickerstaff
*Jane Gray—Rowe
*Jane Shore—Rowe
Jealous Wife—Colman
*Inconstant—Farquhar
†Jovial Crew—Brome
*Isabella—Garrick
†Island Princess—Motteux
*Julius Cæsar—Shakspeare
†King Charles I.—Havard
*King John—Shakspeare
*King Lear--Garrick
Lady's Last Stake—Cibber
†Limberham—Dryden
*Lionel and Clarissa—Bickerstaff

*Love for Love—Congreve
Love in a Mist--Cunningham
Love in a Riddle—Cibber
†Love in a Tub—Etherege
*Love makes a Man—Cibber
Love's Last Shift—Cibber
*Love in a Village—Bickerstaff
*Macbeth—Shakspeare
Magic Cavern, 8vo—Songs
*Mahomet—Miller, &c.
*Maid of the Mill—Bickerstaff
†Man of Mode—Etherege
†Mariamne—Fenton
†Massacre of Paris—Lee
*Measure for Measure—— Shakspeare
*Medea—Glover
*Merope—Hill
*Merry Wives of Windsor —Shakspeare
Miller of Mansfield, &c.— Dodsley
*Minor—Wrighten
*Miser—Fielding
†Mistake—Vanbrugh
*Mourning Bride--Congreve
†Mustapha—Orrery
New Way to pay Old Debts altered
†Nonjuror—Cibber
*Old Bachelor—Congreve

THE

M I N O R

A

COMEDY

IN THREE ACTS:

PERFORMED AT THE

THEATRE ROYAL, DRURY - LANE:

WRITTEN BY THE LATE

S A M U E L   F O O T E, Esq.

Tantam Religio potuit suadere Malorum.

L O N D O N:

Printed for W. Lowndes, J. Barker and H. Lowndes

1798.

Price One Shilling and Sixpence

DRAMATIS PERSONÆ.

Foote, *Canker*, *Smart*, and *Pearse*, Perfons in the Introduction.

	Drury Lane.	Covent Garden.	Hay Market.
Sir William Wealthy,	Mr. Baddeley.	Mr. Wilfon.	Mr. Wewitzer.
Mr. Richard Wealthy,	Mr. Packer.	Mr. Thompfon.	Mr. Ufher.
Sir George Wealthy,	Mr. Whitfield.	Mr. Macready.	Mr. Iliff.
Shift,	Mr. Bannifter, jun.	Mr. Rees.	Mr. Bannifter, jun.
Loader,	Mr. R. Palmer.	Mr. Cubitt.	Mr. R. Palmer.
Dick,	Mr. Burton.	Mr. Blanchard.	Mr. Burton.
Smirk,	Mr. Bannifter, jun.	Mr. Rees.	Mr. Bannifter, jun.
Mrs. Cole,	Mr. Bannifter, jun.	Mr. Bannifter.	Mr. Bannifter, jun.
Lucy,	Mifs Collins.	Mifs Chapman.	Mifs Heard.

WILLIAM DUKE OF DEVONSHIRE,

Lord Chamberlain of his Majesty's Houshold.

MY LORD,

THE MINOR, who is indebted for his appearance on the stage to your Grace's indulgence, begs leave to desire your further protection, at his entering into the world.

Though the allegiance due from the whole dramatic people to your Grace's station, might place this addrefs in the light of a natural tribute; yet, my Lord, I should not have taken that liberty with the Duke of Devonshire, if I could not at the same time, plead some little utility in the design of my piece; and add, that the public approbation has stamped a value on the execution.

The law, which threw the stage under the absolute government of a lord chamberlain, could not fail to fill the minds of all the objects of that power with very gloomy apprehensions; they found themselves (through their own licentioufnefs, it must be confeffed) in a more precarious dependant state, than any other of his Majesty's subjects. But when their direction was lodged in the hands of a nobleman, whose ancestors had so succefsfully struggled for national liberty, they ceased to fear for their own. It was not from a patron of the liberal arts they were to expect an oppressor; it was not from the friend of freedom, and of man, they were to dread partial monopolies, or the establishment of petty tyrannies.

Their

Their warmeſt wiſhes are accompliſhed; none of their rights have been invaded, except what, without the firſt poetic authority, I ſhould not venture to call a right, the Jus Nocendi.

Your tenderneſs, my Lord, for all the followers of the Muſes, has been in no inſtance more conſpicuous, than in your late favour to me, the meaneſt of their train; your Grace has thrown open (for thoſe who are denied admittance into the palaces of Parnaſſus) a cottage on its borders, where the unhappy migrants may be, if not magnificently, at leaſt, hoſpitably entertained.

I ſhall detain your Grace no longer, than juſt to echo the public voice, that, for the honour, progreſs, and perfection of letters, your Grace may long continue their candid CENSOR, who have always been their generous protector.

I have the honour, my Lord, to be, with the greateſt reſpect, and gratitude,

Your Grace's moſt dutiful,

moſt obliged,

and obedient Servant,

Elleſtre,　　　　　SAMUEL FOOTE.
July 8,

The MINOR.

Dodd delin.

W. Walker sc.

Mr FOOTE as Mrs COLE.

My thoughts are fix'd upon a better place.
What, I suppose Mr Loader, you will be
for your old Friend, the black-ey'd Girl, &c.

Act I.

Publish'd 26 July 1777. by T. Lowndes & Partners.

THE MINOR.

INTRODUCTION.

Enter CANKER *and* SMART.

Smart.

BUT are you fure he has leave?
Cank. Certain.

Smart. I'm damn'd glad on't. For now we fhall have a laugh either with him or at him, it does not fignify which.

Cank. Not I. But is not the door of the Little Theatre open.

Smart. Yes. Who is that fellow that feems to ftand centry there?

Cank. By his tattered garb and meagre vifage, he muft be one of the troop.

Smart. I'll call him. Holloa, Mr.——

Enter Pearfe.

What, is there any thing going on over the way?

Pear. A rehearfal.

Smart. Of what?

Pear. A new piece.

Smart. Foote's?

Pear

Pear. Yes.

Cank. Is he there?

Pear. He is.

Smart. Zounds, let's go and fee what he's about.

Cank. With all my heart.

Smart. Come along then.   [*Exeunt.*

Enter Foote and an Actor.

Foote. Sir, this will never do! you muft get rid of your high notes, and country cant. Oh, 'tis the true ftrolling,—

Enter Smart and Canker.

Smart. Ha, ha, ha! what, hard at it, my boy !——Here's your old friend Canker and I come for a peep. Well, and hey, what is your plan?

Foote. Plan?

Smart. Ay, what are your charaɛters? Give us your group; how is your cloth fill'd?

Foote. Charaɛters!

Smart. Ay.—Come, come, communicate. Wha, man, we will lend thee a lift. I have a damn'd fine original for thee, an aunt of my own, juft come from the North, with the true Newcaftle bur in her throat; and a nofe and a chin.—I am afraid fhe is not well enough known: but I have a remedy for that. I'll bring her the firft night of your piece, place her in a confpicuous ftation, and whifper the fecret to the whole houfe. That will be damn'd fine, won't it?

Foote. Oh, delicious!

                                      Smart

Smart. But don't name me. For if fhe fmokes me for the author, I fhall be dafh'd out of her codicil in a hurry.

Foote. Oh, never fear me. But I fhould think your uncle Tom a better charaĉter.

Smart. What the politician?

Foote. Aye; that every day, after dinner, as foon as the cloth is remov'd, fights the battle of Minden, batters the French with cherry-ftones, and purfues 'em to the banks of the Rhine in a ftream of fpilt port.

Smart. Oh, damn it, he'll do.

Foote. Or what fay you to your father-in-law, Sir Timothy? who, tho' as broken-winded as a Hounflow poft-horfe, is eternally chaunting Venetian ballads. Kata tore cara higlia.

Smart. Admirable! by heavens! — Have vou got 'em.

Foote. No.

Smart. Then in with 'em my boy.

Foote. Not one.

Smart. Pr'ythee why not?

Foote. Why look'e, Smart, though you are, in the language of the world, my friend, yet there is one thing you, I am fure, love better than any body.

Smart. What's that?

Foote. Mifchief.

Smart. No, pr'ythee.

Foote. How now am I fure that you, who fo readily give up your relations, may not have fome defign upon me?

Smart. I don't underftand you.

Foote.

Foote. Why, as foon as my characters begin to circulate a little fuccefsfully, my mouth
is ftopp'd in a minute, by the clamour of your
relations,——Oh, dam'me—'tis a fhame,—it
fhould not be,—people of diftinction brought
upon the ftage !—And fo, out of compliment
to your coufins, I am to be beggar'd for
treating the public with the follies of your
family, at your own requeft.

Smart. How can you think I would be
fuch a dog ? What, the devil, then, are we
to have nothing perfonal ? Give us the actors
however.

Foote. Oh that's ftale. Befides, I think
they have, of all men, the beft right to complain.

Smart. How fo?

Foote. Becaufe, by rendering them ridiculous in their profeffion, you at the fame
time injure their pockets. Now as to the
other gentry, they have providentially fomething befides their underftanding to rely on ;
and the only injury they can receive is, that
the whole town is then diverted with what
before was only the amufement of private
parties.

Canker. Give us then a national portrait : a
Scotchman or an Irifhman.

Foote. If you mean merely the dialect of
the two countries, I can't think it either a
fubject of fatire or humour ; it is an acciden-
tal unhappinefs, for which a man is no more
accountable, than for the colour of his hair.
Now affectation, I take to be the true comic
object. If, indeed, a North Briton, ftruck
                                                    with

with a fcheme of reformation, fhould advance from the banks of the Tweed, to
teach the Englifh the true pronunciation of
their own language, he would, I think,
merit your laughter: nor would a Dublin
mechanic, who, from heading the Liberty-
boys in a fkirmifh on Ormond Quay, fhould
think he had a right to prefcribe military laws
to the firft commander in Europe, be a lefs ridiculous object.

Smart. Are there fuch?

Foote. If you mean that the blunders of a
few peafants, or the partial principles of a
fingle fcoundrel, are to ftand as characterifti-
cal marks of a whole country, your pride
may produce a laugh; but believe me, it is at
the expence of your underftanding.

Canker. Heyday, what a fyftem is here!
Laws for laughing! And pray, fage Sir, in-
ftruct us when we may laugh with propriety?

Foote. At an old beau, a fuperannuated
beauty, a military coward, a ftuttering orator,
or a gouty dancer. In fhort, whoever affects
to be what he is not, or ftrives to be what he
cannot, is an object worthy the poet's pen,
and your mirth.

Smart. Pfha, I don't know what you mean
by your is nots, and cannots—damn'd ab-
ftrufe jargon. Ha, Canker!

Cank. Well, but if you' will not give us
perfons, let us have things. Treat us with a
modern amour, and a ftate intrigue, or a——

Foote. And fo amufe the public ear at the
expence of private peace. You muft excufe
me.

Cank.

Cank. And with thefe principles, you expect to thrive on this fpot?

Smart. No, no, it won't do. I tell thee
the plain roaft and boil'd of the theatres will
never do at this table. We muft have high
feafon'd ragouts, and rich fauces.

Foote. Why, perhaps, by way of defert, I
may produce fomething that may hit your pa-
late.

Smart. Your bill of fare?

Foote. What think you of one of thofe
itinerant field orators, who, tho' at declared
enmity with common fenfe, have the addrefs
to poifon the principles, and at the fame time
pick the pockets of half our induftrious fellow fubjects?

Cank. Have a care. Dangerous ground,
Ludere cum facris, you know.

Foote. Now I look upon it in a different
manner. I confider thefe gentlemen in the
light of public performers, like myfelf; and
whether we exhibit at Tottenham-court, or
the Haymarket, our purpofe is the fame, and
the place is immaterial.

Cank. Why, indeed, if it be confidered—

Foote. Nay, more, I muft beg leave to affert,
that ridicule is the only antidote againft this
pernicious poifon. This is a madnefs that
argument can never cure: and fhould a little
wholefome feverity be applied, perfecution
would be the immediate cry; where then
can we have recourfe, but to the comic mufe?
perhaps the archnefs and feverity of her fmile
may redrefs an evil, that the laws cannot
reach, or reafon reclaim.

Cank.

Cank. Why, if it does not cure thofe already diftemper'd, it may be a means to ftop the infeƈtion.

Smart. But how is your fcheme conduƈted?

Foote. Of that you may judge. We are juft going upon a repetition of the piece. I fhould be glad to have your opinion.

Smart. We will give it you.

Foote. One indulgence: As you are Englifhmen, I think, I need not beg, that as from neceffity moft of my performers are new, you will allow for their inexperience, and encourage their timidity.

Smart. But reafonable.

Foote. Come, then, prompter, begin.

Pear. Lord, Sir, we are all at a ftand.

Foote. What's the matter?

Pear. Mrs. O-Schohnefy has return'd the part of the bawd; fhe fays fhe is a gentlewoman, and it would be a refleƈtion on her family to do any fuch thing!

Foote. Indeed!

Pear. If it had been only a whore, fays fhe, I fhould not have minded; becaufe no lady need be afhamed of doing that.

Foote. Well, there is no help for it; but thefe gentlemen muft not be difappointed. Well, I'll do the charaƈter myfelf.

ACT

ACT I.

Enter Sir William Wealthy, and Mr. Richard Wealthy.

COME, come, brother, I know the world. People who have their attention eternally fixed upon one object, can't help being a little narrow in their notions.

R. Weal. A fagacious remark that, and highly probable, that we merchants, who maintain a conftant correfpondence with the four quarters of the world, fhould know lefs of it than your fafhionable fellows, whofe whole experience is bounded by Weftminfter-bridge.

Sir. Will. Nay, brother, as a proof that I am not blind to the benefit of travelling, George, you know, has been in Germany thefe four years.

R. Weal Where he is well grounded in gaming and gluttony; France has furnifhed him with fawning and flattery; Italy equipp'd him with capriols and cantatas: and thus ac-complifh'd, my young gentleman is return'd with a cargo of whores, cooks, valets de chambre, and fiddlefticks, a moft valuable member of the Britifh commonwealth.

Sir. Will. You diflike then my fyftem of education?

R. Weal. Moft fincerely.

Sir. Will. The whole?

R. Weal. Every particular.

Sir.

Sir. Will. The early part, I fhould imagine, might merit your approbation.

R. Weal. Leaft of all. What, I fuppofe, becaufe he has run the gauntlet thro' a public fchool, where, at fixteen, he had practis'd more vices than he would otherwife have heard of at fixty.

Sir, Will. Ha, ha, prejudice.

R. Weal. Then, indeed, you removed him to the univerfity! where, left his morals fhould be mended, and his underftanding improved, you fairly fet him free from the reftraint of the one, and the drudgery of the other, by the priviledged diftinction of a filk gown and a velvet cap.

Sir. Will. And all thefe evils, you think, a city education would have prevented?

R. Weal. Doubtlefs.——Proverbs, proverbs, brother William, convey wholefome inftruction, Idlenefs is the root of all evil. Regular hours, conftant employment, and good example, can't fail to form the mind.

Sir. Will. Why, truly, brother, had you ftuck to your old civic vices, hypocrify, cozenage, and avarice, I don't know whether I might not have committed George to your care; but you cockneys now beat us fuburbians at our own weapons. What, old boy, times are changed fince the date of thy indentures; when the fleek, crop eared prentice ufed to dangle after his miftrefs, with the great bible under his arm, to St. Bride's, on a Sunday; bring home the text, repeat the divifions of the difcourfe, dine at twelve, and

regale,

regale, upon a gaudy day, with buns and beer at Iflington, or Mile-End.

R. Weal. Wonderfully facetious !

Sir. Will. Our modern lads are of a different metal. They have their gaming clubs in the Garden, their little lodgings, the fnug depofitories of their rufty fwords, and occafional bag-wigs; their horfes for the turf; ay, and their commiffions of bankruptcy too, before they are well out of their time.

R. Weal. Infamous afperfion !

Sir. Will. But the laft meeting at New-market, lord Lofty received at the hazard-table the identical note from the individual taylor to whom he had paid it but the day before for a new fet of liveries.

R. Weal. Invention !

Sir. Will. Thefe are anecdotes you will never meet with in your weekly travels from Cateaton-ftreet to your boarded box in Clapham, brother.

R. Wealth. And yet that boarded box, as your prodigal fpendthrift proceeds, will foon be the only feat of the family.

Sir. Will. May be not. Who knows what a reformation our projeck may produce !

R. Wealth. I do. None at all.

Sir. Will. Why fo ?

R. Wealth. Becaufe your means are ill-proportioned to their end. Were he my fon, I would ferve him———

Sir. Will. As you have done your daughter. Difcard him. But confider, I have but one.

R. Wealth.

R. Wealth. That would weigh nothing with me : for, was Charlotte to fet up a will of her own, and reject the man of my choice, fhe muft expect to fhare the fate of her fifter. I confider families as a fmaller kind of king-doms, and would have difobedience in the one as feverely punifhed as rebellion in the other. Both cut off from their refpective focieties.

Sir. Will. Poor Lucy! But furely you begin to relent. Mayn't I intercede?

R. Wealth. Look'e, brother, you know my mind. I will be abfolute. If I meddle with the management of your fon, it is at your own requeft; but if, directly or indirectly, you interfere with my banifhment of that wilful, headftrong, difobedient huffy, all ties between us are broke ; and I fhail no more remember you as a brother, than I do her as a child.

Sir. Will. I have done. But to return. You think there is a probability in my plan?

R. Weath. I fhall attend the iffue.

Sir. Will. You will lend your aid, how-ever?

R. Wealth. We fhall fee how you go on.

Enter Servant.

Serv. A letter, fir.

Sir. Will. Oh, from Capias, my attorney. Who brought it?

Serv. The perfon is without, fir.

Sir. Will. Bid him wait. *(Reads.) Exit. Serv.*

Worthy

Worthy Sir,

 The bearer is the perfon I promifed to pro-cure. I thought it was proper for you to ex-amine him in viva voce. So if you adminifter a few interrogatories, you will find, by crofs-queftioning him, whether he is a competent per-fon to profecute the caufe you wot of. I wifh you a fpeedy iffue: and as there can be no de-fault in your judgment, am of opinion it fhould be carried iuto immediate execution. I am,

Worthy Sir, &c.

Timothy Capias.

P. S. *The party's Name is* Samuel Shift. *He is an admirable mime or mimic, and moft delectable company; as we experience every Tuefday night at our club, the Magpye and Horfe-fhoe, Fetter-lane.*

Very methodical indeed, Mr. Capias!—John

Enter Servant.

Bid the perfon who brought this Letter, walk in. *(Exit Serv.)* Have you any curiofity, brother?

 R. Wealth. Not a jot. I muft to the Change. In the evening you may find me in the counting-houfe, or at Jonathan's. *(Exit.*

 Sir. Will. You fhall hear from me.

Enter Shift and Servant.

Shut the door, John, and remember, I am not at home. [*Exit. Serv.*] You came from Mr. Capias?

Shift.

Shift. I did, fir.

Sir. Will. Your name I think is Shift?

Shift. It is, fir.

Sir. Will. Did Mr. Capias drop any hint of my bufinefs with you?

Shift. None. He only faid, with his fpectacles on his nofe, and his hand upon his chain, Sir William Wealthy is a refpectable perfonage, and my client; he wants to retain you in a certain affair, and will open the cafe, and give you your brief himfelf: if you adhere to his inftructions, and carry your caufe, he is generous, and will difcharge your bill without taxation.

Sir. Will. Ha! ha! my friend Capias to a hair! Well fir, this is no bad fpecimen of your abilities. But fee that the door is faft. Now fir, you are to——

Shift. A moment's paufe, if you pleafe. You muft know, Sir William, I am a propigious admirer of forms. Now Mr. Capias tells me, that it is always the rule to adminifter a retaining fee before you enter upon the merits.

Sir. Will. Oh, fir, I beg your pardon!

Shift. Not that I queftioned your generofity; but forms you know——

Sir. Will. No apology, I beg. But, as we are to have a clofer connection, it may not be amifs, by way of introduction, to underftand one another a little. Pray, fir, where was you born?

Shift. At my father's.

Sir. Will. Hum!——And what was he?

Shift. A gentleman.

Sir.

Sir. Will. What was you bred?

Shift. A gentleman.

Sir. Will. How do you live?

Shift. Like a gentleman.

Sir. Will. Could nothing induce you to un-bofom yourfelf?

Shift. Look'e, Sir William, there is a kind of fomething in your countenance, a certain opennefs and generofity, a je ne fcai quoi in your manner, that I will unlock. You fhall fee me all.

Sir. Will. You will oblige me.

Shift. You muft know then, that Fortune, which frequently delights to raife the nobleft ftructures from the fimpleft foundations; who from a taylor made a pope, from a gin-fhop an emprefs, and many a prime minifter from nothing at all, has thought fit to raife me to my prefent height, from the humble employment of—Light your Ho-nour——A link boy.

Sir. Will. A pleafant fellow.——Who were your parents?

Shift. I was produced, fir, by a left-handed marriage, in the language of the news-papers, between an illuftrious lamp-lighter and an eminent itinerant cat and dog butcher. Cat's meat, and dog's meat.——I dare fay, you have heard my mother fir. But as to this happy pair, I owe little befides my Being, I fhall drop them where they dropt me——in the ftreet.

Sir. Will. Proceed.

Shift. My firft knowledge of the world I owe to a fchool, which has produced many
a great

a great man; the avenues of the Play-houfe.
There, fir, leaning on my extinguifh'd link,
I learn'd dexterity from pick-pockets, con-
nivance from conftables, politics and fafhions
from footmen, and the art of making and
breaking a promife, from their mafters.
Here, firrah, light me a-crofs the kennel
——I hope your honour will remember poor
Jack.——You ragged rafcal I have no half-
pence——I'll pay you the next time I fee
you——But, lack-a-day, fir, that time I faw
as feldom as his tradefmen.

Sir. Will. Very well.

Shift. To thefe accomplifhments from without the Theatre, I muft add one that I obtain'd within.

Sir. Will. How did you gain admittance
there ?

Shift. My merit, fir, that, like my link,
threw a radiance round me——A detach-
ment from the head-quarters here, took poffeffion, in the fummer, of a country corporation, where I did the honours of the barn,
by fweeping the ftage, and clipping the candles. There my fkill and addrefs was fo confpicuous, that it procured me the fame office the enfuing winter, at Drury-Lane, where
I acquired intrepidity; the crown of all my
virtues.

Sir. Will. How did you obtain that?

Shift. By my poft. For I think, fir, he
that dares ftand the fhot of the gallery in
lighting, fnuffing, and fweeping, the firft
night of a new play, may bid defiance to the
pillory, with all its cuftomary compliments.

Sir,

Sir. Will. Some truth in that.

Shift. But an unlucky crab-apple, applied to my right eye, by a patriot gingerbread-baker from the Borough, who would not fuffer three dancers from Switzerland, becaufe he hated the French, forced me to a precipitate retreat.

Sir. Will. Poor devil?

Shift. Broglio and Contades have done the fame. But as it happen'd, like a tennis-ball, I rofe higher than the rebound.

Sir. Will. How fo?

Shift. My misfortune, fir, moved the compaffion of one of our performers, a whimfical man; he took me into his fervice. To him I owe, what I believe will make me ufeful to you.

Sir. Will. Explain.

Shift. Why, fir, my mafter was remarkably happy in an art, which, however difefteem'd at prefent, is by Tully, reckon'd amongft the perfections of an orator; Mimickry.

Sir. Will. Why, you are deeply read Mr. Shift!

Shift. A fmattering—But, as I was faying, fir, nothing came amifs to my mafter. Bipeds, or quadrupeds; rationals, or animals; from the clamour of the bar, to the cackle of the barn-door; from the foporific twang of the tabernacle of Tottenham-Court, to the melodious bray of their long ear'd brethren in Bunhill-Fields; all were objects of his imitation, and my attention. In a word, fir, for two whole years, under this profeffor, I ftudied and ftarved, impoverifh'd my

body,

body, and pamper'd my mind; till thinking myfelf pretty near equal to my mafter, I made him one of his own bows, and fet up for my-felf.

Sir Will. You have been fuccefsful I hope.

Shift. Pretty well; I can't complain. My art, fir, is a pafse-par-tout. I feldom want employment. Let's fee, how ftand my en-gagements. [*Pulls out a pocket-book*] Hum, —hum, Oh! Wednefday, at Mrs. Gam-mut's, near Hanover-fquare; there, there, I fhall make a meal upon the Mingotti; for her ladyfhip is in the opera intereft; but, however, I fhall revenge her caufe upon her rival Mattei. Sunday evening at Lady Su-ftinuto's concert. Thurfday I dine upon the actors, with ten Templars, at the Mitre in Fleet-ftreet. Friday I am to give the amo-rous parley of two intriguing cats in a gutter, with the difturbing of a hen-rooft, at Mr. Deputy Sugarfops, near the Monument. So fir, you fee my hands are full. In fhort, Sir William, there is not a buck or a turtle de-voured within the bills of mortality, but there I may, if I pleafe, ftick a napkin under my chin.

Sir Will. I'm afraid, Mr. Shift, I muft break in a little upon your engagements; but you fhall be no lofer by the bargain.

Shift. Command me.

Sir Will. You can be fecret as well as fer-viceable?

Shift. Mute as a mackarel.

Sir Will. Come hither then. If you betray me to my fon.———

Shift. Scalp me.

Sir

Sir Will. Enough.—You muſt know then, the hopes of our family, are, Mr. Shift, cen-tered in one boy.

Shift. And I warrant he is a hopeful one.

Sir Will. No interruption, I beg. George has been abroad theſe four years, and from his late behaviour, I have reaſon to believe, that had a certain event happened, which I am afraid he wiſhed,—my death——

Shift. Yes ; that's natural enough.

Sir Will. Nay, pray,—there would ſoon be an end to an ancient and honourable family.

Shift. Very melancholy, indeed. But fa-milies, like beſoms, will wear to the ſtumps, and finally fret out, as you ſay.

Sir Will. Pr'ythee peace for five minutes.

Shift. I am tongue-tied.

Sir Will. Now I have projected a ſcheme to prevent this calamity.

Shift. Ay, I ſhould be glad to hear that.

Sir Will. I am going to tell it you.

Shift. Proceed.

Sir Will. George, as I have contrived it, ſhall experience all the miſery of real ruin, without running the leaſt riſque.

Shift. Ay, that will be a coup de maitre.

Sir Will. I have prevailed upon his uncle, a wealthy citizen.——

Shift. I don't like a city plot.

Sir Will. I tell thee it is my own.

Shift. I beg pardon.

Sir Will. My brother, I ſay, ſome time ſince wrote him a circumſtantial account of my death ; upon which he is returned, in full expectation of ſucceeding to my eſtate.

Shift.

Shift. Immediately?

Sir Will. No; when at age. In about three months.

Shift. I underftand you.

Sir Will. Now, fir, guefling into what hands my heedlefs boy would naturally fall, on his return, I have in a feign'd character, affociated myfelf with a fet of rafcals, who will fpread every bait that can flatter folly, inflame extravagance, allure inexperience, or catch credulity. And when, by their means, he thinks himfelf reduced to the laft extremity; loft even to the moft diftant hope——

Shift. What then?

Sir Will. Then will I ftep in, like his guardian-angel, and fnatch him from perdition. If mortified by mifery, he becomes confcious of his errors, I have faved my fon; but if, on the other hand, gratitude can't bind, nor ruin reclaim him, I will caft him out, as an alien to my blood, and truft for the fupport of my name and family to a remoter branch.

Shift. Bravely refolved. But what part am I to fuftain in this drama?

Sir Will. Why George, you are to know, is already ftript of what money he could command, by two fharpers: but as I never truft them out of my fight they can't deceive me.

Shift. Out of your fight!

Sir Will. Why, I tell thee, I am one of the knot: an adept in their fcience, can flip, fhuffle, cog, or cut with the beft of 'em.

Shift. How do you efcape your fon's notice?

Sir Will. His firm perfuafion of my death, with the extravagance of my difguife.——

tion

Why, I would engage to elude your penetration, when I am beau'd for the baron. But of that by and by. He has recourfe, after his ill fuccefs, to the cent. per cent. gentry, ufurers, for a further fupply.

Shift. Natural enough.

Sir Will. Pray do you know,—I forgot his name,—a wrinkled old fellow, in a threadbare coat? He fits every morning, from twelve till two, in the left corner of Lloyd's coffeehoufe ; and every evening, from five till eight, under the clock, at the Temple-exchange.

Shift. What, little Transfer the broker !

Sir Will. The fame. Do you know him ?

Shift. Know him ! Ay, rot him. It was but laft Eafter Tuefday, he had me turn'd out at a feaft, in Leather-feller's Hall, for finging Room for Cuckolds, like a parrot; and vowed it meant a reflection upon the whole body corporate.

Sir Will. You have reafon to remember him.

Shift. Yes, yes, I recommended a minor to him myfelf, for the loan only of fifty pounds; and would you believe it, as I hope to be faved, we dined, fupped, and wetted five-and-thirty guineas upon tick, in meetings at the Crofskeys, in order to fettle the terms; and after all, the fcoundrel would not lend us a ftiver.

Sir Will. Could you perfonate him ?

Shift. Him ! Oh, you fhall fee me fhift into his fhamble in a minute: and with a withered face, a bit of a purple nofe, a cautionary ftammer, and a fleek filver head, I would undertake to deceive even his banker. But to fpeak the truth, I have a friend that can do this inimi-

inimitably well. Have not you fomething of more confequence for me?

Sir Will. I have. Could not you, mafter Shift, affume another fhape? You have attended auctions.

Shift. Auctions! a conftant puff. Deep in the myftery; a profeffed connoiffeur, from a Niger to a nautilus, from the Apollo Belvidere to a butterfly.

Sir Will. One of thefe infinuating, oily orators I will get you to perfonate: for we muft have the plate and jewels in our poffeffion, or they will foon fall into other hands.

Shift. I will do it.

Sir Will. Within I'll give you farther inftructions.

Shift. I'll follow you.

Sir Will. [*Going, returns.*] You will want materials.

Shift. Oh, my drefs I can be furnifhed with in five minutes. [*Exit Sir Will.*] A whimfical old blade this. I fhall laugh if this fcheme mifcarries. I have a ftrange mind to lend it a lift—never had a greater—Pho, a damn'd unnatural connection this of mine! What have I to do with fathers and guardians! a parcel of preaching, prudent, careful, curmudgeonly— dead to pleafures themfelves, and the blafters of it in others——Mere dogs in a manger—No, no, I'll veer, tack about, open my budget to the boy, and join in a counter-plot. But hold, hold, friend Stephen, fee firft how the land lies. Who knows whether this Germaniz'd genius has parts to comprehend, or fpirit to reward thy merit. There's danger in that, aye, marry

1s

is there. 'Egad before I fhift the helm, I'll
firft examine the coaft; and then if there be
but a bold fhore, and a good bottom, have a
care old Square Toes, you will meet with your
match.

Enter Sir George, Loader, and Servant.

Sir Geo. Let the Martin pannels for the vis-
a-vis be carried to Long-Acre, and the pye-
balls fent to Hall's to be bitted——You will
give me leave to be in your debt till the evening, Mr. Loader. I have juft enough left to
difcharge the baron; and we muft, you know,
be punctual with him, for the credit of the
country.

Load. Fire him, a fnub-nofed fon of a bitch.
Levant me, but he got enough laft night to
purchafe a principality amongft his countrymen, the High-dutchians and Huffarians.

Sir Geo. You had your fhare, Mr. Loader.

Load. Who, I! Lurch me at four, but I
was marked to the top of your trick, by the
baron, my dear. What, I am no cinque and
quartre man. Come, fhall we have a dip in
the hiftory of the Four Kings this morning?

Sir Geo. Rather too early. Befides, it is
the rule abroad, never to engage a-frefh, till
our old fcores are difcharged.

Load. Capot me, but thofe lads abroad are
pretty fellows, let'em fay what they will.
Here, fir, they will vowel you, from father to
fon, to the twentieth generation. They
would as foon now-a-days pay a tradefman's
bill, as a play debt. All fenfe of honour is
gone

gone, not a ſtiver ſtirring. They could as ſoon raiſe the dead as two pounds two; nick me, but I have a great mind to tie up, and ruin the raſcals—What, has Transfer been here this morning?

Enter Dick.

Sir Geo. Any body here this morning, Dick?

Dick. No body, your honour.

Load. Repique the raſcal. He promiſed to be here before me.

Dick. I beg your honour's pardon. Mrs. Cole from the Piazza was here, between ſeven and eight,

Sir Geo. An early hour for a lady of her calling.

Dick. Mercy on me! The poor gentle-woman is mortally altered ſince we uſed to lodge there, in our jaunts from Oxford; wrapt up in flannels: all over the rheumatiſe.

Load. Ay, ay, old Moll is at her laſt ſtake.

Dick. She bade me ſay, ſhe juſt ſtopt in her way to the tabernacle; after the exhortations, ſhe ſays, ſhe'll call again.

Sir Geo. Exhortation! Oh, I recollect. Well, whilſt they only make proſelytes from that profeſſion, they are heartily welcome to them.——She does not mean to make me a convert?

Dick. I believe ſhe has ſome ſuch deſign upon me: for ſhe offered me a book of hymns, a ſhilling, and a dram, to go along with her.

Sir Geo. No bad ſcheme, Dick. Thou haſt

a fine

a fine fober, pfalm-finging countenance; and
when thou haft been fome time in their tram-
mels, may make as able a teacher as the beft
of· 'em.

Dick. Laud fir, I want learning,

Sir Geo. Oh, the fpirit, the fpirit will fupply all that, Dick, never fear.

Enter Sir William, as a German Baron.

My dear baron, what news from the Haymarket? What fays the Florenza? Does fhe
yield? Shall I be happy? Say yes, and command my fortune.

Sir Will. I was never did fee fo fine a woman fince I was leave Hamburgh; dere was
all de colour, all red and white, dat was quite
natural; point d'artifice. Then fhe was dance
and fing—I vow to heaven, I was never fee de
like!

Sir Geo. But how did fhe receive my em-
baffy? What hopes?

Sir Will. Why dere was, monfieur le chevalier, when I firft enter, dree or four damn'd
queer people! ah, ah, dought I, by gad I
guefs your bufinefs. Dere was one fat big
woman's, dat I know long time: le valet de
chambre was tell me dat fhe came from a
grand merchant; ha, ha, dought I, by your
leave, ftick to your fhop; or, if you muft have de
pritty girl, dere is de play-hous, dat do very
well for you; but for de opera, pardonnez, by
gar dat is meat for your mafter.

Sir Geo. Infolent mechanic!—but fhe de-
fpifed him?

Sir

Sir Will. Ah', may foy, he is damn'd rich, has beaucoup de guineas ; but after de fat woman go, I was tell the fignora, madam, dere is one certain chevalier of dis country, who has travelled, fee de world, bien fait, well made, beaucoup d'Efprit, a great deal of monies, who beg, by gar, to have de honour to drow himfelf at your feet.

Sir Geo. Well, well, baron.

Sir Will. She afka your name ; as foon as I tell her, aha, by gar, dans an inftant, fhe melt like de lomp of fugar ; fhe run to her bureau, and, in de minute, return wid de paper.

Sir Geo. Give it me.

Les preliminaires d'une traité entre le chevalier Wealthy, and la Signora Florenza.

A bagatelle, a trifle : fhe fhall have it.

Load. Hark'e, knight, what is all that there outlandifh ftuff?

Sir Geo. Read, read. The eloquence of angels, my dear baron!

Load. Slam me, but the man's mad ! I don't underftand their gibberifh—What is it in Englifh ?

Sir Geo. The preliminaries of a fubfidy treaty, between Sir G. Wealthy, and Signora Florenza ? that the faid. Signora will refign the poffeffion of her perfon to the faid Sir George, on the payment of three hundred guineas monthly, for equipage, table, domeftics, drefs, dogs, and diamonds ; her debts to be duly difcharged, and a note advanced of five hundred by way of entrance.

Load.

Load. Zounds, what a cormorant! She muſt be deviliſh handſome.

Sir Geo. I am told ſo.

Load. Told ſo! Why, did you never ſee her?

Sir Geo. No; and poſſibly never may, but from my box at the opera.

Load. Hey-dey! Why, what the devil——

Sir Geo. Ha, ha, you ſtare, I don't wonder at it. This is an elegant refinement, unknown to the groſs voluptuaries of this part of the world. This is, Mr. Loader, what may be called a debt to your dignity: for an opera girl is as eſſential a piece of equipage for a man of faſhion, as his coach.

Load. The devil!

Sir Geo. 'Tis for the vulgar only to enjoy what they poſſeſs: the diſtinction of ranks and conditions are, to have hounds, and never hunt; cooks, and dine at taverns; houſes you never inhabit; miſtreſſes, you never enjoy——

Load. And debts, you never pay. Egad, I am not ſurpriz'd at it; if this be your trade, no wonder that you want money for neceſſaries, when you give ſuch a damn'd deal for nothing at all.

Enter Servant.

Serv. Mrs. Cole, to wait upon your honour.

Sir Geo. My dear baron, run, diſpatch my affair, conclude my treaty, and thank her for the very reaſonable conditions.

Sir Will. I fall.

Sir

Sir Geo. Mr. Loader, fhall I trouble you to introduce the lady? She is, I think, your acquaintance.

Load. Who, old Moll? Ay, ay, fhe's your market-woman. I wou'd not give fix-pence for your fignoras. One armful of good, wholefome Britifh beauty, is worth a fhip-load of their trapfing, tawdry trollops. But hark'e, baron, how much for the table? Why, fhe muft have a devilifh large family, or a mon-ftrous ftomach.

Sir Will. Ay, ay, dere is her moder, la complaifante to walk in de Park, and to go to de play; two broders, deux valets, dree Spanifh lap-dogs, and de monkey.

Load. Strip me, if I wou'd fet five fhil-lings againft the whole gang. May my part-ner renounce with the game in his hand, if I were you, knight, if I would not———
                                                [*Ex. Bar,*

Sir Geo. But the lady waits.   [*Ex.* Load.] A ftrange fellow this! What a whimfical jargon he talks! Not an idea abftra&ted from play? To fay truth, I am fincerely fick of my acquaintance: But, however, I have the firft people in the kingdom to keep me in countenance. Death and the dice level all diftin&tions.

Enter Mrs. Cole, fupported by Loader and Dick.

Mrs. Cole. Gently, gently, good Mr· Loader.

Load. Come along, old Moll. Why, you jade, you look as rofy this morning, I muft
                                                have

have a fmack at your mums. Here, tafte her,
fhe is as good as old hock to get yc i a ftomach.

Mrs. Cole. Fie, Mr. Loader, I thought you
had forgot me.

Load. I forgot you! I would as foon foreget
what is trumps.

Mrs. Cole. Softly, foftly, young man.
There, there, mighty well. And how does
your honour do? I han't feen your honour,
I can't tell the—Oh! mercy on me, there's
a twing————

Sir Geo. What is the matter, Mrs. Cole?

Mrs. Cole. My old diforder, the rheuma-
tife; I han't been able to get a wink of—
Oh la! What, you have been in town thefe
two days?

Sir Geo. Since Wednefday.

Mrs. Cole. And never once call'd upon old
Cole. No, no, I am worn out, thrown by
and forgotten, like a tatter'd garment, as Mr.
Squintum fays. Oh, he is a dear man! But
for him I had been a loft fheep; never known
the comforts of the new birth; no,—There's
your old friend, Kitty Carrot, at home ftill.
—What, fhall we fee you this evening? I have
kept the green room for you ever fince I heard
you were in town.

Load. What fhall we take a fnap at old
Moll's Hey, beldam, have you a good batch
of Burgundy abroch?

Mrs. Cole. Bright as a ruby; and for fla-
vour! You know the colonel—He and Jenny
Cummins drank three flafks, hand to fift, laft
night.

Load.

Load. What, bilk thee of thy fhare?

Mrs. Cole. Ah, don't mention it, Mr. Loader. No, that's all over with me. The time has been, when I could have earned thirty fhillings a day by my own drinking, and the next morning was neither fick nor forry: But now, O laud, a thimbleful turns me topfy-turvy.

Load. Poor old girl!

Mrs. Cole. Aye, I have done with thefe idle vanities; my thoughts are fix'd upon a better place.—What, I fuppofe, Mr. Loader, you will be for your old friend the black-eyed girl, from Rofemary-lane. Ha, ah! Well, 'tis a merry little tit. A thoufand pities fhe's fuch a reprobate!——But fhe'll mend; her time is not come: all fhall have their call, as Mr. Squin*t*cm fays, fooner or later; regeneration is not the work of a day. No, no, no,——Oh!

Sir Geo. Not worfe I hope.

Mrs. Cole. Rack, rack, gnaw, gnaw, never eafy, a-bed or up all's one. Pray, honeft friend, have you any clary, or mint-water in the houfe?

Dick. A cafe of French drams.

Mrs. Cole. Heaven defend me! I would not touch a dram for the world.

Sir Geo. They are but cordials, Mrs. Cole. —Fetch 'em, you blockhead. [*Ex.* Dick.]

Mrs. Cole. Aye, I am a going; a wafting and a wafting, Sir George. What will become of the houfe when I am gone, heaven knows————No.——When people are mifs'd, then they are mourned. Sixteen years have

have I lived in the Garden, comfortably and creditably; and, though I fay it, could have got bail any hour of the day: Reputable tradefmen, Sir George, neighbours Mr. Loader knows; no knock-me-down doings in my houfe. A fet of regular, fedate, fober cuftomers. No rioters.—Sixteen did I fay— Aye, eighteen years I have paid fcot and lot in the parifh of St. Paul's, and during the whole time, nobody have faid, Mrs. Cole, why do you fo? Unlefs twice that I was be- fore Sir Thomas De Val, and three times in the round-houfe.

Sir Geo. Nay, don't weep, Mrs. Cole.

Load. May I lofe deal, with an honour at bottom, if old Moll does not bring tears into my eyes.

Mrs. Cole. However, it is a comfort, after all, to think one has paft through the world with credit and charaĉter. Ah! a good name, as Mr. Squintum fays, is better than a gallipot of ointment.

Enter Dick, with a dram.

Load. Come, hafte, Dick, hafte;—forrow is dry. Here, Moll, fhall I fill thee a bum- per?

Mrs. Cole. Hold, hold, Mr. Loader! Hea- ven help you, I could as foon fwallow the Thames. Only a fip, to keep the gout out of my ftomach.

Load. Why then, here's to thee.—Levant me, but it is fupernaculum—Speak when you have enough.

Mrs. Cole. I won't trouble you for the glafs; my

my hands do fo tremble and fhake, I fhall but
fpill the good creature.

Load. Well pull'd. But now to bufinefs.
Pr'ythee, Moll, did not I fee a tight young
wench, in a linen gown, knock at your door
this morning?

Mrs. Cole. Aye; a young thing from the
country.

Load. Could we not get a peep at her this
evening?

Mrs. Cole. Impoffible! She is engaged to
Sir Timothy Totter. I have taken earneft for
her thefe three months.

Load. Pho! what fignifies fuch a fellow as
that. Tip him an old trader, and give her to
the knight.

Mrs. Cole. Tip him an old trader! Mercy
on us! where do you expect to go when you
die, Mr, Loader?

Load. Crop me, but this Squintum has
turned her brains!

Sir Geo. Nay, Mr. Loader, I think the
gentleman has wrought a moft happy reformation.

Mrs. Cole. Oh, it was a wonderful work!
There had I been toffing in a fea of fin without rudder or compafs; and had not the good
gentleman piloted me into the harbour of
grace, I muft have ftruck againft the rocks of
reprobation, and have been quite fwallowed
up in the whirlpool of defpair. He was the
precious inftrument of my fpiritual fprinkling.
—But, however, Sir George, if your mind be
fet upon a young country thing, to-morrow
night, I believe, I can furnifh you.

Load.

Load. As how?

Mrs. Cole. I have advertifed this morning, in the regifter office, for fervants under feven-teen : and ten to one but I light on fomething that will do.

Load. Pillor me, but it has a face.

Mrs. Cole. Truly, confiftently with my confcience, I would do any thing for your honour.

Sir Geo. Right, Mrs. Cole, never lofe fight of that monitor. But, pray, how long has this heavenly change been wrought in you?

Mrs. Cole. Ever fince my laft vifitation of the gout. Upon my firft fit, feven years ago, I began to have my doubts, and my waverings ; but I was loft in a labyrinth, and no body to fhew me the road. One time I thought of dying a Roman, which is truly a comfortable communion enough for one of us : but it would not do.

Sir Geo. Why not?

Mrs. Cole. I went, one fummer, over to Boulogne, to repent ; and, would you believe it, the bare-footed, bald-pate beggars would not give me abfolution without I quitted my bufinefs——Did you ever hear of fuch a fet of fcabby——Befides, I could not bear their bar-barity. Would you believe it, Mr. Loader, they lock up for their lives, in a nunnery, the prettieft, fweeteft, tender young things!—— Oh, fix of them for a feafon would finifh my bufinefs here ; and then I fhould have nothing to do, but to think of hereafter.

Load. Brand me, what a country !

Sir Geo. Oh, fcandalous !

Mrs.

Mrs. Cole. O no, it would not do. So, in my laft illnefs, I was wifhed to Mr. Squintum, who ftepped in with his faving grace, got me with the new birth, and I became, as you fee, regenerate, and another creature.

Enter Dick.

Dick. Mr. Transfer, Sir, has fent to know if you be at home.

Sir Geo. Mrs. Cole, I am mortified to part with you. But, bufinefs, you know——.

Mrs. Cole. True, Sir George. Mr. Loader, your arm——Gently——oh!—oh!

Sir Geo. Would you take another thimble-ful, Mrs. Cole?

Mrs. Cole. Not a drop—I fhall fee you this evening?

Sir Geo. Depend upon me.

Mrs. Cole. To-morrow I hope to fuit you—We are to have, at the tabernacle, an occa-fional hymn, with a thankfgiving fermon for my recovery. After which I fhall call at the regifter office, and fee what goods my adver-tifement has brought in.

Sir Geo. Extremely obliged to you, Mrs. Cole.

Mrs. Cole. Or, if that fhould not do, I have a tid bit at home, will fuit your ftomach. Never brufhed by a beard. Well, heaven blefs you——Softly—have a care, Mr. Loader —Richard, you may as well give me the bot-tle into the chair, for fear I fhould be taken ill on the road. Gently—fo, fo!

[*Exit Mrs. Cole and Loader.*

Sir

Sir Geo. Dick, fhew Mr. Transfer in— Ha, ha, what a hodge podge! How the jade has jumbled together the carnal and the fpiritual; with what eafe fhe reconciles her new birth to her old calling! —No wonder thefe preachers have plenty of profelytes, whilft they have the addrefs fo comfortably to blend the hitherto jarring interefts of the two worlds.

Enter Loader.

Well, knight, I have houfed her; but they want you within, fir.

Sir Geo. I'll go to them immediately.

ACT II.

Dick.

MY mafter will come to you prefently.

Enter Sir George.

Sir Geo. Mr. Transfer, your fervant.

Tranf. Your honour's very humble. I thought to have found Mr. Loader here.

Sir Geo. He will return immediately. Well, Mr. Transfer——but take a chair— you have had a long walk. Mr Loader, I prefume, opened to you the urgency of my bufinefs.

Tranf. Aye, aye, the general cry, money, money! I don't know, for my part, where all the money is flown to. Formerly a note, with a tolerable endorfement, was as current

as

as cafh. If your uncle Richard now would join in this fecurity————

Sir Geo. Impoffible.

Tranf. Aye, like enough. I wifh you were of age.

Sir Geo. So do I. But as that will be confidered in the premium————

Tranf. True, true,——I fee you underftand bufinefs ——And what fum does your honour lack at prefent?

Sir Geo. Lack!——How much have you brought?

Tranf. Who, I? Dear me! none.

Sir Geo. Zounds, none!

Tranf. Lack-a-day, none to be had, I think. All the morning have I been upon the hunt. There, Ephraim Barebones, the tallow chandler, in Thames-ftreet, ufed to be a never-failing chap; not a guinea to be got there. Then I tottered away to Nebuchadnezzar Zebulon, in the Old Jewry, but it happened to be Saturday; and they never touch on the Sabbath, you know.

Sir Geo. Why what the devil can I do?

Tranf. Good me, I did not know your honour had been fo preffed.

Sir Geo. My honour preffed! Yes, my honour is not only preffed, but ruined, unlefs I can raife money to redeem it. That blockhead, Loader, to depend upon this old doating——

Tranf. Well, well, now I declare, I am quite forry to fee your honour in fuch a taking.

Sir Geo. Damn your forrow.

Tranf. But come, don't be caft down: Tho'

Tho' money is not to be had, money's worth may, and that's the fame thing.

Sir Geo. How, dear Transfer?

Tranf. Why I have, at my warehoufe in the city, ten cafks of whale-blubber, a large cargo of Dantzick dowlas, with a curious affortment of Birmingham hafts, and Whitney blankets for exportation..

Sir Geo. Hey!

Tranf. And ftay, ftay, then, again, at my country-houfe, the bottom of Gray's Inn-Lane, there's a hundred ton of fine old hay, only damaged a little laft winter, for want of thatching; with forty load of flint ftones.

Sir Geo. Well.

Tranf. Your honour may have all thefe for a reafonable profit, and convert them into cafh.

Sir Geo. Blubber and blankets? Why, you old rafcal, do you banter me?

Tranf. Who I? O la', marry, heaven forbid.

Sir Geo. Get out of my—you ftuttering fcoundrel.

Tranf. If your honour would but hear me——

Sir Geo. Troop, I fay, unlefs you have a mind to go a fhorter way than you came. [*Exit. Tr.*] And yet there is fomething fo uncommonly ridiculous in his propofal, that were my mind more at eafe—[*Enter Loader.*] So, fir, you have recommended me to a fine fellow.

Load. What's the matter?

Sir

Sir Geo. He can't fupply me with a fhilling; and wants, befides, to make me a dealer in dowlas.

Load. Aye, and a very good commodity too. People that are upon ways and means, muft not be nice, knight. A pretty piece of work you have made here! Thrown up the cards, with the game in your hands.

Sir Geo. Why, pr'ythee of what ufe would his——

Load. Ufe! of every ufe.—Procure you the fpankers, my boy. I have a broker, that in a twinkling, fhall take off your bargain.

Sir Geo. Indeed!

Load. Indeed! Aye, indeed. You fit down to hazard and not know the chances! I'll call him back.—Holloa, Transfer.—A pretty little, bufy, buftling—You may travel miles, before you will meet with his match. If there is one pound in the city, he will get it. He creeps, like a ferret, into their bags, and makes the yellow boys bolt again.

Enter Transfer.

Come hither, little Transfer; what, man, our Minor was a little too hafty; he did not underftand trap: knows nothing of the game, my dear.

Tranf. What I faid, was to ferve Sir George; as he feem'd————

Load. I told him fo; well, well, we will take thy commodities, were they as many more. But try, pr'ythee, if thou could'ft not procure us fome of the ready, for prefent fpending.

Tranf. Let me confider.

Load.

Load. Aye, do, come: fhuffle thy brains;
never fear the baronet.   To let a lord of lands
want fhiners; 'tis a fhame.

Tranf. I do recolle&, in this quarter of
the town, an old friend, that ufed to do things
in this way.

Load. Who ?

Tranf. Statute, the fcrivener.

Load Slam me, but he has nicked the
chance.

Tranf. A hard man, mafter Loader!

Sir Geo. No matter.

Tranf. His demands are exorbitant.

Sir Geo. That is no fault of ours.

Load. Weil faid, knight!

Tranf. But to fave time, I had better mention his terms.

Load. Unneceffary.

Tranf. Five per cent, legal intereft.

Sir Geo He fhall have it.

Tranf. Ten, the premium.

Sir Geo. No more words.

Tranf. Then, as you are not of age, five
more for enfuring your life.

Load. We will give it.

Tranf. As for what he will demand for the
rifque——

Sir Geo. He fhall be fatisfied.

Tranf. You pay the attorney.

Sir Geo. Amply, amply; Loader, difpatch
him.

Load. There, there, little Transfer; now
every thing is fettled.   All terms fhall be
complied with, reafonable or unreafonable.

                                    What,

What, our principal is a man of honour. [*Exit. Tr.*] Hey, my knight, this is doing bufinefs. This pinch is a fure card.

Re-enter Transfer.

Tranf. I had forgot one thing. I am no^t the principal ; you pay the brokerage.

Load. Aye, aye ; and a handfome prefent into the bargain, never fear.

Tranf. Enough, enough.

Load. Hark'e, Transfer, we'll take the Birmingham hafts and Whitney wares.

Tranf. They fhall be forthcoming——You would not have the hay, with the flints ?

Load. Every pebble of 'em. The magiftrates of the baronet's borough are infirm and gouty. He fhall deal them as new pavement. [*Ex. Tr.*] So that's fettled. I believe, knight, I can lend you a helping hand as to the laft article. I know fome traders that will truck: fellows with finery ; not commodities of fuch clumfy conveyance as old Transfer's.

Sir Geo. You are obliging.

Load. I'll do it, boy ; and get you, into the bargain, a bonny auctioneer, that fhall difpofe of 'em all in a crack. [*Exit.*

Enter Dick.

Dick. Your uncle, fir, has been waiting fome time.

Sir Geo. He comes in a lucky hour. Shew him in. [*Ex. Dick.*] Now for a lecture. My fituation fhan't - fink my fpirits, however.

Here

Here comes the mufty trader, running over with remonftrances. I muft banter the cit.

Enter Richard Wealthy.

R. Weal. So, fir, what I fuppofe this is a fpice of your foreign breeding, to let your uncle kick his heels in your hall, whilft your prefence chamber is crouded with pimps, bawds, and gamefters.

Sir Geo. Oh, a proof of my refpeﬅ, dear nuncle. Would it have been decent now, nuncle, to have introduced you into fuch company?

R. Weal. Wonderfully confiderate! Well, young man, and what do you think will be the end of all this? Here I have received, by the laft mail, a quire of your draughts from abroad. I fee you are determined our neighbours fhould tafte of your magnificence.

Sir Geo. Yes, I think I did fome credit to my country.

R. Weal. and how are all thefe to be paid?

Sir Geo. That I fubmit to you, dear nuncle.

R. Weal. From me!——Not a foufe to keep you from the counter.

Sir Geo. Why then let the fcoundrels ftay. It is their duty. I have other demands, debts of honour, which muft be difcharged.

R. Weal. Here's a diabolical diftinﬅion! Here's a proftitution of words!—Honour! 'Sdeath, that a rafcal, who has picked your pocket, fhall have his crime gilded with the moft facred diftinﬅion, and his plunder punc-
tually

tually paid, whilst the induftrious mechanic, who minifters to your very wants, fhall have his debts delayed, and his demand treated as infolent.

Sir Geo. Oh! a truce to this thread-bare trumpery, dear nuncle.

R. Weal. I confefs my folly; but make yourfelf eafy; you won't be troubled with many more of my vifits. I own I was weak, enough to defign a fhort expoftulation with you; but as we in the city know the true value of time, I fhall take care not to fquander away any more of it upon you.

Sir Geo. A prudent refolution.

R. Weal. One commiffion, however, I can't difpenfe with myfelf from executing.——It was agreed between your father and me, that as he had but one fon and I one daughter——

Sir Geo. Your gettings fhould be added to his eftate, and my coufin Margery and I fquat down together in the comfortable ftate of matrimony.

R. Weal. Puppy! fuch was our intention. Now his laft will claims this contract.

Sir Geo. Difpatch, dear nuncle.

R. Weal. Why then, in a word, fee me here demand the execution.

Sir Geo. What dy'e mean? For me to marry Margery.

R. Weal. I do.

Sir Geo. What, moi-me?

R. Weal. You, you——Your anfwer, aye or no?

Sir

Sir Geo. Why then, concisély and briefly, without evasion, equivocation, or further circumlocution.———No.

R. Weal. I am glad of it.

Sir Geo. So am I.

R. Weal. But pray, if it would not be too great a favour, what objections can you have to my daughter? Not that I want to remove 'em, but merely out of curiosity. What objections?

Sir Geo. None. I neither know her, have seen her, enquired after her, or ever intend it.

R. Weal. What, perhaps, I am the stumbling block?

Sir Geo. You have hit it.

R. Weal. Aye, now we come to the point. Well, and pray——

Sir Geo. Why, it is not so much a dislike to your person, tho' that is exceptionable enough, but your profession, dear nuncle, is an insuperable obstacle.

R. Weal. Good lack! And what harm has that done, pray?

Sir Geo. Done! So stained, polluted, and tainted the whole mass of your blood, thrown such a blot on your escutcheon, as ten regular successions can hardly efface.

R. Weal. The deuce!

Sir Geo. And could you now, consistently with your duty as a faithful guardian, recommend my union with a daughter of a trader?

R. Weal. Why, indeed, I ask pardon; I am afraid I did not weigh the matter as maturely as I ought.

Sir Geo. Oh, a horrid barbarous scheme!

R. Weal.

R. Weal. But then I thought, her having the honour to partake of the fame flefh and blood with yourfelf, might prove in fome meafure, a kind of fuller's-earth, to fcour out the dirty fpots contracted by commerce.

Sir Geo. Impoffible!

R. Weal. Befides, here it has been the practice even of peers.

Sir Geo. Don't mention the unnatural intercourfe! Thank heav'n, Mr. Richard Wealthy, my education has been in another country, where I have been too well inftructed in the value of nobility, to think of intermixing it with the offspring of a Bourgeois. Why, what apology could I make to my children, for giving them fuch a mother?

R. Weal. I did not think of that. Then I muft defpair, I am afraid.

Sir Geo. I can afford but little hopes. Tho', upon recollection——Is the Griffette pretty?

R. Weal. A parent may be partial. She is thought fo.

Sir Geo. Ah la jolie petite Bourgeoife! Poor girl, I fincerely pity her. And I fuppofe, to procure her emerfion from the mercantile mud, no confideration would be fpared.

R. Weal. Why, to be fure, for fuch an honour, one would ftrain a point.

Sir Geo. Why then, not totally to deftroy your hopes, I do recollect an edict in favour of Brittany; that when a man of diftinction engages in commerce, his nobility is fuffer'd to fleep.

R. Weal.

R. Weal. Indeed!

Sir Geo. And upon his quitting the contagious connection, he is permitted to refume his rank.

R. Weal. That's fortunate.

Sir Geo. So nuncle Richard, if you will fell out of the ftocks, fhut up your counting-houfe, and quit St. Mary Axe for Grofvenor-fquare——

R. Weal. What then?

Sir Geo. Why, when your rank has had time to roufe itfelf, for I think your nobility, nuncle, has had a pretty long nap, if the girl's perfon is pleafing, and the purchafe-money is adequate to the honour, I may in time be prevailed upon to reftore her to the right of her family.

R. Weal. Amazing condefcenfion!

Sir Geo. Good-nature is my foible. But, upon my foul, I would not have gone fo far for any body elfe.

R. Weal. I can contain no longer. Hear me, fpendthrift, prodigal, do you know, that in ten days your whole revenue won't purchafe you a feather to adorn your empty head?——

Sir Geo. Hey day, what's the matter now?

R. Weal. And that you derive every acre of your boafted patrimony from you great uncle, a foap boiler!

Sir Geo. Infamous afperfion!

R. Weal. It was his bags, the fruits of his honeft induftry, that preferved your lazy, beggarly nobility. His wealth repair'd your
tottering

tottering hall, from the ruins of which, even the rats had run.

Sir Geo. Better our name had perifh'd! Infupportable! foap-boiling, uncle!

R. Weal. Traduce a trader in a country of commerce! It is treafon againft the community; and, for your punifhment, I would have you reftored to the fordid condition from whence we drew you, and like your predeceffors, the Picts, ftript, painted, and fed upon hips, haws and blackberries.

Sir Geo. A truce, dear haberdafher.

R. Weal. One pleafure I have, that to this goal you are upon the gallop; but have a care, the fword hangs but by a thread. When next we meet, know me for the mafter of your fate.   [*Exit.*

Sir Geo. Infolent mechanic! But that his Bourgeois blood would have foiled my fword—

Enter Baron and Loader.

Sir Will. What is de matter?

Sir Geo. A fellow here, upon the credit of a little affinity, has dared to upbraid me with being fprung from a foap-boiler.

Sir Will. Vat, you from the boiler of foap!

Sir Geo. Me.

Sir Will. Aha, begar, dat is anoder ting —And harka you, mifter monfieur, ha— how dare a you have d'affrontary—

Sir Geo. How!

Sir Will. De impertinence to fit down, play wid me?

Sir Geo. What is this?

Sir

Sir Will. A beggarly Bourgeois vis-a-vis, a baron of twenty defcents.

Load. But baron——

Sir Will. Bygar, I am almoft afhamed to win of fuch a low, dirty—Give me my monies, and let me never fee your face.

Load. Why, but baron, you miftake this thing. I know the old buck this fellow prates about.

Sir Will. May be.

Load. Pigeon me, as true a gentleman as the grand fignor. He was, indeed, a good-natured, obliging, friendly fellow; and being a great judge of foap, tar, and train-oil, he ufed to have it home to his houfe, and fell it to his acquaintance for ready money, to ferve them.

Sir Will. Was dat all?

Load. Upon my honour.

Sir Will. Oh, dat, dat is anoder ting. By-gar I was afraid he was negotiant.

Load. Nothing like it.

Enter Dick.

Dick. A gentleman to enquire for Mr. Loader.

Load. I come—A pretty fon of a bitch, this baron! pimps for the man, picks his pocket, and then wants to kick him out of company, becaufe his uncle was an oilman.

Exit.

Sir Will. I beg pardon, chevalier, I was miftake.

Sir Geo. Oh, don't mention it; had the flam been faɛt, your, behavour was natural enough.

Enter

Enter Loader.

Load. Mr. Smirk, the auctioneer.

Sir Geo. Shew him in, by all means.

[*Exit. Loader.*

Sir Will. You have affairs.

Sir Geo. If you'll walk into the next room, they will be finished in five minutes.

Enter Loader, with Shift as Smirk.

Load. Here, master Smirk, this is the gentleman. Hark'e, knight, did I not tell you, old Moll was your mark? Here she has brought a pretty piece of man's meat already; as sweet as a nosegay, and as ripe as a cherry, you rogue. Dispatch him, mean time we'll manage the girl. [*Exit.*

Smirk You are the principal.

Sir Geo. Even so. I have, Mr. Smirk, some things of a confiderable value, which I want to dispose of immediately.

Smirk. You have?

Sir Geo. Could you affist me?

Smirk. Doubtlefs.

Sir Geo. But directly?

Smirk. We have an auction at twelve. I'll add your cargo to the catalogue.

Sir Geo. Can that be done?

Smirk. Every day's practice: it is for the credit of the fale. Laft week, amongft the valuable effects of a gentleman, going abroad, I fold a choice collection of china, with a curious fervice of plate; though the real party was never mafter of above two Delf diſhes, and a dozen of pewter, in all his life.

Sir

Sir Geo. Very artificial. But this muſt be concealed.

Smirk. Buried here. Oh, many an aigrette and ſolitaire have I ſold, to diſcharge a lady's play-debt. But then we muſt know the parties; otherwiſe it might be knockt down to the huſband himſelf. Ha, ha——Hey ho!

Sir Geo. True. Upon my word, your profeſſion requires parts.

Smirk. No body's more. Did you ever hear, Sir George, what firſt brought me into the buſineſs?

Sir Geo. Never.

Smirk. Quite an accident, as I may ſay. You muſt have known my predeceſſor, Mr. Prig, the greateſt man in the world, in his way; aye, or that ever was, or ever will be; quite a jewel of a man: he would touch you up a lot! there was no refiſting him. He would force you to bid, whether you would or no. I ſhall never ſee his equal.

Sir Geo. You are modeſt, Mr. Smirk.

Smirk. No, no, but his ſhadow. Far be it from me, to vie with ſo great a man. But, as I was ſaying, my predeceſſor, Mr. Prig, was to have a ſale as it might be on Saturday. On Friday at noon, I ſhall never forget the day, he was ſuddenly ſeized with a violent cholic. He ſent for me to his bedſide, ſqueezed me by the hand; Dear Smirk, ſaid he, what an accident! You know what is to-morrow; the greateſt ſhew this ſeaſon; prints, pictures, bronzes, butterflies, medals, and minionettes; all the world will be

be there; Lady Dy Jofs, Mrs. Nankyn, the
dutchefs of Dupe, and every body at all.
You fee my ftate, it will be impoffible for
me to mount. What can I do?—It was not
for me, you know, to advife that great man.

Sir Geo. No, no.

Smirk. At laft, looking wifhfully at me,
Smirk, fays he, d'you love me?—Mr. Prig,
can you doubt it?——I'll put it to the teft,
fays he; fupply my place to-morrow.—I, eager
to fhew my love, rafhly and rapidly replied, I
will.

Sir Geo. That was bold.

Smirk. Abfolute madnefs. But I had
gone too far to recede. Then the point was,
to prepare for the awful occafion. The firft
want that occurred to me, was a wig; but
this was too material an article to depend on
my own judgement. I refolved to confult my
friends. I told them the affair——You hear,
gentlemen, what has happened; Mr. Prig,
one of the greateft men in his way, the world
ever faw, or ever will, quite a jewel of a man,
is taken with a violent fit of the cholic; to-morrow, the greateft fhew this feafon ; prints, pictures, bronzes, butterflies, medals, and minionettes ; every body in the world to be there;
Lady Dy Jofs, Mrs. Nankyn, dutchefs of
Dupe, and all mankind; it being impoffible
he fhould mount, I have confented to fell——
They ftared—It is true, gentlemen. Now I
fhould be glad to have your opinions as to a
wig. They were divided: fome recommended
a tye, others a bag: one mentioned a bob,
but was foon over-ruled. Now, for my part,

I own,

I own, I rather inclined to the bag; but to avoid the imputation of rafhnefs, I refolved to take Mrs. Smirk's judgement, my wife, a dear good woman, fine in figure, high in tafte, a fuperior genius, and knows old china like a Nabob.

Sir Geo. What was her decifion?

Smirk. I told her the cafe—My dear, you know what has happened. My good friend, Mr. Prig, the greateft man in the world, in his way, that ever was, or ever will be, quite a jewel of a man—a violent fit of the cholic ——the greateft fhew this feafon, to-morrow, pictures, and every thing in the world; all the world will be there : now, as it is im- poffible he fhould, I mount in his ftead. You know the importance of a wig; I have afked my friends—fome recommended a tye, others a bag—what is your opinion? Why, to deal freely, Mr. Smirk, fays fhe, a tye for your round, regular, fmiling face, would be rather too formal, and a bag too boyifh, deficient in dignity for the folemn occafion; were I worthy to advife, you fhould wear a fomething between both.—I'll be hanged if you don't mean a major. I jumpt at the hint, and a ma- jor it was.

Sir Geo So, that was fixt.

Smirk. Finally. But next day, when I came to mount the roftrum, then was the trial. My limbs fhook, and my tongue trem- bled. The firft lot was a chamber utenfil, in Chelfea china, of the pea-green pattern. It occafioned a great laugh; but I got thro' it. Her grace, indeed, gave me great encourage- ment. I overheard her whifper to lady Dy,
                                                    Upon

Upon my word, Mr. Smirk does it very well. Very well, indeed, Mr. Smirk, addreffing her-felf to me. I made an acknowledging bow to her grace, as in duty bound But one flower flounced involuntarily from me that day, as I may fay. I remember, Dr. Trifle called it enthufiaftic, and pronounced it a pre-fage of my future greatnefs.

Sir Geo. What was that?

Smirk. Why, fir, the lot was a Guido; a fingle figure, a marvellous fine performance; well preferved, and highly finifhed. It ftuck at five and forty; I, charmed with the pic-ture, and piqued at the people, A going for five and forty, no body more than five and forty?——Pray, ladies and gentlemen, look at this piece, quite flefh and blood, and only wants a touch from the torch of Prometheus to ftart from the canvas, and fall a bidding. A general plaudit enfued, I bowed, and in three minutes knocked it down at fixty three, ten.

Sir Geo. That was a ftroke at leaft equal to your mafter.

Smirk. O dear me! You did not know the great man, alike in every thing. He had as much to fay upon a ribbon, as a Raphael. His manner was inimitably fine. I remember, they took him off at the playhoufe, fome time ago; pleafant, but wrong. Public charaƈters fhould not be fported with—They are facred ——But we lofe time.

Sir Geo. Oh, in the lobby, on the table, you will find the particulars.

Smirk.

Smirk. We fhall fee you. There will be a world of company. I fhall pleafe you. But the great nicety of our art is, the eye. Mark how mine fkims round the room. Some bidders are fhy, and only advance with a nod; but I nail them. One, two, three, four, five. You will be furprized—Ha, ha, ha,—heigh ho.

[*Exeunt.*

ACT. III.

Enter Sir George and Loader.

Sir George.

A Moft infernal run. Let's fee, *(Pulls out a card.)* Loader a thoufand, the Baron two, Tally——Enough to beggar a banker. Every fhilling of Transfer's fupply exhaufted! nor will even the fale of my moveables prove fufficient to difcharge my debts. Death and the devil! In what a complication of calamities has a few days plunged me! And no refource?

Load. Knight, here's old moll come to wait on you; fhe has brought the tid-bit I fpoke of. Shall I bid her fend her in?

Sir Geo. Pray do.   [*Exit Loader.*

Enter Mrs. Cole and Lucy.

Mrs. Cole. Come along, Lucy. You bafhful baggage, I thought I had filenced your fcruples. Don't you remember what Mr. Squintum faid? A woman's not worth faving,
that

that wont be guilty of a fwinging fin; for they have matter to repent upon. Here, your honour, I leave her to your management. She is young, tender, and timid; does not know what is for her own good; but your honour will foon teach her. I would willingly ftay, but I muft not lofe the lecture.   [*Exit.*

Sir Geo. Upon my credit, a fine figure! Aukward——Can't produce her publicly as mine; but fhe will do for private amufement ——Will you be feated, mifs?——Dumb! quite a picture! She too wants a touch of the Promethean torch—Will you be fo kind, ma'am, to walk from your frame and take a chair?——Come, pry'thee, why fo coy? Nay, I am not very adroit in the cuftom of this country. I fuppofe I muft conduct you——Come, mifs.

Lucy. O, fir!

Sir Geo. Child!

Lucy. If you have any humanity, fpare me.

Sir Geo. In tears! What can this mean? Artifice. A project to raife the price, I fuppofe. Look'e, my dear, you may fave this piece of pathetic for another occafion. It won't do with me; I am no novice——So, child, a truce to your tragedy, I beg.

Lucy. Indeed you wrong me, fir; indeed you do.

Sir Geo. Wrong you! how came you here, and for what purpofe?

Lucy. A fhameful one; I know it all, and yet believe me, fir, I am innocent.

Sir Geo. Oh, I don't queftion that. Your pious patronefs is a proof of your innocence.
                                                    Lucy,

Lucy. What can I fay to gain your credit?
And yet, fir, ftrong as appearances are againſt
me, by all that's holy, you fee me here, a poor,
diſtreſt, involuntary victim.

Sir Geo. Her ſtyle's above the common claſs;
her tears are real.—Riſe, child.—How the poor,
creature trembles!

Lucy. Say then I am ſafe!

Sir Geo. Fear nothing.

Lucy. May heaven reward you. I cannot.

Sir Geo. Pr'ythee child, collect yourſelf,
and help me to unravel this myſtery. You
came hither willingly? There was no force?

Lucy. None.

Sir Geo. You know Mrs Cole.

Lucy. Too well.

Sir Geo. How came you then to truſt her?

Lucy. Mine, fir, is a tedious, melancholy tale.

Sir Geo. And artleſs too?

Lucy. As innocence.

Sir Geo. Give it me.

Lucy. It will tire you.

Sir Geo. Not if it be true. Be juſt, and
you will find me generous.

Lucy. On that, fir, I relied in venturing
hither.

Sir Geo. You did me juſtice. Truſt me with
all your ſtory. If you deſerve, depend upon
my protection.

Lucy. Some months ago, fir, I was conſidered as the joint heireſs of a reſpectable, wealthy
merchant; dear to my friends, happy in my
proſpects, and my father's favourite.

Sir Geo. His name.

Lucy.

Lucy. There you muſt pardon me. Unkind and cruel tho' he has been to me, let me diſcharge the duty of a daughter, ſuffer in ſilence, nor bring reproach on him who gave me being.

Sir Geo. I applaud your piety.

Lucy. At this happy period, my father, judging an addition of wealth muſt bring an increaſe of happineſs, reſolved to unite me with a man, ſordid in his mind, brutal in his manners, and riches his only recommendation. My refuſal of this ill-ſuited match, tho' mildly given, enflamed my father's temper, naturally choleric, alienated his affections, and baniſhed me his houſe, diſtreſt and deſtitute.

Sir Geo. Would no friend receive you?

Lucy. Alas, how few are friends to the unfortunate! Beſides, I knew, ſir, ſuch a ſtep would he conſidered by my father, as an appeal from his juſtice. I therefore retired to a remote corner of the town, truſting, my only advocate, to the tender calls of nature, in his cool, reflecting hours.

Sir Geo. How came you to know this woman?

Lucy. Accident placed me in a houſe, the miſtreſs of which profeſſed the ſame principles with my infamous conductreſs. There, as enthuſiaſm is the child of melancholy, I caught the infection. A conſtant attendance on their aſſemblies, procured me the acquaintance of this woman, whoſe extraordinary zeal and devotion firſt drew my attention and confidence. I truſted her with my ſtory, and in return received the warmeſt invitation to take the protection of her houſe. This I unfortunately accepted.

Sir

Sir Geo. Unfortunately indeed!

Lucy. By the decency of appearances, I was some time impofed upon. But an accident, which you will excufe my repeating, revealed all the horror of my fituation. I will not trouble you with a recital of all the arts ufed to feduce me; happily they hitherto have failed. But this morning I was acquainted with my deftiny; and no other election left me, but immediate compliance, or a jail. In this defperate condition, you cannot wonder, fir, at my choofing rather to rely on the generofity of a gentleman, than the humanity of a creature infenfible to pity, and void of every virtue.

Sir Geo. The event fhall juftify your choice. You have my faith and honour for your fecurity. For tho' I can't boaft of my own goodnefs, yet I have an honeft feeling for afflicted virtue ; and, however unfafhionable, a fpirit that dares afford it protection. Give me your hand. As foon as I have difpatched fome prefling bufinefs here, I will lodge you in an afylum, facred to the diftreffes of your fex; where indigent beauty is guarded from temptations, and deluded innocence refcued from infamy. [*Exeunt.*

Enter Shift.

Shif. Zooks, I have toiled like a horfe ; quite tired, by Jupiter. And what fhall I get for my pains ? The old fellow here talks of making me eafy for life. Eafy! and what does he mean by eafy? He'll make me an excife-man, I fuppofe ; and fo with an ink-horn at my button-hole, and a taper fwitch in my hand, I fhall run about gauging of beer-barrels. No, that will neve

never do. This lad here is no fool. Foppifh
indeed. He does not want parts, no, nor principles neither. I overheard his fcene with the
girl. I think I may truft him. I have a great
mind to venture it. It is a fhame to have him
duped by this old don. It muft not be. I'll
in and unfold—Ha!—Egad I have a thought
too, which, if my heir apparent can execute, I
fhall ftill lie concealed, and perhaps be rewarded on both fides.

 I have it,—'tis engendered, piping hot,
  And now, Sir knight, I'll match you with
   a plot.   [*Exit.*

Enter Sir William and Richard Wealthy.

R. Weal. Well, I fuppofe, by this time, you
are fatisfied what a fcoundrel you have brought
into the world, and are ready to finifh your fool-
ery.

Sir Will. Got to the cataftrophe, good brother.

R. Weal. Let us have it over then.

Sir Will. I have already alarmed all his
tradefmen. I fuppofe we fhall foon have him
here, with a legion of bailiffs and conftables.
——Oh, you have my will about you?

R. Weal. Yes, yes.

Sir Will. It is almoft time to produce it, or
read him the claufe that relates to his rejecting
your daughter. That will do his bufinefs.
But they come. I muft return to my character.

Enter Shift.

Shift. Sir, fir, we are all in the wrong box;
our fcheme is blown up; your fon has detected
          Loader

Loader and Tally, and is playing the very devil within.

Sir Will. Oh, the bunglers!

Shift. Now for it, youngster.

Enter Sir George, driving in Loader and another.

Sir Geo. Rafcals, robbers, that, like the locuft, mark the road you have taken, by the ruin and defolation you leave behind you.

Load. Sir George!

Sir Geo. And can youth, however cautious, be guarded againft fuch deep-laid, complicated villainy? Where are the reft of your diabolical crew? your auctioneer, ufurer, and——O, fir, are you here?——I am glad you have not eicaped us, however.

Sir Will. What de devil is de matter?

Sir Geo. Your birth, which I believe an impofition, preferves you, however, from the difcipline thofe rogues have received. A baron, a nobleman, a fharper! O fhame! It is enough to banifh all confidence from the world. On whofe faith can we rely, when thofe, whofe honour is held as facred as an oath, unmindful of their dignity, defcend to rival pick-pockets in their infamous arts. What are thefe [*pulls out dice*] pretty implements? The fruits of your leifure hours! They are dexteroufly done. You have a fine mechanical turn.—Dick, fecure the door.

Mrs. Cole, fpeaking as entering.

Mrs. Cole. Here I am, at laft. Well, and how is your honour, and the little gentlewoman?—Blefs me! what is the matter here?

Sir

Sir Geo. I am, madam, treating your friends with a cold collation, and you are opportunely come for your fhare. The little gentlewoman is fafe, and in much better hands than you de-figned her. Abominable hypocrite! who, tottering under the load of irreverent age and infamous difeafes, inflexibly proceeds in the practice of every vice, impioufly proftituting the moft facred inftitutions to the moft infernal purpofes.

Mrs Cole. I hope your honour——

Sir Geo. Take her away. As you have been fingular in your penitence, you ought to be diftinguifhed in your penance; which I promife you, fhall be moft publickly and plentifully beftowed. [*Exit Cole.*

Enter Dick.

Dick. The conftables, fir.

Sir Geo. Let them come in, that I may confign thefe gentlemen to their care.[*To Sir Will.*] Your letters of nobility you will produce in a court of juftice. Tho', if I read you right, you are one of thofe indigent, itinerant nobles of your own creation, which our reputation for hofpitality draws hither in fhoals, to the fhame of our underftanding, the imparing of our fortunes, and when you are trufted, the betraying of our defigns. Officers, do your duty.

Sir Will. Why, don't you know me?

Sir Geo. Juft as I gueffed. An impoftor. He has recovered the free ufe of his tongue already.

Sir Will. Nay, but George.

Sir

Sir Geo. Infolent familiarity! away with him.

Sir Will. Hold, hold, a moment. Brother Richard, fet this matter to rights.

R. Weal. Don't you know him?

Sir Geo. Know him! The very queftion is an affront.

R. Weal. Nay, I don't wonder at it. 'Tis your father, you fool.

Sir Geo. My father! Impoffible!

Sir Will. That may be, but 'tis true.

Sir Geo. My father alive! Thus let me greet the blefling.

Sir Will. Alive! Aye, and I believe I fhan't be in a hurry to die again.

Sir Geo. But, dear fir, the report of your death——and this difguife——to what——

Sir Will. Don't afk any queftions. Your uncle will tell you all. For my part, I am fick of the fcheme.

R. Weal. I told you what would come of your politicks.

Sir Will. You did fo. But if it had not been for thofe clumfy fcoundrels, the plot was as good a plot——O George, fuch difcoveries I have to make. Within I'll unravel the whole.

Sir Geo. Perhaps, fir, I may match 'em.

Shift. Sir.   *[Pulls him by the fleeve.*

Sir Geo. Never fear. It is impoffible, gentlemen, to determine your fate, till this matter is more fully explained; till when, keep 'em in fafe cuftody.——Do you know them, fir?

Sir Will. Yes, but that's more than they did me. I can cancel your debts there, and, I believe, prevail on thofe gentlemen to refund too ——But

———But you have been a fad profligate young
dog, George,

Sir Geo. I can't boaft of my goodnefs, fir ;
but I think I could produce you a proof, that
I am not fo totally deftitute of———

Sir Will. Aye ! Why then pr'ythee do.

Sir Geo. I have, fir, this day, refifted a temptation, that greater pretenders to morality
might have yielded to. But I will truft myfelf
no longer, and muft crave your interpofition
and protection.

Sir Will. To what?

Sir Geo. I will attend you with the explanation in an inftant.

Sir Will. Pr'ythee, Shift, what does he mean?

Shift. I believe I can guefs.

Sir Will. Let us have it.

Shift. I fuppofe the affair I overheard juft
now, a prodigious fine elegant girl, faith, that
difcarded by her family, for refufing to marry
her grandfather, fell into the hands of the ve-
nerable lady you faw, who being the kind cate-
rer for your fon's amufements, brought her hither for a purpofe obvious enough. But the
young gentleman, touched with her ftory, truth
and tears, was converted from the fpoiler of
her honour to the protector of her innocence.

Sir Will. Look'e there, brother, did not I tell
you that George was not fo bad at the bottom !

R. Weal. This does indeed atone for half the
———But they are here.

Enter Sir George and Lucy.

Sir Geo. Fear nothing, madam, you may
fafely rely on the———

Lucy.

Lucy. My father!

R. Weal. Lucy!

Lucy. O, fir, can you forgive your poor diftreft unhappy girl? You fcarce can guefs how hardly I've been ufed, fince my banifh-ment from your paternal roof. Want, pining want, anguifh and fhame, have been my con-ftant partners.

Sir Will. Brother!

Sir Geo. Sir!

Lucy. Father!

R. Weal. Rife, child, 'tis I muft afk thee forgivenefs. Canft thou forget the woes I've made thee fuffer? Come to my arms once more thou darling of my age.—What mifchief had my rafhnefs nearly compleated. Nephew, I fcarce can thank you, as I ought, but——

Sir Geo. I am richly paid, in being the happy inftrument——Yet, might I urge a wifh——

R. Weal. Name it.

Sir Geo. That you would forgive my follies of to-day; and, as I have been providentially the occafional guardian of your daughter's ho-nour, that you would beftow on me that right for life.

R. Weal. That muft depend on Lucy; her will, not mine, fhall now direct her choice— What fays your father?

Sir Will. Me, oh, I'll fhew you in an inftant. Give me your hands. There children, now you are joined, and the devil take him that wifhes to part you.

Sir Geo. I thank you for us both.

R. Weal. Happinefs attend you.

Sir

Sir Will. Now, brother, I hope you will allow me to be a good plotter. All this was brought to bear by my means.

Shift. With my affiftance, I hope you'll own, fir.

Sir Will. That's true, honeft Shift, and thou fhalt be richly rewarded; nay, George fhall be your friend too. This Shift is an ingenious fellow, let me tell you, fon.

Sir Geo. I am no ftranger to his abilities, fir. But, if you pleafe, we will retire. The various ftruggles of this fair fufferer require the foothing foftnefs of a fifter's love. And now, fir, I hope your fears for me are over ; for had I not this motive to reftrain my follies, yet I now know the town too well to be ever its bubble, and will take care to preferve, at leaft,

Some more eftate, and principles, and wit,
Than brokers, bawds, and gamefters fhall think
    fit.

SHIFT, *addreffing himfelf to* SIR GEORGE.

And what becomes of your poer fervant Shift?
Your father talks of lending me a lift——
A great man's promife, when his turn is ferved!
Capons on promifes would foon be ftarved:
No, on myfelf alone, I'll now rely:
'Gad I've a thriving traffic in my eye——
Near the mad manfions of Moorfields I'll bawl;
Friends, fathers, mothers, fifters, fons, and all,
Shut up your fhops, and liften to my call.
With labour, toil, all fecond means difpenfe,
And live a rent-charge upon Providence.
Prick up your ears; a ftory now I'll tell,
Which once a widow, and her child befel,
I knew the mother, and her daughter well;
Poor, it is true, they were; but never wanted,
For whatfoe'er they afk'd, was always granted.

One

One fatal day, the matron's truth was tried,
She wanted meat and drink, and fairly cried.
[*Child.*] Mother, you cry! [*Moth.*]Oh, child, I've got no
    bread.
[*Child.*] What matter that? Why Providence an't dead!
With reafon good, this truth the child might fay,
For there came in at noon, that very day,
Bread, greens, potatoes, and a leg of mutton,
A better fure a table ne'er was put on:
Aye, that might be, ye cry, with thofe poor fouls;
But we ne'er had a rafher for the coals.
And d'ye deferve it? How d'ye fpend your days?
In paftimes, prodigality, and plays!
Let's go fee Foote? ah, Foote's a precious limb!
Old-nick will foon a foot-ball make of him!
For foremoft rows in fide-boxes you fhove,
Think you to meet with fide-boxes above?
Where gigling girls, and powder'd fops may fit?⎤
No, you will all be cramm'd into the pit,   ⎬
And croud the houfe for Satan's benefit.   ⎦
Oh, what you fnivel! well, do fo no more,   ⎫
Drop, to atone, your money at the door,   ⎬
And, if I pleafe——I'll give it to the poor. ⎭

FINIS.

THE

L Y A R;

A

COMEDY

IN THREE ACTS:

WRITTEN BY THE LATE

SAMUEL FOOTE, Esq.

PERFORMED AT THE

THEATRES ROYAL

IN

DRURY LANE AND THE HAYMARKET.

LONDON:

PRINTED FOR W. LOWNDES, 38, BEDFORD STREET.

1805.

Price One Shilling and Sixpence.

Knight and Compton, Printers, Middle-street,
Cloth Fair.

PROLOGUE.

—

WHAT various revolutions in our art
Since Thefpis firft fold ballads in a cart!
By nature fram'd the witty war to wage,
And lay the deep foundations of the ftage,
From his own foil that bard his pictures drew;
The gaping crowd the mimic features knew,
And the broad jeft with fire electric flew.
Succeeding times, more polifh'd and refin'd,
To rigid rules the comic mufe confin'd.
Robb'd of the nat'ral freedom of her fong,
In artful meafures now fhe floats along.
No fprightly fallies roufe the flumb'ring pit:
Thalia, grown mere architect in wit,
To doors and ladders has confin'd her cares,
Convenient clofets, and a fnug back-ftairs;
'Twixt her and Satire has diffolv'd the league,
And jilted Humour to enjoy Intrigue.
To gain the fuff'rage of this polifh'd age,
We bring to-night a ftranger on the ftage:
His fire, De Vega; we confefs this truth,
Left you miftake him for a Britifh youth.
Severe the cenfure on my feeble pen,
Neglecting manners, that fhe copies men.
Thus, if I hum or hah, or name report,
'Tis Serjeant Splitcaufe from the Inns of Court ·
If at the age that ladies ceafe to dance,
To romp at Ranelagh, or read romance,
I draw a dowager inclin'd to man,
Or paint her rage for china or japan,
The true original is quickly known,
And Lady Squab proclaim'd throughout the town:
But in the following group let no man dare
To claim a limb, nay, not a fingle hair;
What gallant Briton can be fuch a fot
To own the child a Spaniard has begot?

DRAMATIS

DRAMATIS PERSONÆ.

	Drury Lane.	*Haymarket.*
	Men.	*Men.*
Sir James Elliot	Mr. De Camp	Mr. Bartley
Old Wilding	Mr. Powell	Mr. Denman
Young Wilding	Mr. Dwyer	Mr. Ellifton
Papillion	Mr. Wewitzer	Mr. Chapman
	Women.	*Women.*
Mifs Grantham	Mifs Mellon	Mrs. Harlowe
Mifs Godfrey	Mrs. Gunning	Mrs. Gaudry
Kitty	Mifs Tidfwell	Mrs. Cleland.

THE

THE LYAR.

ACT I.

SCENE—*Young Wilding's Lodgings.*
Young Wilding and Papillion difcovered.

Young Wilding.

AND am I now, Papillion, perfe&tly equipp'd?

Pap. Perfonne mieux. Nobody better.

Y. Wild. My figure?

Pap. Fait a peindre.

Y. Wild. My air?

Pap. Libre.

Y. Wild. My addrefs?

Pap. Parifiene.

Y. Wild. My hat fits eafily under my arm; not like the draggled tail of my tatter'd academical habit.

Pap. Ah, bien autre chofe.

Y. Wild. Why, then, adieu Alma Mater, and bien venue la ville de Londre; farewell to the fchools, and welcome the theatres; prefidents, pro&tors, fhort commons with long graces, muft now give place to plays, bagnios, long tavern bills with no graces at all.

Pap. Ah, bravo! bravo!

Y. Wild. Well, but my dear Papillion, you muft give me the chart du pays. This town is a new world to me: my provident papa, you know, would never fuffer me near the fmoke of London; and what can be his mo-

tive

tive for permitting me now, I can't readily conceive.

Pap. Ni moi.

Y. Wild. I fhall, however, take the liberty to conceal my arrival from him for a few days.

Pap. Vous avez raifon.

Y. Wild. Well, my Mentor, and how am I to manage? Direct my road: where muft I begin? But the debate is, I fuppofe, of confequence?

Pap. Vraiment.

Y. Wild. How long have you left Paris, Papillion?

Pap. Twelve, dirteen year.

Y. Wild. I can't compliment you upon your progrefs in Englifh.

Pap. The accent is difficult.

Y. Wild. But here you are at home.

Pap. C'eft vrai.

Y. Wild. No ftranger to fafhionable places.

Pap. Au fait!

Y. Wild. Acquainted with the fafhionable figures of both fexes.

Pap. Sans doute.

Y. Wild. Well, then, open your lecture:—and, d'ye hear, Papillion, as you have the honour to be promoted from the mortifying condition of an humble valet to the important charge of a private tutor, let us difcard all diftance between us. See me ready to flake my thirft at your fountain of knowledge, my Magnus Apollo.

Pap. Here, then, I difclofe my Helicon to my poetical pupil.

Y. Wild. Hey, Papillion?

Pap. Sir?

Y. Wild. What is this? Why, you speak English!

Pap. Without doubt.

Y. Wild. But, like a native!

Pap. To be sure.

Y. Wild. And what am I to conclude from all this?

Pap. Logically thus, Sir: whoever speaks pure English is an Englishman. I speak pure English; ergo, I am an Englishman. There's a categorical syllogism for you, major, minor, and consequence. What! do you think, Sir, that, whilst you was busy at Oxford, I was idle? No, no, no.

Y. Wild. Well, Sir, but, notwithstanding your pleasantry, I must have this matter explain'd.

Pap. So you shall, my good Sir; but don't be in such a hurry. You can't suppose I would give you the key, unless I meant you should open the door.

Y. Wild. Why, then, prythee unlock it.

Pap. Immediately. But, by way of entering upon my post as preceptor, suffer me first to give you a hint. You must not expect, Sir, to find here, as at Oxford, men appearing in their real characters: every body there, Sir, knows that Dr. Muffy is a fellow of Maudlin, and Tom Trifle a student of Christ-church; but this town is one great comedy, in which not only the principles, but frequently the persons, are feign'd.

Y. Wild. A useful observation.

Pap. Why now, Sir, at the first coffee-house I shall enter you, you will perhaps meet a man, from whose decent sable dress, placid

cid countenance, infinuating behaviour, fhort
fword, with the waiter's civil addition of *A
difh of coffee for Dr. Julap*, you would fuppofe him to be a phyfician.

Y. Wild. Well?

Pap. Does not know diafcordium from di-
achylon.   An abfolute French fpy, concealed
under the fhelter of a huge medicinal perri-
wig.

Y. Wild. Indeed !

Pap. A martial figure, too, it is odds but
you will encounter, from whofe fcars, title,
drefs, and addrefs, you would fuppofe to have
had a fhare in every action fince the peace of
the Pyrenees ; runner to a gaming table, and
bully to a bawdy houfe.   Battles, to be fure,
he has been in—with the watch ; and frequently a prifoner, too, in the round-houfe.

Y. Wild. Amazing !

Pap. In fhort, Sir, you will meet with lawyers who practife fmuggling, and merchants
who trade upon Hounflow-heath ; reverend
atheifts, right honourable fharpers, and Frenchmen from the county of York.

Y. Wild. In the laft lift I prefume you roll.

Pap. Juft my fituation.

Y. Wild. And pray, Sir, what may be your
motive for this whimfical transformation ?

Pap. A very harmlefs one, I promife you.
I would only avail myfelf at the expence of
folly and prejudice.

Y. Wild. As how?

Pap. Why, Sir——But, to be better underftood, I believe it will be neceffary to
give you a fhort fketch of the principal inci-
dents of my life.

                              Y. Wild.

Y. Wild. Prythee do.

Pap. Why then, you are to know, Sir, that my former fituation has been rather above my prefent condition, having once fuftained the dignity of fub-preceptor to one of thofe cheap rural academies with which our county of York is fo plentifully ftock'd.

Y. Wild. But to the point: Why this dif-guife? why renounce your country?

Pap. There, Sir, you make a little miftake; it was my country that renounced me.

Y. Wild. Explain.

Pap. In an inftant: upon quitting the fchool, and firft coming to town, I got re-commended to the compiler of the Monthly Review.

Y. Wild. What, an author too?

Pap. Oh, a voluminous one. The whole region of the belles lettres fell under my in-fpection; phyfic, divinity, and the mathematics, my miftrefs managed herfelf. There, Sir, like another Ariftarch, I dealt out fame and dam-nation at pleafure. In obedience to the ca-price and commands of my mafter, I have con-demn'd books I never read; and applauded the fidelity of a tranflation, without under-ftanding one fyllable of the original.

Y. Wild. Ah! why, I thought acutenefs of difcernment and depth of knowledge were neceffary to accomplifh a critic.

Pap. Yes, Sir; but not a monthly one. Our method was very concife. We copy the title-page of a new book; we never go any further. If we are ordered to praife it, we have at hand about ten words, which, fcat-ter'd through as many periods, effectually does

the

the bufinefs; as, " laudable defign, happy ar-
" rangement, fpirited language, nervous fen-
" timent, elevation of thought, conclufive ar-
" gument." If we are to decry, then we have,
" unconnected, flat, falfe, illiberal, ftricture,
" reprehenfible, unnatural." And thus, Sir,
we pepper the author, and foon rid our hands
of his work.

Y. Wild. A fhort recipe!

Pap And yet, Sir, you have all the materials
that are neceffary? Thefe are the arms with
which we engage authors of every kind. To
us all fubjects are equal; plays or fermons,
poetry or politics, mufic or midwifery, it is
the fame thing.

Y. Wild. How came you to refign this eafy
employment?

Pap. It would not anfwer. Notwithftanding what we fay, people will judge for themfelves: our work hung upon hand, and all
I could get from the Publifher was four fhil-
lings a-week and my fmall beer. Poor pittance!

Y. Wild. Poor, indeed.

Pap. Oh, half ftarved me.

Y. Wild. What was your next change?

Pap. I was mightily puzzled to choofe.
Some would have me turn player, and others
methodift preacher; but as I had no money to
build me a tabernacle, I did not think it
could anfwer; and as to player,——whatever
might happen to me, I was determined
not to bring a difgrace upon my family; and
fo I refolved to turn footman.

Y. Wild. Wifely refolved.

Pap. Yes, Sir, but not fo eafily executed.

Y. Wild.

Y. Wild. No!

Pap. Oh no, Sir. Many a weary ſtep have I taken after a place. Here I was too old, there I was too young; here the laſt livery was too big, there it was too little; here I was aukward, there I was knowing: Madam diſliked me at this houſe, her ladyſhip's woman at the next: ſo that I was as much puzzled to find out a place, as the great Cynic philoſopher to diſ-cover a man. In ſhort I was quite in a ſtate of deſpair, when chance threw an old friend in my way that quite retrieved my affairs.

Y. Wild. Pray, who might he be?

Pap. A little bit of a Swiſs genius, who had been French uſher with me at the ſame ſchool in the country. I open'd my melancholy ſtory to him over threepenny-worth of beef-a-la-mode, in a cellar in St. Ann's. My little fo-reign friend purſed up his lanthorn jaws, and, with a ſhrug of contempt, " Ah, maitre Jean, vous n'avez pas la politique; you have no fineſſe: to thrive here, you muſt ſtudy the folly of your own country." " How, Monſieur?" " Taiſez vous: keep a your tongue. Au-trefois I teach you ſpeak French, now I teach-a you to forget Engliſh. Go vid me to my lodgement, I vil give you proper dreſs: den go preſent yourſelf to de ſame hotels, de very ſame houſe; you will find all de doors dat was ſhut in your face as footman Anglois, vil fly open demſelves to a French valet de chambre."

Y. Wild. Well, Papillion?

Pap. Gad, Sir, I thought it was but an ho-neſt artifice, ſo I determined to follow my friend's advice.

Y. Wild.

Y. Wild. Did it fucceed?

Pap. Better than expectation. My tawny face, long quieu, and broken Englifh, was a paffe-partout. Befides, when I am out of place, this difguife procures me many refources.

Y. Wild. As how?

Pap. Why, at a pinch, Sir, I am either a teacher of tongues, a frifeur, a dentift, or a dancing-mafter: thefe, Sir, are hereditary profeffions to Frenchmen. But now, Sir, to the point: As you were pleafed to be fo candid with me, I was determined to have no referve with you. You have ftudied books, I have ftudied men; you want advice, and I have fome at your fervice.

Y. Wild. Well, I'll be your cuftomer.

Pap. But guard my fecret. If I fhould be fo unfortunate as to lofe your place, don't fhut me out from every other.

Y. Wild. You may rely upon me.

Pap. In a few years I fhall be in a condition to retire from bufinefs; but whether I fhall fettle at my family-feat, or pafs over to the continent, is as yet undetermined. Perhaps, in gratitude to the country, I may purchafe a marquifate near Paris, and fpend the money I have got by their means generoufly amongft them.

Y. Wild. A grateful intention. But let us fally. Where do we open?

Pap. Let us fee—one o'clock—it is a fine day: the Mall will be crowded.

Y. Wild. Allons.

Pap. But don't ftare, Sir: furvey every thing with an air of habit and indifference.

Y. Wild. Never fear.

Pap.

Pap. But I would, Sir, crave a moment's audience, upon a fubject that may prove very material to you.

Y. Wild. Proceed.

Pap. You will pardon my prefumption; but you have, my good mafter, one little foible that I could wifh you to correct.

Y. Wild. What is it?

Pap. And yet it is a pity, too; you do it fo very well.

Y. Wild. Prythee be plain.

Pap. You have, Sir, a lively imagination, with a moft happy turn for invention.

Y. Wild. Well.

Pap. But now and then in your narratives you are hurried, by a flow of fpirits, to border upon the improbable; a little given to the marvellous.

Y. Wild. I underftand you: what, I am fomewhat fubject to lying?

Pap. Oh, pardon me, Sir; I don't fay that; no, no: only a little apt to embellifh; that's all. To be fure it is a fine gift; that there is no difputing: but men in general are fo ftupid, fo rigoroufly attach'd to matter of fact—And yet this talent of yours is the very foul and fpirit of poetry; and why it fhould not be the fame in profe, I can't for my life determine.

Y. Wild. You would advife me, then, not to be quite fo poetical in my profe?

Pap. Why, Sir, if you would defcend a little to the grovelling comprehenfion of the million, I think it would be as well.

Y. Wild. I'll think of it.

Pap. Befides, Sir, in this town, people are more fmoky and fufpicious. Oxford, you know, is the feat of the mufes; and a man is

naturally

naturally permitted more ornament and garni-
ture to his converfation than they will allow in
this latitude.

Y. Wild. I believe you are right.   But we
fhall be late.   D'ye hear me, Papillion : if at
any time you find me too poetical, give me a
hint ; your advice fhan't be thrown away.

[*Exit.*

Pap. I wifh it mayn't ; but the difeafe is
too rooted to be quickly removed.   Lord, how
I have fweat for him ! yet he is as unembarraff-
ed, eafy, and fluent, all the time, as if he
really believed what he faid.   Well, to be
fure, he is a great mafter : it is a thoufand pities his genius could not be converted to fome
public fervice.   I think the government fhould
employ him to anfwer the Moniteur.   I'll be
hang'd if he is not too many for Monfieur Tal-
leyrand, at his own weapons.   [*Exit.*

SCENE—*The Park.*

*Enter Mifs Grantham, Mifs Godfrey, and
Servant.*

M. Gr. John, let the chariot go round to
Spring-gardens ; for your miftrefs and I fhall
call at Lady Bab's, Mifs Arabella Allnight's,
the Countefs of Crumple's, and the tall man's,
this morning.   My dear Mifs Godfrey, what
trouble I have had to get you out !   Why,
child, you are as tedious as a long morning.—
Do you know, now, that of all places of public rendezvous I honour the Park ?—forty
thoufand million of times preferable to the
play houfe !   Don't you think fo, my dear ?

M. God. They are both well in their way.

M. Gr. Way ! why, the purpofe of both is
the

the fame ; to meet company, isn't it ? What, d'ye think I go there for the plays, or come here for the trees?—ha, ha!—well, that is well enough. But, O Gemini! I beg a million of pardons; you are a prude, and have no relifh for the little innocent liberties with which a fine woman may indulge herfelf in public.

M. God. Liberties in public !

M. Gr. Yes, child; fuch as encoring a fong at an opera, interrupting a play in a critical fcene of diftrefs, hallooing to a pretty fellow 'crofs the Mall as loud as if you were calling a coach. Why, do you know, now, my dear, that by a lucky ftroke in drefs, and a few high airs of my own making, I have had the good fortune to be gazed at and followed by as great a crowd, on a Sunday, as if I was the Turkifh ambaffador?

M. God. The good fortune, Ma'am ! Surely the wifh of every decent woman is to be un-noticed in public.

M. Gr. Decent ! oh, my dear queer crea-ture, what a phrafe have you found out for a woman of fafhion ! Decency is, child, a mere bourgeois, plebeian quality, and fit only for thofe who pay court to the world, and not for us to whom the world pays court. Upon my word, you muft enlarge your ideas. You are a fine girl, and we muft not have you loft: I'll undertake you myfelf. But, as I was faying —Pray, my dear, what was I faying ?

M. God. I profefs I don't recollect.

M. Gr. Hey!——Oh, ah ! the Park. One great reafon for my loving the Park is, that one has fo many opportunities of creating con-nections.

M. God.

M. God. Ma'am!

M. Gr. Nay, don't look grave. Why, do you know that all my male friendſhips are form'd in this place?

M. God. It is an odd ſpot: but you muſt pardon me if I doubt the poſſibility.

M. Gr. Oh, I will convince you in a moment; for here ſeems to be coming a good ſmart figure that I don't recollect. I will throw out a lure.

M. God. Nay, for Heaven's ſake!

M. Gr. I am determined, child: that is—

M. God. You will excuſe my withdrawing.

M. Gr. Oh, pleaſe yourſelf, my dear.

[*Exit Miſs Godfrey.*

Enter Young Wilding with Papillion.

Y. Wild. Your Ladyſhip's handkerchief, Ma'am.

M. Gr. I am, Sir, concern'd at the trouble—

Y. Wild. A moſt happy incident for me, Madam; as chance has given me an honour, in one lucky minute, that the moſt diligent attention has not been able to procure for me in the whole tedious round of a revolving year.

M. Gr. Is this meant to me, Sir?

Y. Wild. To whom elſe, Madam? Surely, you muſt have mark'd my reſpectful aſſiduity, my uninterrupted attendance: to plays, operas, balls, routs, and ridottos, I have purſued you like your ſhadow; I have beſieged your door for a glimpſe of your exit and entrance, like a diſtreſſed creditor, who has no arms againſt privilege but perſeverance.

Pap. So, now he is in for it; ſtop him who can.

Y. Wild.

Y. Wild. In fhort, Madam, ever finçe I quitted America, which I take now to be about a year, I have as faithfully guarded the live-long night your ladyfhip's portal, as a centinel the powder magazine in a fortified city.

Pap. Quitted America! well pull'd.

M. Gr. You have ferved in America, then?

Y. Wild. Full four years, Ma'am: and during that whole time, not a fingle action of confequence but I had an opportunity to fignalize myfelf; and I think I may, without vanity, affirm, I did not mifs the occafion.— You have heard of Quebec, I prefume?

Pap. What the deuce is he driving at now?

Y. Wild. The project to furprife that place was thought a happy expedient, and the firft mounting the breach a gallant exploit. There, indeed, the whole army did me juftice.

M. Gr. I have heard the honour of that conqueft attributed to another name.

Y. Wild. The mere taking the town, Ma'am. But that's a trifle: fieges, now-a-days, are reduced to certainties. It is amazing how minutely exact we, who know the bufinefs, are at calculation. For inftance, now, we will fuppofe the commander in chief, addreffing himfelf to me, was to fay, " Colonel, I want to reduce that fortrefs; what will be the expence?"—" Why, pleafe your highnefs, the reduction of that fortrefs will coft you one thoufand and two lives, fixty-nine legs, ditto arms, fourfcore fractures, with about twenty dozen of flefh wounds."

M. Gr. And you fhould be near the mark?

Y. Wild. To an odd joint, Ma'am. But,

B   Madam,

Madam, it is not to the French alone that my feats are confined: Cherokees, Catabaws, with all the Aws and Eees of the continent, have felt the force of my arms.

Pap. This is too much, Sir.

Y. Wild. Hands off!—Nor am I lefs adroit at a treaty, Madam, than terrible in battle. To me we owe the friendfhip of the Five Nations; and I had the firft honour of fmoking the pipe of peace with the Little Carpenter.

M. Gr. And fo young!

Y. Wild. This gentleman, though a Frenchman and an enemy, I had the fortune to deliver from the Mohawks, whofe prifoner he had been for nine years. He gives a moft entertaining account of their laws and cuftoms: he fhall prefent you with the wampum belt and a fcalping-knife. Will you permit him, Madam, juft to give you a tafte of the military-dance, with a fhort fpecimen of their war-hoop?

Pap. For Heaven's fake!

M. Gr. The place is too public.

Y. Wild. In fhort, Madam, after having gathered as many laurels abroad as would garnifh a Gothic cathedral at Chriftmas, I return'd to reap the harveft of the well-fought field. Here it was my good fortune to encounter you. Then was the victor vanquifhed: what the enemy could never accomplifh, your eyes in an inftant atchieved; prouder to ferve here than command in chief elfewhere; and more glorious in wearing your chains, than in triumphing over the vanquifh'd world.

M. Gr. I have got here a moft heroical lover. But I fee Sir James Elliot coming, and
must

muft difmifs him.——[*Afide.*]——Well, Sir, I accept the tendre of your paffion, and may find a time to renew our acquaintance; at prefent it is neceffary we fhould feparate.

Y. Wild. " Slave to your will, I live but to obey you." But, may I be indulged with the knowledge of your refidence?

M. Gr. Sir?

Y. Wild. Your place of abode.

M. Gr. Oh, Sir, you can't want to be acquainted with that; you have a whole year ftood centinel at my ladyfhip's portal.

Y. Wild. Madam, I—I—I——.

M. Gr. Oh, Sir, your fervant. Ha, ha, ha! What, you are caught? ha, ha, ha! Well, he has a moft intrepid affurance. Adieu, my Mars. Ha, ha, ha! [*Exit.*

Pap. That laft was an unlucky queftion, Sir.

Y. Wild. A little mal-a-propos, I muft confefs.

Pap. A man fhould have a good memory who deals much in this poetical profe.

Y. Wild. Poh! I'll foon re-eftablifh my credit. But I muft know who this girl is. Hark ye, Papillion; could not you contrive to pump out of her footman—I fee there he ftands—the name of his miftrefs?

Pap. I will try. [*Exit.*
[*Wilding retires to the back of the ftage.*

Enter Sir James Elliot and Servant.

Sir Ja. Mufic and an entertainment?

Ser. Yes, Sir.

Sir Ja. Laft night, upon the water!

Ser. Upon the water, laft night.

Sir Ja. Who gave it?

Ser. That, Sir, I can't fay.

To

To them Wilding.

Y. Wild. Sir James Elliot, your moſt devoted.

Sir Ja. Ah, my dear Wilding! you are welcome to town.

Y. Wild. You will pardon my impatience; I interrupted you; you ſeem'd upon an intereſting ſubjeƈt?

Sir Ja. Oh, an affair of gallantry.

Y. Wild. Of what kind?

Sir Ja. A young lady regaled laſt night by her lover on the Thames.

Y. Wild. As how?

Sir Ja. A band of muſic in boats.

Y. Wild. Were they good performers?

Sir Ja. The beſt. Then conduƈted to Marblehall, where ſhe found a magnificent collation.

Y. Wild. Well order'd?

Sir Ja. With elegance. After ſupper a ball; and, to conclude the night, a firework.

Y. Wild. Was the laſt well deſign'd?

Sir Ja Superb.

Y. Wild. And happily executed?

Sir Ja. Not a ſingle faux pas.

Y. Wild. And you don't know who gave it?

Sir Ja. I can't even gueſs.

Y. Wild. Ha, ha, ha!

Sir Ja. Why do you laugh?

Y. Wild. Ha, ha, ha! It was me.

Sir Ja. You!

Pap. You, Sir!

Y. Wild. Moi——me.

Pap. So, ſo, ſo; he's enter'd again.

Sir Ja. Why, you are fortunate to find a miſtreſs in ſo ſhort a ſpace of time.

Y. Wild.

Y. Wild. Short! why, man, I have been in London thefe fix weeks.

Pap. O Lord, O Lord!

Y. Wild. It is true, not caring to encounter my father, I have rarely ventured out but at nights.

Pap. I can hold no longer. Dear Sir——

Y. Wild. Peace, puppy.

Pap. A curb to your poetical vein.

Y. Wild. I fhall curb your impertinence——But fince the ftory is got abroad, I will, my dear friend, treat you with all the particulars.

Sir Ja. I fhall hear it with pleafure——This is a lucky adventure: but he muft not know he is my rival. [*Afide.*

Y. Wild. Why, Sir, between fix and feven my goddefs embarked at Somerfet-ftairs, in one of the companies barges, gilt and hung with damafk, exprefsly for the occafion.

Pap. Mercy on us!

Y. Wild. At the cabin-door fhe was ac-cofted by a beautiful boy, who, in the garb of a Cupid, paid her fome compliments in verfe of my own compofing. The conceits were pretty; allufions to Venus and the fea—the lady and the Thames—no great matter; but, however, well timed, and, what was better, well taken.

Sir Ja. Doubtlefs.

Pap. At what a rate he runs!

Y. Wild. As foon as we had gained the centre of the river, two boats, full of trumpets, French-horns, and other martial mufic, ftruck up their fprightly ftrains from the Surry fide, which were echoed by a fuitable number of lutes, flutes, and hautboys, from the oppofite fhore.

shore. In this state, the oars keeping time, we majestically sail'd along, till the arches of the New Bridge gave a pause, and an opportunity for an elegant dessert in Dresden China, by Robinson. Here the repast closed with a few favourite airs from Eliza, Tenducci, and the Mattei.

Pap. Mercy on us!

Y. Wild. Opposite Lambeth I had prepared a naval engagement, in which Boscawen's victory over the French was repeated: the action was conducted by one of the commanders on that expedition, and not a single incident omitted.

Sir Ja. Surely you exaggerate a little.

Pap. Yes, yes, this battle will sink him.

Y. Wild. True to the letter, upon my honour. I shan't trouble you with a repetition of our collation, ball, feu d'artifice, with the thousand little incidental amusements that chance or design produced: it is enough to know, that all that could flatter the senses, fire the imagination, or gratify the expectation, was there produced in a lavish abundance.

Sir Ja. The sacrifice was, I presume, grateful to your deity.

Y. Wild. Upon that subject you must pardon my silence.

Pap. Modest creature!

Sir Ja. I wish you joy of your success—For the present you will excuse me.

Y. Wild. Nay, but stay and hear the conclusion.

Sir Ja. For that I shall seize another occasion.   [*Exit.*

Pap. Nobly perform'd, Sir.

                                                    Y. Wild.

Y. Wild. Yes, I think happily hit off.

Pap. May I take the liberty to offer one queftion?

Y. Wild. Freely.

Pap. Pray, Sir, are you often vifited with thefe waking dreams?

Y. Wild. Dreams! what doft mean by dreams?

Pap. Thofe ornamental reveries, thofe frolics of fancy, which, in the judgment of the vulgar, would be deem'd abfolute fiams.

Y. Wild. Why, Papillion, you have but a poor, narrow, circumfcribed genius.

Pap. I muft own, Sir, I have not fublimity fufficient to relifh the full fire of your Pindaric mufe.

Y. Wild. No; a plebeian foul! But I will animate thy clay: mark my example, follow my fteps, and in time thou may'ft rival thy mafter.

Pap. Never, never, Sir; I have not talents to fight battles without blows, and give feafts that don't coft me a farthing—Befides, Sir, to what purpofe are all thefe embellifhments? Why tell the lady you have been in London a year?

Y. Wild. The better to plead the length, and confequently the ftrength, of my paffion.

Pap. But why, Sir, a foldier?

Y. Wild. How little thou know'ft of the fex! What, I fuppofe thou would'ft have me attack them in mood and figure, by a pedantic claffical quotation, or a pompous parade of jargon from the fchools. What, do'ft think that women are to be got like degrees?

Pap. Nay, Sir——

Y. Wild.

Y. Wild. No, no; the fçavoir vivre is the
fcience for them ; the man of war is their man:
they muft be taken, like towns, by lines of
approach, counter-fcarps, angles, trenches,
coehorns, and covert-ways ; then enter fword-
in-hand, pell-mell! Oh, how they melt at
the Gothic names of General Swapinback,
Count Roufomoufky, Prince Montecuculi, and
Marfhal Fuftenburg! Men may fay what they
will of their Ovid, their Petrarch, and their
Waller; but I'll undertake to do more bufinefs by the fingle aid of the London Gazette,
than by all the fighing, dying, crying crotchets,
that the whole race of rhymers have ever produced.

Pap. Very well, Sir; this is all very lively :
but remember the travelling pitcher. If you
don't one time or other, under favour, lie
yourfelf into fome confounded fcrape, I will
be content to be hanged.

Y. Wild. Do you think fo, Papillion ?—And
whenever that happens, if I don't lie myfelf
out of it again, why then I will be content to
be crucified. And fo, along after the lady—
[*Stops fhort, going out.*] Zounds, here comes
my father! I muft fly. Watch him, Papillion, and bring me word to Cardigan.

[*Exeunt feparately.*

ACT II.

SCENE—*A Room in a Tavern.*

Young Wilding and Papillion rifing from table.

Young Wilding.

GAD, I had like to have run into the old gentleman's mouth.

Pap. It is pretty near the fame thing, for I faw him join Sir James Elliot: fo your arrival is no longer a fecret.

Y. Wild. Why then I muft lofe my plea-fure, and you your preferment: I muft fubmit to the dull decency of a fober family, and you to the cuftomary duties of brufhing and pow-dering. But I was fo flutter'd at meeting my father, that I forgot the fair: prythee, who is fhe?

Pap. There were two.

Y. Wild. That I faw.

Pap. From her footman I learnt her name was Godfrey.

Y. Wild. And her fortune?

Pap. Immenfe.

Y. Wild. Single, I hope?

Pap. Certainly.

Y. Wild. Then will I have her.

Pap. What! whether fhe will or no?

Y. Wild. Yes.

Pap. How will you manage that?

Y. Wild. By making it impoffible for her to marry any one elfe.

Pap. I don't underftand you, Sir.

Y. Wild.

Y. Wild. Oh! I fhall only have recourfe to that talent you fo mightily admire. You will fee, by the calculation of a few anecdotes, how foon I will get rid of my rivals.

Pap. At the expence of the lady's reputation, perhaps.

Y. Wild. That will be as it happens.

Pap. And have you no qualms, Sir?

Y. Wild. Why, where's the injury?

Pap. No injury to ruin her fame!

Y. Wild. I will reftore it to her again.

Pap. How?

Y. Wild. Turn tinker, and mend it my el.

Pap. Which way?

Y. Wild. The old way; folder it by marriage: that, you know, is the modern falve for every fore.

Enter Waiter.

Waiter. An elderly gentleman to enquire for Mr. Wilding.

Y. Wild. For me! what fort of a being is it?

Wait. Being, Sir!

Y. Wild. Ay; how is he drefs'd?

Wait. In a tye-wig and fnuff-colour'd coat.

Pap. Zooks, Sir, it is your father.

Y. Wild. Show him up.   [*Exit Waiter.*

Pap. And what muft I do?

Y. Wild. Recover your broken Englifh, but preferve your rank; i have a reafon for it.

Enter Old Wilding.

O. Wild. Your fervant, Sir: you are welcome to town.

Y. Wild. You have juft prevented me, Sir: I was preparing to pay my duty to you.

O. Wild.

O. Wild. If you thought it a duty, you should, I think, have fooner difcharged it.

Y. Wild. Sir!

O. Wild. Was it quite fo decent, Jack, to be fix weeks in town, and conceal yourfelf only from me?

Y. Wild. Six weeks! I have fcarce been fix hours.

O. Wild. Come, come; I am better informed.

Y. Wild. Indeed, Sir, you are impos'd upon. This gentleman (whom firft give me leave to have the honour of introducing to you), this, Sir, is the Marquis de Chatteau Brilliant, of an ancient houfe in Brittany; who, travelling through England, chofe to make Oxford for fome time the place of his refidence, where I had the happinefs of his acquaintance.

O. Wild. Does he fpeak Englifh?

Y. Wild. Not fluently, but underftands it perfectly.

Pap. Pray, Sir——

O. Wild. Any fervices, Sir, that I can render you here, you may readily command.

Pap. Beaucoup d'honneur.

Y. Wild. This gentleman, I fay, Sir, whofe quality and country are fufficient fecurities for his veracity, will affure you, that yefterday we left Oxford together.

O. Wild. Indeed!

Pap. C'eft vrai.

O. Wild. This is amazing. I was at the fame time inform'd of another circumftance too, that, I confefs, made me a little uneafy,

as

as it interfered with a favourite fcheme of my own.

Y. Wild. What could that be, pray, Sir?

O. Wild. That you had conceived a violent affection for a fair lady.

Y. Wild. Sir!

O. Wild. And had given her very gallant and very expenfive proofs of your paffion.

Y. Wild. Me, Sir!

O. Wild. Particularly laft night; mufic, collations, balls, and fireworks.

Y. Wild. Monfieur le Marquis!—And pray, Sir, who could tell you all this?

O. Wild. An old friend of yours.

Y. Wild. His name, if you pleafe?

O. Wild. Sir James Elliot.

Y. Wild. Yes; I thought he was the man.

O. Wild. Your reafon.

Y. Wild. Why, Sir, though Sir James Elliot has a great many good qualities, and is upon the whole a valuable man, yet he has one fault which has long determined me to drop his acquaintance.

O. Wild. What may that be?

Y. Wild. Why you can't, Sir, be a ftranger to his prodigious fkill in the traveller's talent?

O. Wild. How!

Y. Wild. Oh, notorious to a proverb. His friends, who are tender of his fame, glofs over his foible, by calling him an agreeable novelift; and fo he is with a vengeance. Why, he will tell ye more lies in an hour, than all the circulating libraries put together will publifh in a year.

O. Wild. Indeed!

Y. Wild. Oh, he is the modern Mandeville

at

at Oxford : he was always diftinguifhed by the facetious appellation of the Bouncer.

O. Wild. Amazing !

Y. Wild. Lord, Sir, he is fo well underftood in his own country, that, at the laft Hereford affize, a caufe, as clear as the fun, was abfolutely thrown away by his being merely mentioned as a witnefs.

O. Wild. A ftrange turn!

Y. Wild. Unaccountable. But there, I think, they went a little too far; for if it had come to an oath, I don't think he would have bounced neither ; but in common occurrences, there is no repeating after him. Indeed, my great reafon for dropping him was, that my credit began to be a little fufpefted too.

Pap. Poor gentleman!

O. Wild. Why, I never heard this of him.

Y. Wild. That may be ; but can there be a ftronger proof of his practice than the flam he has been telling you of fireworks, and the Lord-knows-what ? And I dare fwear, Sir, he was very fluent and florid in his defcription.

O. Wild. Extremely.

Y. Wild. Yes, that is juft his way ; and not a fyllable of truth from the beginning to the ending, Marquis !

Pap. Oh, dat is all a fiftion, upon mine honour.

Y. Wild. You fee, Sir, Sir——

O. Wild. Clearly. I really can't help pitying the poor man. I have heard of people, who, by long habit, become a kind of conftitutional lyars.

Y. Wild.

Y. Wild. Your obfervation is juft; that is exactly his cafe.

Pap. I'm fure it is yours.   [*Afide.*

O. Wild. Well, Sir, I fuppofe we fhall fee you this evening.

Y. Wild. The Marquis has an appointment with fome of his countrymen, which I have promifed to attend: befides, Sir, as he is an entire ftranger in town, he may want my little fervices.

O. Wild. Where can I fee you in about an hour? I have a fhort vifit to make, in which you are deeply concern'd.

Y. Wild. I fhall attend your commands; but where?

O. Wild. Why, here. Marquis, I am your obedient fervant.

Pap. Votre ferviteur tres humble.

              [*Exit Old Wilding.*

Y. Wild. So, Papillion, that difficulty is dif-patch'd. I think I am even with Sir James for his tattling.

Pap. Moft ingenioufly managed:—but are not you afraid of the confequence?

Y. Wild. I don't comprehend you.

Pap. A future explanation between the parties.

Y. Wild. That may embarrafs: but the day is diftant. I warrant I will bring myfelf off.

Pap. It is in vain for me to advife.

Y. Wild. Why, to fay truth, I do begin to find my fyftem attended with danger. Give me your hand, Papillion—I will reform.

Pap. Ah, Sir!

Y. Wild. I pofitively will. Why, this prac-tice may in time deftroy my credit.

              Pap.

Pap. That is pretty well done already.[*Aside.*] —Ay, think of that, Sir.

Y. Wild. Well, if I don't turn out the meereft dull matter-of-fact fellow—But, Papillion, I muft fcribble a billet to my new flame. I think her name is——

Pap. Godfrey; her father, an India governor fhut up in the ftrong room at Calcutta, left her all his wealth : fhe lives near Mifs Grantham, by Grofvenor fquare.

Y. Wild. A governor!—Oh ho!—Bufhels of rupees and pecks of pagodas, I reckon. Well, I long to be rummaging. But the old gentleman will foon return : I will haften to finifh my letter. But, Papillion, what could my father mean by a vifit in which I am deeply concern'd ?

Pap. I can't guefs.

Y. Wild. I fhall know prefently. To Mifs Godfrey, formerly of Calcutta, now refiding in Grofvenor-fquare. Papillion, I won't tell her a word of a lie.

Pap. You won't, Sir?

Y. Wild. No; it would be ungenerous to deceive a lady. No ; I will be open, candid, and fincere.

Pap. And if you are, it will be the firft time. [*Exeunt.*

SCENE—*An Apartment in Mifs Grantham's Houfe.*

Enter Mifs Grantham and Mifs Godfrey.

M. God. And you really like this gallant fpark?

M. Gr. Prodigioufly! Oh, I'm quite in love with his affurance! I wonder who he is : he

can't

can't have been long in town. A young fellow of his eafy impudence muft have foon
made his way into the beft of company.

M. God. By way of amufement he may
prove no difagreeable acquaintance; but you
can't furely have any ferious defigns upon
him?

M. Gr. Indeed but I have.

M. God. And poor Sir James Elliot is to be
difcarded at once?

M. Gr. Oh, no!

M. God. What is your intention in regard
to him?

M. Gr. Hey?—I can't tell you. Perhaps,
if I don't like this new man better, I may marry him.

M. God. Thou art a ftrange giddy girl.

M. Gr. Quite the reverfe! a perfect pattern
of prudence; why, would you have me lefs
careful of my perfon than my purfe?

M. God. My dear?

M. Gr. Why, I fay, child, my fortune being in money, I have fome in India-bonds,
fome in the bank, fome on this loan, fome on
the other! fo that if one fund fails, I have
a fure refource in the reft.

M. God. Very true.

M. Gr. Well, my dear, juft fo I manage my
love affairs: if I fhould not like this man—if
he fhould not like me—if we fhould quarrel—
if, if—or in fhort, if any of the ifs fhould happen which you know break engagements every day, why, by this means I fhall be never at
a lofs.

M. God. Quite provident. Well, and pray
on

on how many different fecurities have you at prefent plac'd out your love ?

M. Gr. Three : the fober Sir James Elliot ; the new America-man; and this morning I expect a formal propofal from an old friend of my father.

M. God. Mr. Wilding ?

M. Gr. Yes; but I don't reckon much upon him: for you know, my dear, what can I do with an aukward, raw, college cub! Though upon fecond thoughts, that mayn't be too bad neither; for as I muft have the fa-fhioning of him, he may be eafily moulded to one's mind.

Enter a Servant.

Ser. Mr. Wilding, Madam.

M. Gr. Show him in. [*Exit Servant.*]— You need not go, my dear; we have no par-ticular bufinefs.

M. God. I wonder, now, what fhe calls particular bufinefs.

Enter Old Wilding.

O. Wild. Ladies, your fervant. I wait up-on you, Madam, with a requeft from my fon, that he may be permitted the honour of kiffing your hand.

M. Gr. Your fon is in town then ?

O. Wild. He came laft night, Ma'am; and though but juft from the univerfity, I think I may venture to affirm with as little the air of a pedant as——

M. Gr. I don't, Mr. Wilding, queftion the accomplifhments of your fon ; and fhall own too, that his being defcended from the old
friend

friend of my father is to me the strongest recommendation.

O. Wild. You honour me, Madam.

M. Gr. But, Sir, I have something to say—

O. Wild. Pray, Madam, speak out ; it is impossible to be too explicit on these important occasions.

M. Gr. Why then, Sir, to a man of your wisdom and experience, I need not observe, that the loss of a parent to counsel and direct at this solemn crisis, has made a greater degree of personal prudence necessary in me.

O. Wild. Perfectly right, Ma'am.

M. Gr. We live, Sir, in a very censorious world ; a young woman can't be too much on her guard ; nor should I choose to admit any man in the quality of a lover, if there was not at least a strong probability——

O. Wild. Of a more intimate connection. I hope, Madam, you have heard nothing to the disadvantage of my son.

M. Gr. Not a syllable : but you know, Sir, there are such things in nature as unaccountable antipathies, aversions, that we take at first sight. I should be glad there could be no danger of that.

O. Wild. I understand you, Madam : you shall have all the satisfaction imaginable : Jack is to meet me immediately ; I will conduct him under your window ; and if his figure has the misfortune to displease, I will take care his addresses shall never offend you. Your most obedient servant.   [*Exit.*

M. Gr. Now, there is a polite, sensible, old father for you.

M. God. Yes ; and a very discreet, prudent
                                        daughter

daughter he is likely to have. Oh, you are a great hypocrite, Kitty.

Enter a Servant.

Ser. A letter for you, Madam. [*To Mifs Godfrey.*] Sir James Elliot to wait on your ladythip. [*To Mifs Grantham.*]

M. Gr. Lord, I hope he won't ftay long here. He comes, and feems entirely wrapt up in the difmals: what can be the matter now?

Enter Sir James Elliot.

Sir Ja. In paffing by your door, I took the liberty, Ma'am, of enquiring after your health.

M. Gr. Very obliging. I hope, Sir, you received a favourable account.

Sir Ja. I did not know but you might have caught cold laft night.

M. Gr. Cold! why, Sir, I hope I didn't fleep with my bed-chamber window open.

Sir Ja. Ma'am!

M. Gr. Sir!

Sir Ja. No, Ma'am; but it was rather hazardous to ftay fo late upon the water.

M. Gr. Upon the water!

Sir Ja. Not but the variety of amufements, it muft be owned, were a fufficient temptation.

M. Gr. What can he be driving at now?

Sir Ja. And pray, Madam, what think you of young Wilding? Is not he a gay, agreeable, fprightly—

M. Gr. I never give my opinion of people I don't know.

Sir Ja. You don't know him!

M. Gr. No.

Sir Ja.

Sir Ja. And his father I did not meet at your door!

M. Gr. Moſt likely you did.

Sir Ja. I am glad you own that, however. But for the ſon, you never——

M. Gr. Set eyes upon him.

Sir Ja. Really!

M. Gr. Really.

Sir Ja. Finely ſupported! Now, Madam, do you know that one of us is juſt going to make a very ridiculous figure?

M. Gr. Sir, I never had the leaſt doubt of your talents for excelling in that way.

Sir Ja. Ma'am, you do me honour: but it does not happen to fall to my lot upon this occaſion, however.

M. Gr. And that is a wonder!—what, then I am to be the fool of the comedy, I ſuppoſe?

Sir Ja. Admirably rallied! But I ſhall daſh the ſpirit of that triumphant laugh.

M. Gr. I dare the attack. Come on, Sir.

Sir Ja. Know then, and bluſh, if you are not all loſt to ſhame as dead to decency, that I am no ſtranger to laſt night's tranſactions.

M. Gr. Indeed!

Sir Ja. From your firſt entering the barge at Somerſet-houſe, to your laſt landing at Whitehall.

M. Gr. Surpriſing!

Sir Ja. Cupids, collations, feaſts, fireworks, all have reach'd me.

M. r. Why, you deal in magic.

Sir Ja. My intelligence is as natural as it is infallible.

M. Gr. May I be indulged with the name of your informer?

Sir Ja.

Sir Ja. Freely, Madam. Only the very individual fpark to whofe folly you were indebted for this gallant profufion.

M. Gr. But his name?

Sir Ja. Young Wilding.

M. Gr. You had this ftory from him?

Sir Ja. I had.

M. Gr. From Wilding!—That is amazing.

Sir Ja. Oh ho! what, you are confounded at laft; and no evafion, no fubterfuge, no—

M. Gr. Look ye, Sir James; what you can mean by this ftrange ftory, and very extraordinary behaviour, it is impoffible for me to conceive; but if it is meant as an artifice to palliate your infidelity to me, lefs pains would have anfwer'd your purpofe.

Sir Ja. Oh, Madam, I know you are provided.

M. Gr. Matchlefs infolence! As you can't expeƈt that I fhould be prodigioufly pleafed with the fubjeƈt of this vifit, you won't be furpris'd at my wifhing it as fhort as poffible.

Sir Ja. I don't wonder you feel pain at my prefence; but you may reft fecure you will have no interruption for me; and I really think it would be a pity to part two people fo exaƈtly formed for each other. Your Ladyfhip's fervant. [*Going*]—But, Madam, though your fex fecures you from any farther refentment, yet the prefent objeƈt of your favour may have fomething to fear. [*Exit.*

M. Gr. Very well. Now, my dear, I hope you will acknowledge the prudence of my plan. To what a pretty condition I muft have been reduced, if my hopes had refted upon one lover alone!

M. God.

M. God. But are you fure that your method to multiply may not be the means to reduce the number of your flaves?

M. Gr. Impoffible!—Why, can't you difcern that this flam of Sir James Elliot's is a mere fetch to favour his retreat?

M. God. And you never faw Wilding!

M. Gr. Never.

M. God. There is fome myftery in this. I have, too, here in my hand, another mortification that you muft endure.

M. Gr. Of what kind?

M. God. A little allied to the laft: it is from the military fpark you met this morning.

M. Gr. What are the contents?

M. God. Only a formal declaration of love.

M. Gr. Why, you did not fee him.

M. God. But it feems he did me.

M. Gr. Might I perufe it?——" Battles— no wounds fo fatal—cannon-balls—Cupid— fpring a mine—cruelty—die on a counterfcarp —eyes—artillery—death—the ftranger." It is addrefs'd to you.

M. God. I told you fo.

M. Gr. You will pardon me, my dear; but I really can't compliment you upon the fuppofition of a conqueft at my expence.

M. God. That would be enough to make me vain. But why do you think it was fo impoffible?

M. Gr. And do you pofitively want a reafon?

M. God. Pofitively.

M. Gr. Why, then, I fhall refer you for an anfwer to a faithful counfellor and moft accomplifh'd critic.

M. God. Who may that be?

M. Gr.

M. Gr. The mirror upon your toilette.

M. God. Perhaps you may differ in judgment.

M. Gr. Why, can glaffes flatter?

M. God. I can't fay I think that neceffary.

M. Gr. Saucy enough !—But come, child, don't let us quarrel upon fo whimfical an occafion : time will explain the whole. You will favour me with your opinion of Young Wilding at my window.

M. God. I attend you.

M. Gr. You will forgive me, my dear, the little hint I dropt ; it was meant merely to ferve you ; for indeed, child, there is no quality fo infufferable in a young woman as felf-conceit and vanity.

M. God. You are moft prodigioufly obliging.

M. Gr. I'll follow you, Mifs. [*Exit Mifs Godfrey.*] Pert thing !—She grows immoderately ugly. I always thought her aukward, but fhe is now an abfolute fright.

M. God. (within.) Mifs, Mifs Grantham, your hero's at hand.

M. Gr. I come.

M. God. As I live, the very individual ftranger !

M. Gr. No fure !—Oh Lord, let me have a peep !

M. God. It is he !—it is he !—it is he !
[*Exeunt.*

SCENE—*The Street.*

Enter Old Wilding, Young Wilding, and Papillion.

O. Wild. There, Marquis, you muft pardon me ; for though Paris be more compact, yet furely

furely London covers a much great quantity—
Oh, Jack, look at that corner houfe : how
d'ye like it ?

Y. Wild. Very well; but I don't fee any
thing extraordinary.

O. Wild. I wifh, though, you were the
mafter of what it contains.

Y. Wild. What may that be, Sir?

O. Wild. The miftrefs, you rogue you: a
fine girl, and an immenfe fortune ; ay, and a
prudent fenfible wench into the bargain.

Y. Wild. Time enough yet, Sir.

O. Wild. I don't fee that: you are, lad,
the laft of our race, and I fhould be glad to
fee fome probability of its continuance.

Y. Wild. Suppofe, Sir, you were to repeat
your endeavours; you have cordially my confent.

O. Wild. No; rather too late in life for that
experiment.

Y. Wild. Why, Sir, would you recommend
a condition to me, that you difapprove of
yourfelf ?

O. Wild. Why, firrah, I have done my duty to the public and my family, by producing
you. Now, Sir, it is incumbent on you to
difcharge your debt.

. *Y. Wild.* In the college cant, I fhall beg
leave to tick a little longer.

O. Wild. Why, then, to be ferious, fon,
this is the very bufinefs I wanted to talk with
you about. In a word, I wifh you married;
and, by providing the lady of that manfion for
the purpofe, I have proved myfelf both a father and a friend.

Y. Wild. Far be it from me to queftion
your

your care; yet some preparation for so important a change——

O. Wild. Oh, I will allow you a week.

Y. Wild. A little more knowledge of the world.

O. Wild. That you may study at leisure.

Y. Wild. Now all Europe is in arms, my design was to serve my country abroad.

O. Wild. You will be full as useful to it by recruiting her subjects at home.

Y. Wild. You are then resolved?

O. Wild. Fix'd.

Y. Wild. Positively?

O. Wild. Peremptorily.

Y. Wild. No prayers——

O. Wild. Can move me.

Y. Wild. How the deuce shall I get out of this toil? [*Aside.*]—But suppose, Sir, there should be an unsurmountable objection?

O. Wild. Oh, leave the reconciling that to me: I am an excellent casuist.

Y. Wild. But I say, Sir, if it should be impossible to obey your commands?

O. Wild. Impossible!—I don't understand you.

Y. Wild. Oh, Sir!—But on my knees first let me crave your pardon.

O. Wild. Pardon! for what?

Y. Wild. I fear I have lost all title to your future favour.

O. Wild. Which way?

Y. Wild. I have done a deed——

O. Wild. Let's hear it.

Y. Wild. At Abingdon, in the county of Berks.

O. Wild. Well?

Y. Wild.

Y. Wild. I am——

O. Wild. What?

Y. Wild. Already married.

O. Wild. Married!

Pap. Married!

Y. Wild. Married.

O. Wild. And without my confent?

Y. Wild. Compell'd; fatally forced. Oh, Sir, did you but know all the circumftances of my fad, fad ftory, your rage would foon convert itfelf to pity.

O. Wild. What an unlucky event!—But rife, and let me hear it all.

Y. Wild. The fhame and confufion I now feel renders that tafk at prefent impoffible; I muft therefore rely for the relation on the good offices of this faithful friend.

Pap. Me, Sir! I never heard one word of the matter.

O. Wild. Come, Marquis, favour me with the particulars.

Pap. Upon my vard, Sire, dis affair has fo fhock me, dat I am almoft as incapable to tell de tale as your fon.—[*To Young Wilding.*]— Dry-a your tears. What can I fay, Sir?

Y. Wild. Any thing.—Oh!——[*Seems to weep.*]

Pap. You fee, Sire.

O. Wild. Your kind concern at the misfortunes of my family calls for the moft grateful acknowledgment.

Pap. Dis is great misfortune, fans doute.

O. Wild. But if you, a ftranger, are thus affected, what muft a father feel?

Pap. Oh, beaucoup; a great deal more.

O. Wild. But fince the evil is without a remedy,

medy, let us know the worft at once. Well,
Sir, at Abingdon?

Pap. Yes, at Abingdon.

O. Wild. In the county of Berks?

Pap. Dat is right, in the county of Berks.

Y. Wild. Oh, oh!

O. Wild. Ah, Jack, Jack! are all my hopes
then—Though I dread to afk, yet it muft be
known; who is the girl, pray, Sir?

Pap. De girl, Sir—[*Afide to Young Wilding.*]
——Who fhall I fay?

Y. Wild. Any body.

Pap. For de girl, I can't fay, upon my vard.

O. Wild. Her condition?

Pap. Pas grande condition; dat is to be
fure. But dere is no help—[*Afide to Young
Wilding.*]—Sir, I am quite a-ground.

O. Wild. Yes, I read my fhame in his referve: fome artful huffey.

Pap. Dat may be. Vat you call huffey?

O. Wild. Or perhaps fome common creature. But I'm prepared to hear the worft.

Pap. Have you no mercy?

Y. Wild. I'll ftep to your relief, Sir.

Pap. O Lord, a happy deliverance.

Y. Wild. Though it is almoft death for me
to fpeak, yet it would be infamous to let the
reputation of the lady fuffer by my filence.
She is, Sir, of an ancient houfe and unble-
mifh'd charaĉter.

O. Wild. That is fomething.

Y. Wild. And though her fortune may not
be equal to the warm wifhes of a fond father,
yet—

O. Wild. He. name?

Y. Wild. Mifs Lydia Sybthorp.

O. Wild.

O. Wild. Sybthorp—I never heard of the name.—But proceed.

Y. Wild. The latter end of laft long vacation, I went with Sir James Elliot to pafs a few days at a new purchafe of his near Abingdon. There, at an affembly, it was my chance to meet and dance with this lady.

O. Wild. Is fhe handfome?

Y. Wild. Oh, Sir, more beautiful——

O. Wild. Nay, no raptures; but go on.

Y. Wild. But to her beauty fhe adds politenefs, affability, and difcretion; unlefs fhe forfeited that charaƈter by fixing her affeƈtion on me.

O. Wild. Modeftly obferved.

Y. Wild. I was deterr'd from a public declaration of my paffion, dreading the fcantinefs of her fortune would prove an objeƈtion to you. Some private interviews fhe permitted.

O. Wild. Was that fo decent?—But love and prudence, madnefs and reafon.

Y. Wild. One fatal evening, the twentieth of September, if I miftake not, we were in a retired room innocently exchanging mutual vows, when her father, whom we expeƈted to fup abroad, came fuddenly upon us. I had juft time to conceal myfelf in a clofet.

O. Wild. What, unobferved by him?

Y. Wild. Entirely. But, as my ill ftars would have it, a cat, of whom my wife is vaftly fond, had a few days before lodged a litter of kittens in the fame place: I unhappily trod upon one of the brood; which fo provoked the implacable mother, that fhe flew at me with the fury of a tiger.

O. Wild.

O. Wild. I have obferved thofe creatures very fierce in defence of their young.

Pap. I fhall hate a cat as long as I live.

Y. Wild. The noife roufed the old gentleman's attention : he open'd the door, and there difcovered your fon.

Pap. Unlucky.

Y. Wild. I rufh'd to the door; but fatally my foot flipt at the top of the ftairs, and down I came tumbling to the bottom. The piftol in my hand went off by accident : this alarmed her three brothers in the parlour, who, with all their fervants, rufh'd with united force upon me.

O. Wild. And fo furprized you!

Y. Wild. No, Sir; with my fword I for fome time made a gallant defence, and fhould have inevitably efcaped; but a raw-boned, over-grown clumfy cook-wench ftruck at my fword with a kitchen-poker, broke it in two, and compell'd me to furrender at difcretion; the confequence of which is obvious enough.

O. Wild. Natural. The lady's reputation, your condition, her beauty, your love, all combined to make marriage an unavoidable meafure.

Y. Wild. May I hope, then, you rather think me unfortunate than culpable?

O. Wild. Why, your fituation is a fufficient excufe: all I blame you for is, your keeping it a fecret from me. With Mifs Grantham I fhall make an aukward figure; but the beft apology is the truth: I'll haften and explain it to her all——Oh, Jack, Jack, this is a mortifying bufinefs!

Y. Wild.

Y. Wild. Moſt melancholy.

[*Exit Old Wilding.*

Pap. I am amazed, Sir, that you have ſo carefully conceal'd this tranſaction from me.

Y. Wild. Heyday! what, do you believe it too?

Pap. Believe it! why, is not the ſtory of the marriage true?

Y. Wild. Not a ſyllable.

Pap. And the cat, and the piſtol, and the poker?

Y. Wild. All invention.—And were you really taken in!

Pap. Lord, Sir, how was it poſſible to avoid it?—Mercy on us! what a collection of cir-cumſtances have you crowded together!

Y. Wild. Genius; the mere effects of ge-nius, Papillion. But to deceive you, who ſo thoroughly know me!

Pap. But to prevent that for the future, could you not juſt give your humble ſervant a hint when you are bent upon bouncing? Be-ſides, Sir, if 'you recollect your fixt reſolution to reform——

Y. Wild. Ay, as to matter of fancy, the mere ſport and frolic of invention: but in caſe of neceſſity——why, Miſs Godfrey was at ſtake, and I was forced to uſe all my fineſſe.

Enter a Servant.

Ser. Two letters, Sir. [*Exit.*

Pap. There are two things in my conſcience my maſter will never want;—a prompt lie, and a ready excuſe for telling of it.

Y. Wild. Hum! buſineſs begins to thicken upon us: a challenge from Sir James Elliot, and

and a rendezvous from the pretty Miſs Godfrey They ſhall both be obſerved, but in
their order; therefore the lady firſt. Let me
ſee—I have not been twenty hours in town,
and I have already got a challenge, a miſtreſs,
and a wife: now, if I can get engaged in a
chancery ſuit, I ſhall have my hands pretty
full of employment. Come, Papillion, we
have no time to be idle.   [*Exeunt.*

ACT III.

SCENE—*An Apartment in Miſs Godfrey's
House.*

Miſs Grantham and Miſs Godfrey.

Miſs Godfrey.

UPON my word, Miſs Grantham, this is
but an idle piece of curioſity: you know the
man is already diſpoſed of, and therefore——

M. Gr. That is true, my dear; but there is
in this affair ſome myſtery that I muſt and will
have explain'd.

M. God. Come, come, I know the griev-
ance.—You can't brook that this ſpark, though
even a married man, ſhould throw off his allegiance to you, and enter a volunteer in my
ſervice.

M. Gr. And ſo you take the fact for granted?

M. God. Have I not his letter?

M. Gr. Conceited creature!—I fancy, Miſs,
by your vaſt affection for this letter, it is the
firſt of the kind you have ever received.

M. God.

M. God. Nay, my dear, why fhould you be piqued at me? the fault is none of mine. I dropt no handkerchief; I threw out no lure: the bird came willingly to hand, you know.

M. Gr. Metaphorical too! What, you are fetting up for a wit as well as a belle! Why, really, Madam, to do you juftice, you have full as fine pretenfions to one as the other.

M. God. I fancy, Madam, the world will not form their judgment of either from the report of a difappointed rival.

M. Gr. Rival!—admirably rallied! But let me tell you, Madam, this fort of behaviour, Madam, at your own houfe, whatever may be your beauty, is no great proof of your breeding, Madam.

M. God. As to that, Ma'am, I hope I fhall always fhow a proper refentment to any infult that is offer'd me, let it be in whofe houfe it will. The affignation, Ma'am, both time and place, was of your own contriving.

M. Gr. Mighty well, Ma'am!

M. God. But if, dreading a mortification, you think proper to alter your plan, your chair, I believe, is in waiting.

M. Gr. It is, Madam!—then let it wait.— Oh, what that was your fcheme! but it won't take, Mifs: the contrivance is a little too fhallow.

M. God. I don't underftand you.

M. Gr. Cunning creature! So all this infolence was concerted, it feems; a plot to drive me out of the houfe, that you might have the fellow all to yourfelf: but I have a regard for your chara&ter, though you negle& it.—

Fie,

Fie, Mifs; a paffion for a married man! I really blufh for you.

M. God. And I moft fincerely pity you.— But curb your choler a little: the inquiry you are about to make requires rather a cooler dif- pofition of mind; and by this time the hero is at hand.

M. Gr. Mighty well; I am prepared. But, Mifs Godfrey, if you really wifh to be acquit- ted of all artificial underhand dealings in this affair, fuffer me in your name to manage the interview.

M. God. Moft willingly: but he will recol- lect your voice.

M. Gr. Oh, that is eafily alter'd. [*Enter a maid, who whifpers Mifs Grantham, and ex- it.*]—It is he; but hide yourfelf, Mifs, if you pleafe.

M. God. Your hood a little forwarder, Mifs; you may be known, and then we fhall have the language of politenefs inflam'd to proofs of a violent paffion.

M. Gr. You are prodigioufly cautious.

SCENE—*The Street.*

Enter Young Wilding.

Y. Wild. This rendezvous is fomething in the Spanifh tafte, imported, I fuppofe, with the guitar. At prefent, I prefume the cuftom is confined to the great: but it will defcend; and in a couple of months I fhall not be fur- prized to hear an attorney's hackney clerk roufing at midnight a milliner's prentice, with an *Ally, Ally Croker.* But that, if I miftake not, is the temple; and fee my goddefs herfelf. Mifs Godfrey!

[*Mifs Grantham appears at the balcony.*

M. Gr.

M. Gr. Hufh!

Y. Wild. Am I right, Mifs?

M. Gr. Softly.   You received my letter I fee, Sir.

Y. Wild. And flew to the appointment with more—

M. Gr. No raptures, I beg.   But you muft not fuppofe this meeting meant to encourage your hopes.

Y. Wild. How, Madam?

M. Gr. Oh, by no means, Sir, for though I own your figure is pleafing, and your converf-ation——

M. God. Hold, Mifs; when did I ever con-verfe with him? [*from within.*]

M. Gr. Why, did not you fee him in the park?

M. God. True, Madam; but the converfa-tion was with you.

M. Gr. Blefs me! you are very difficult.   I fay, Sir, though your perfon may be unexcep-tionable, yet your chara&ter—

Y. Wild. My chara&ter!

M. Gr. Come, come, you are better known than you imagine.

Y. Wild. I hope not.

M. Gr. Your name is Wilding.

Y. Wild. How the deuce came fhe by that! —True, Madam.

M. Gr. Pray, have you never heard of a Mifs Grantham?

Y. Wild. Frequently.

M. Gr. You have.   And had you never any favourable thoughts of that lady?   Now mind, Mifs.

Y. Wild. If you mean as a lover, never.

The

The lady did me the honour to have a small defign upon me.

M. God. I hear every word, Mifs.

M. Gr. But you need not lean fo heavy upon me; he fpeaks loud enough to be heard. —I have been told, Sir, that—

Y. Wild. Yes, Ma'am, and very likely by the lady herfelf.

M. Gr. Sir !

Y. Wild. Oh, Madam, I have another obligation in my pocket to Mifs Grantham, which muft be difcharg'd in the morning.

M. Gr. Of what kind?

Y. Wild. Why, the lady, finding an old humble fervant of hers a little lethargic, has thought fit to adminifter me in a jealous draught, in order to quicken his paffion.

M. Gr. Sir, let me tell you——

M. God. Have a care; you will betray yourfelf.

Y. Wild. Oh, the whole ftory will afford you infinite diverfion; fuch a farrago of fights and feafts. But, upon my honour, the girl has a fertile invention.

M. God. So! what, that ftory was yours; was it?

Y. Wild. Pray, Madam, don't I hear another voice?

M. Gr. A diftant relation of mine.—Every fyllable falfe.—But, Sir, we have another charge againft you. Do you know any thing of a lady at Abingdon?

Y. Wild. Mifs Grantham again. Yes, Madam, I have fome knowledge of that lady.

M. Gr. You have? Well, Sir, and that being the cafe, how could you have the affurance——

Y. Wild.

Y. Wild. A moment's patience, Ma'am.—
That lady, that Berkſhire lady, will, I can aſ-
fure you, prove no bar to my hopes.

M. Gr. How, Sir; no bar!

Y. Wild. Not in the leaſt, Ma'am; for that
lady exiſts in idea only.

M. Gr. No ſuch perſon!

Y. Wild. A mere creature of the imagination.

M. Gr. Indeed!

Y. Wild. The attacks of Miſs Grantham
were ſo powerfully enforced, too, by paternal
authority, that I had no method of avoiding
the blow, but by the ſheltering myſelf under
the conjugal ſhield.

M. Gr. You are not married, then?—But
what credit can I give to the profeſſions of a
man, who in an article of ſuch importance, and
to a perſon of ſuch reſpect——

Y. Wild. Nay, Madam, ſurely Miſs Godfrey
ſhould not accuſe me of a crime her own
charms have occaſion'd. Could any other motive, but the fear of loſing her, prevail on me
to trifle with a father; or compel me to in-
fringe thoſe laws which I have hitherto ſo in-
violably obſerved?

M. Gr. What laws, Sir?

Y. Wild. The ſacred laws of truth, Ma'am.

M. Gr. There, indeed, you did yourſelf an
infinite violence. But, when the whole of
the affair is diſcover'd, will it be ſo eaſy to get
rid of Miſs Grantham? The violence of
her paſſion, and the old gentleman's obſti-
nacy——

Y. Wild. Are nothing to a mind reſolved.

M. Gr. Poor Miſs Grantham!

Y. Wild. Do you know her, Madam?

M. Gr.

M. Gr. I have heard of her; but you, Sir, I suppose, have been long on an intimate footing?

Y. Wild. Bred up together from children.

M. Gr. Brave!—Is she handsome?

Y. Wild. Her paint comes from Paris, and her femme de chambre is an excellent artist.

M. Gr. Very well!—Her shape?

Y. Wild. Pray, Madam, is not Curzon esteemed the best stay-maker for people inclined to be crooked?

M. Gr. But as to the qualities of her mind; for instance, her understanding?

Y. Wild. Uncultivated.

M. Gr. Her wit?

Y. Wild. Borrowed.

M. Gr. Her taste?

Y. Wild. Trifling.

M. Gr. And her temper?

Y. Wild. Intolerable.

M. Gr. A finish'd picture. But come, these are not your real thoughts: this is a sacrifice you think due to the vanity of our sex.

Y. Wild. My honest sentiments: and, to convince you how thoroughly indifferent I am to that lady, I would, upon my veracity, as soon take a wife from the Grand Signior's seraglio.—Now, Madam, I hope you are satisfied.

M. Gr. And you would not scruple to acknowledge this before the lady's face?

Y. Wild. The first opportunity.

M. Gr. That I will take care to provide you. Dare you meet me at her house?

Y. Wild. When?

M. Gr. In half an hour.

Y. Wild.

Y. Wild. But won't a declaration of this fort appear odd at—a—

M. Gr. Come, no evafion; your conduct and character feem to me a little equivocal, and I muft infift on this proof at leaft of——

Y. Wild. You fhall have it.

M. Gr. In half an hour?

Y. Wild. This inftant.

M. Gr. Be punctual.

Y. Wild. Or may I forfeit your favour.

M. Gr. Very well; till then, Sir, adieu.— Now I think I have my fpark in the toil; and if the fellow has any feeling, if I don't make him fmart for every article——Come, my dear, I fhall ftand in need of your aid. [*Exit.*

Y. Wild. So I am now, I think, arrived at a critical period. If I can but weather this point——But why fhould I doubt it? it is in the day of diftrefs only that a great man difplays his abilities. But I fhall want Papillion? where can the puppy be?

Enter Papillion.

Y. Wild. So, Sir, where have you been rambling?

Pap. I did not fuppofe you would want——

Y. Wild. Want!——you are always out of the way. Here have I been forced to tell forty lies upon my own credit, and not a fingle foul to vouch for the truth of them.

Pap. Lord, Sir, you know———

Y. Wild. Don't plague me with your apologies; but it is lucky for you that I want your affiftance. Come with me to Mifs Grantham's.

Pap. On what occafion?

Y. Wild.

Y. Wild. An important one: but I'll prepare you as we walk.

Pap. Sir, I am really—I could wifh you
would be fo good as to——

Y. Wild. What, defert your friend in the
heat of battle! Oh, you poltroon!

Pap. Sir, I would do any thing, but you
know I have not talents.

Y. Wild. I do; and for my own fake fhall
not tafk them too high.

Pap. Now I fuppofe the hour is come
when we fhall pay for all.

Y. Wild. Why, what a daftardly, hen-
hearted—But come, Papillion, this fhall be
your laft campaign. Don't droop, man; con-
fide in your leader, and remember, *Sub auf-
pice Teucro nil defperandum.*   [*Exeunt.*

SCENE—*An Apartment in Mifs Grantham's
Houfe.*

Enter a Servant, conducting in Old Wilding.

Ser. My lady, Sir, will be at home immediately: Sir James Elliot is in the next room
waiting her return.

O. Wild. Pray, honeft friend, will you tell
Sir James that I beg the favour of a word
with him? [*Exit Ser.*] This unthinking boy!
Half the purpofe of my life has been to plan
this fcheme for his happinefs, and in one
heedlefs hour has he mangled all.

Enter Sir James Elliot.

Sir, I afk your pardon; but upon fo interefting a fubject, I know you will excufe my
intrufion. Pray, Sir, of what credit is the
family of the Sybthorps in Berkfhire?

Sir Ja. Sir!

O. Wild.

O. Wild. I don't mean as to property; that I am not fo folicitous about; but as to their character: Do they live in reputation? Are they refpected in the neighbourhood?

Sir Ja. The family of the Sybthorps!

O. Wild. Of the Sybthorps.

Sir Ja. Really I don't know, Sir.

O. Wild. Not know!

Sir Ja. No; it is the very firft time I ever heard of the name.

O. Wild. How fteadily he denies it! Well done, Baronet! I find Jack's account was a juft one. [*Afide.*] Pray, Sir James, recollect yourfelf.

Sir Ja. It will be to no purpofe.

O. Wild. Come, Sir, your motive for this affected ignorance is a generous but unneceffary proof of your friendfhip for my fon: but I know the whole affair.

Sir Ja. What affair?

O. Wild. Jack's marriage.

Sir Ja. What Jack?

O. Wild. My fon Jack.

Sir Ja. Is he married?

O. Wild. Is he married! why, you know he is.

Sir Ja. Not I, upon my honour.

O. Wild. Nay, that is going a little too far: but to remove all your fcruples at once, he has own'd it himfelf.

Sir Ja. He has!

O. Wild. Ay, ay, to me. Every circumftance: going to your new purchafe at Abingdon—meeting Lydia Sybthorp at the affembly —their private interviews—furprifed by the father—piftol—poker—and marriage; in fhort, every particular. *Sir Ja.*

Sir Ja. And this account you had from your fon?

O. Wild. From Jack; not two hours ago.

Sir Ja. I wifh you joy, Sir.

O. Wild. Not much of that, I believe.

Sir Ja. Why, Sir, does the marriage difpleafe you?

O. Wild. Doubtlefs.

Sir Ja. Then I fancy you may make yourfelf eafy.

O. Wild. Why fo?

Sir Ja. You have got, Sir, the moft prudent daughter-in-law in the Britifh dominions.

O. Wild. I am happy to hear it.

Sir Ja. For tho' fhe mayn't have brought you much, I'm fure fhe'll not coft you a farthing.

O. Wild. Ay; exactly Jack's account.

Sir Ja. She'll be eafily jointured.

O. Wild. Juftice fhall be done her.

Sir Ja. No provifion neceffary for younger children.

O. Wild. No, Sir! why not?—I can tell you, if fhe anfwers your account, not the daughter of a duke——

Sir Ja. Ha, ha, ha, ha!

O. Wild. You are merry, Sir.

Sir Ja. What an unaccountable fellow!

O. Wild. Sir!

Sir Ja. I beg your pardon, Sir. But with regard to this marriage——

O. Wild. Well, Sir!

Sir Ja. I take the whole hiftory to be neither more nor lefs than an abfolute fable.

O. Wild. How, Sir?

Sir Ja. Even fo.

O. Wild. Why, Sir, do you think my fon would dare to impofe upon me?   *Sir Ja.*

Sir Ja. Sir, he would dare to impofe upon any body. Don't I know him?

O. Wild. What do you know?

Sir Ja. I know, Sir, that his narratives gain him more applaufe than credit; and that, whether from conftitution or habit, there is no believing a fyllable he fays.

O. Wild. Oh, mighty well, Sir!—He wants to turn the tables upon Jack.—But it won't do; you are foreftall'd; your novels won't pafs upon me.

Sir Ja. Sir!

O. Wild. Nor is the character of my fon to be blafted with the breath of a bouncer.

Sir Ja. What is this?

O. Wild. No, no, Mr. Mandeville, it won't do; you are as well known here as in your own county of Hereford.

Sir Ja. Mr. Wilding, but that I am fure this extravagant behaviour owes its rife to fome impudent impofitions of your fon, your age would fcarce prove your protection.

O. Wild. Nor, Sir, but that I know my boy equal to the defence of his own honour, fhould he want a protector in this arm, wither'd and impotent as you may think it.

Enter Mifs Grantham.

M. Gr. Blefs me, gentlemen, what is the meaning of this?

Sir Ja. No more at prefent, Sir: I have another demand upon your fon; we'll fettle the whole together.

O. Wild. I am fure he will do you juftice.

M. Gr. How, Sir James Elliot! I flatter'd myfelf that you had finifh'd your vifits here,
Sir.

Sir. Muft I be the eternal objeƈt of your out-
rage? not only infulted in my own perfon, but
in that of my friends! Pray, Sir, what right—

O. Wild. Madam, I afk your pardon; a difagreeable occafion brought me here: I come,
Madam, to renounce all hopes of being nearer
allied to you, my fon unfortunately being married already.

M. Gr. Married!

Sir Ja. Yes, Madam, to a lady in the
clouds: and becaufe I have refufed to acknowledge her family, this old gentleman has
behaved in a manner very inconfiftent with
his ufual politenefs.

O. Wild. Sir, I thought this affair was to
be referved for another occafion; but you, it
feems——

M. Gr. Oh, is that the bufinefs!—Why, I
begin to be afraid that we are here a little in
the wrong, Mr. Wilding.

O. Wild. Madam!

M. Gr. Your fon has juft confirm'd Sir
James Elliot's opinion, at a conference under
Mifs Godfrey's window.

O. Wild. Is it poffible?

M. Gr. Moft true; and affign'd two moft
whimfical motives for the unaccountable tale.

O. Wild. What can they be?

M. Gr. An averfion for me, whom he has
feen but once; and an affeƈtion for Mifs Godfrey, whom I am almoft fure he never faw in
his life.

O. Wild. You amaze me.

M. Gr. Indeed, Mr. Wilding, your fon is
a moft extraordinary youth; he has finely perplex'd

plex'd us all. I think, Sir James, you have
a fmall obligation to him.

Sir Ja. Which I fhall take care to acknowledge the firft opportunity.

O. Wild. You have my confent. An abandon'd profligate! Was his father a proper
fubject for his——But I difcard him.

M. Gr. Nay, now, gentlemen, you are rather too warm: I can't think Mr. Wilding
bad-hearted at the bottom. This is a levity.—

O. Wild. How, Madam, a levity!

M. Gr. Take my word for it, no more; in-
flamed into habit by the approbation of his
juvenile friends. Will you fubmit his punifhment to me? I think I have the means in my
hands, both to fatisfy your refentments, and
accomplifh his cure into the bargain.

Sir Ja. I have no quarrel to him, but for
the ill offices he has done me with you.

M. Gr. D'ye hear, Mr. Wilding? I am
afraid my opinion with Sir James muft cement
the general peace.

O. Wild. Madam, I fubmit to any——

Enter a Servant.

Ser. Mr. Wilding to wait upon you, Madam. [*Exit.*

M. Gr. He is punctual, I find. Come, good
folks, you all act under my direction. You,
Sir, will get from your fon, by what means
you think fit, the real truth of the Abingdon
bufinefs. You muft likewife feemingly confent to his marriage with Mifs Godfrey, whom
I fhrewdly fufpect he has, by fome odd accident, miftaken for me; the lady herfelf fhall
appear at your call. Come, Sir James, you
will

will withdraw. I intend to produce another performer, who will want a little inftruction.——Kitty?

Enter Kitty.

Let John fhow Mr. Wilding in to his father; then come to my drefling-room : I have a fhort fcene to give you in ftudy. [*Exit Kitty.*]—— The girl is lively, and, I warrant, will do her character juftice. Come, Sir James. Nay, no ceremony ; we muft be as bufy as bees.

[*Exit Mifs Grantham and Sir James.*

O. Wild. This ftrange boy!—But I muft command my temper.

Y. Wild. (fpeaking as he enters.)—People to fpeak with me ! See what they want, Papillion.—My father here!——that's unlucky enough.

O. Wild. Ha, Jack, what brings you here?

Y. Wild. Why, I thought it my duty to wait upon Mifs Grantham, in order to make her fome apology for the late unfortunate——

O. Wild. Well, now, that is prudently as well as politely done.

Y. Wild. I am happy to meet, Sir, with your approbation.

O. Wild. I have been thinking, Jack, about my daughter-in-law : as the affair is public, it is not decent to let her continue longer at her father's.

Y. Wild. Sir!

O. Wild. Would it not be right to fend for her home?

Y. Wild. Doubtlefs, Sir.

O. Wild. I think fo. Why, then, to-morrow my chariot fhall fetch her.

Y. Wild.

Y. Wild. The devil it fhall! [*Afide.*]—Not quite fo foon, if you pleafe, Sir.

O. Wild. No! Why not?

Y. Wild. The journey may be dangerous in her prefent condition.

O. Wild. What's the matter with her?

Y. Wild. She is big with child, Sir.

O. Wild. An audacious——Big with child! —that is fortunate. But, however, an eafy carriage and fhort ftages can't hurt her.

Y. Wild. Pardon me, Sir, I dare not truft her: fhe is fix months gone.

O. Wild. Nay, then, there may be danger indeed. But fhould not I write to her father, juft to let him know that you have difcover'd the fecret?

Y. Wild. By all means, Sir; it will make him extremely happy.

O. Wild. Why, then, I will inftantly about it. Pray, how do you direct to him?

Y. Wild. Abingdon, Berkfhire.

O. Wild. True; but his addrefs?

Y. Wild. You need not trouble yourfelf, Sir: I fhall write by this poft to my wife, and will fend your letter inclofed.

O. Wild. Ay, ay, that will do. [*Going.*

Y. Wild. So, I have parried that thruft.

O. Wild. Though, upon fecond thoughts, Jack, that will rather look too familiar for an introductory letter.

Y. Wild. Sir!

O. Wild. And thefe country gentlemen are full of punctilios——No, I'll fend him a letter apart; fo give me his direction.

Y. Wild. You have it, Sir.

O. Wild. Ay, but his name: I have been fo hurried that I have entirely forgot it.

Y. Wild.

Y. Wild. I am fure fo have I. [*Afide.*]—His name—his name, Sir—Hopkins.

O. Wild. Hopkins!

Y. Wild. Yes, Sir.

O. Wild. That is not the fame name that you gave me before : that, if I recollect, was either Sypthorp or Sybthorp.

Y. Wild. You are right, Sir; that is his paternal appellation : but the name of Hopkins he took for an eftate of his mother's: fo he is indifcriminately called Hopkins or Sybthorp: and now I recollect I have his letter in my pocket—he figns himfelf Sybthorp Hopkins.

O. Wild. There is no end of this : I muft ftop him at once. Hark ye, Sir; I think you are call'd my fon?

Y. Wild. I hope, Sir, you have no reafon to doubt it.

O. Wild. And look upon yourfelf as a gentleman?

Y. Wild. In having the honour of defcending from you.

O. Wild. And that you think a fufficient pretenfion?

Y. Wild. Sir—pray, Sir——

O. Wild. And by what means do you imagine your anceftors obtain'd that diftinguifhing title? By their pre-eminence in virtue, I fuppofe.

Y. Wild. Doubtlefs, Sir.

O. Wild. And has it never occurr'd to you, that what was gain'd by honour might be loft by infamy?

Y. Wild. Perfectly, Sir.

O. Wild. Are you to learn what redrefs even the imputation of a lie demands; and
·that

that nothing lefs than the life of the adverfary can extinguifh the affront?

Y. Wild. Doubtlefs, Sir.

O. Wild. Then, how dare you call yourfelf a gentleman? you, whofe life has been one continued fcene of fraud and falfity! And would nothing content you but making me a partner in your infamy? Not fatisfied with violating that great band of fociety, mutual confidence, the moft facred rights of nature muft be invaded, and your father made the innocent inftrument to circulate your abominable impofitions.

Y. Wild. But, Sir!

O. Wild. Within this hour my life was nearly facrificed in defence of your fame : but perhaps that was your intention; and the ftory of your marriage merely calculated to fend me out of the world, as a grateful return for my bringing you into it.

Y. Wild. For heaven's fake, Sir!

O. Wild. What other motive?

Y. Wild. Hear me, I intreat you, Sir.

O. Wild. To be again impofed on! No, Jack; my eyes are open'd at laft.

Y. Wild. By all that's facred, Sir—

O. Wild. I am now deaf to your delufions.

Y. Wild. But hear me, Sir. I own the Abingdon bufinefs—

O. Wild. An abfolute fiction.

Y. Wild. I do.

O. Wild. And how dare you——

Y. Wild. I crave but a moment's audience.

O. Wild. Go on.

Y. Wild. Previous to the communication of your intention for me, I accidentally met with a lady, whofe charms——　　　*O. Wild.*

O. Wild. So!—what, here's another marriage trump'd out? but that is a ftale device. And, pray, Sir, what place does this lady inhabit? Come, come, go on; you have a fertile invention, and this is a fine opportunity. Well, Sir, and this charming lady, refiding, I fuppofe, *in nubibus*——

Y. Wild. No, Sir; in London.

O. Wild. Indeed!

Y. Wild. Nay, more, and at this inftant in his houfe.

O. Wild. And her name—

Y. Wild. Godfrey.

O. Wild. The friend of Mifs Grantham?

Y. Wild. The very fame, Sir.

O. Wild. Have you fpoke to her?

Y. Wild. Parted from her not ten minutes ago; nay, am here by her appointment.

O. Wild. Has fhe favoured your addrefs?

Y. Wild. Time, Sir, and your approbation, will, I hope.

O. Wild. Look ye, Sir, as there is fome little probability in this ftory, I fhall think it worth farther inquiry. To be plain with you, I know Mifs Godfrey; am intimate with her family: and though you deferve but little from me, I will endeavour to aid your intention. But if, in the progrefs of this affair, you practife any of your ufual arts; if I difcover the leaft falfehood, the leaft duplicity, remember you have loft a father.

Y. Wild. I fhall fubmit without a murmur.

[*Exit Old Wilding.*

Enter Papillion.

Y. Wild. Well, Papillion.

Pap.

Pap. Sir, here has been the devil to pay within.

Y. Wild. What's the matter?

Pap. A whole legion of cooks, confectioners, muficians, waiters, and watermen.

Y. Wild. What do they want?

Pap. You, Sir.

Y. Wild. Me!

Pap. Yes, Sir; they have brought in their bills.

Y. Wild. Bills! for what?

Pap. For the entertainment you gave laft night upon the water.

Y. Wild. That I gave?

Pap. Yes, Sir; you remember the bill of fare: I am fure the very mention of it makes my mouth water.

Y. Wild. Prythee, are you mad? There muft be fome miftake; you know that I—

Pap. They have been vaftly puzzled to find out your lodgings; but Mr. Robinfon meeting by accident with Sir James Elliot, he was kind enough to tell him where you lived. Here are the bills: Almack's, twelve dozen of Claret, ditto Champagne, Frontiniac, Sweetmeats, Pine-apples: the whole amount is 372*l*. 9*s*. befides mufic and fireworks.

Y. Wild. Come, Sir, this is no time for trifling.

Pap. Nay, Sir, they fay they have gone full as low as they can afford; and they were in hopes, from the great fatisfaction you expreffed to Sir James Elliot, that you would throw them in an additional compliment.

Y. Wild. Hark ye, Mr. Papillion, if you
                                              don't

don't ceafe your impertinence, I fhall pay you
a compliment that you would gladly excufe.

Pap. Upon my faith, I relate but the mere
matter of fact. You know, Sir, I am but bad
at invention ; though this incident, I can't help
thinking, is the natural fruit of your happy one.

Y. Wild. But are you ferious ? is this poffible ?

Pap. Moft certain. It was with difficulty
I reftrain'd their impatience ; but, however, I
have difpatch'd them to your lodgings, with a
promife that you fhall immediately meet them.

Y. Wild. Oh, there we fhall foon rid our
hands of the troop.—Now, Papillion, I have
news for you. My father has got to the bottom of the whole Abingdon bufinefs.

Pap. The deuce !

Y. Wild. We parted this moment. Such a
fcene !

Pap. And what was the iffue ?

Y. Wild. Happy beyond my hopes. Not
only an act of oblivion, but a promife to plead
my caufe with the fair.

Pap. With Mifs Godfrey !

Y. Wild. Who elfe ?—He is now with her
in another room.

Pap. And there is no—you underftand me
—in all this ?

Y. Wild. No, no ; that is all over now—
my reformation is fixt.

Pap. As a weather-cock.

Y. Wild. Here comes my father.

Enter Old Wilding.

Y. Wild. Well, Sir, I find in this laft article
you have condefcended to tell me the truth :
the

the young lady is not averfe to your union ;
but, in order to fix fo mutable a mind, I have
drawn up a flight contract, which you are
both to fign.

Y. Wild. With tranfport.

O. Wild. I will introduce Mifs Godfrey.[*Exit*

Y. Wild. Did not I tell you, Papillion?

Pap. This is amazing, indeed !

Y. Wild. Am not I a happy fortunate ?——
But they come.

Enter Old Wilding and Mifs Godfrey.

O. Wild. If, Madam, he has not the higheft
fenfe of the great honour you do him, I fhall
ceafe to regard him.——There, Sir, make
your own acknowledgments to that lady.

Y. Wild. Sir !

O. Wild. This is more than you merit ; but
let your future behaviour teftify your gratitude.

Y. Wild. Papillion ! Madam ! Sir !

O. Wild. What, is the puppy petrified !—
Why don't you go up to the lady ?

Y. Wild. Up to the lady !—That lady ?

O. Wild. That lady !—To be fure. What
other lady ?—To Mifs Godfrey.

Y. Wild. That lady Mifs Godfrey ?

O. Wild. What is all this?—Hark ye, Sir ;
I fee what you are at : but no trifling ; I'll be
no more the dupe of your double deteftable—
Recollect my laft refolution : This inftant your
hand to the contract, or tremble at the confequence.

Y. Wild. Sir, that, I hope, is—might not I
—to be fure——

O. Wild. No further evafions ! There, Sir.

Y. Wild. Heigh ho ! [*Signs it.*]

O. Wild.

O. Wild. Very well.　Now, Madam, your name if you pleafe.

Y. Wild. Papillion, do you know who fhe is?

Pap. That's a queftion indeed!　Don't you, Sir?

Y. Wild. Not I, as I hope to be faved.

Enter a Servant.

Ser. A young lady begs to fpeak with Mr. Wilding.

Y. Wild. With me?

M. God. A young lady with Mr. Wilding!

Ser. Seems diftreft, Madam, and extremely prefling for admittance.

M. God. Indeed!　There may be fomething in this.　You muft permit me, Sir, to paufe a little: who knows but a prior claim may prevent——

O. Wild. How, Sir, who is this lady?

Y. Wild. It is impoffible for me to divine, Sir.

O. Wild. You know nothing of her?

Y. Wild. How fhould I?

O. Wild. You hear, Madam.

M. God. I prefume your fon can have no objeftion to the lady's appearance.

Y. Wild. Not in the leaft, Madam.

M. God. Show her in, John.　　[*Exit Ser.*

O. Wild. No, Madam, I don't think there is the leaft room for fufpefting him: he can't be fo abandon'd as to——But fhe is here.　Upon my word, a fightly woman.

Enter Kitty as Mifs Sybthorp.

Kit. Where is he?—Oh, let me throw my arms—my life—my——

Y. Wild. Heyday!

Kit.

Kit. And could you leave me? and for fo long a fpace? Think how the tedious time has lagg'd along.

Y. Wild. Madam!

Kit. But we are met at laft, and now will part no more.

Y. Wild. The deuce we won't!

Kit. What, not one kind look! no tender word to hail our fecond meeting!

Y. Wild. What the devil is all this?

Kit. Are all your oaths, your proteftations, come to this? Have I deferved fuch treatment? Quitted my father's houfe, left all my friends, and wander'd here alone in fearch of thee, thou firft, laft, only object of my love!

O. Wild. To what can all this tend? Hark ye, Sir; unriddle this myftery.

Y. Wild. Davus, non Edipus fum. It is beyond me, I confefs. Some lunatic efcaped from her keeper, I fuppofe.

Kit. Am I difown'd then, contemn'd, flighted?

O. Wild. Hold!—let me inquire into this matter a little. Pray, Madam——You feem to be pretty familiar here.—Do you know this gentleman?

Kit. Too well.

O. Wild. His name?

Kit. Wilding.

O. Wild. So far fhe is right. Now yours, if you pleafe.

Kit. Wilding.

Omnes. Wilding!

O. Wild. And how came you by that name, pray?

Kit. Moft lawfully, Sir: by the facred band, the holy tie that made us one.   *O. Wild.*

O. Wild. What, married to him?

Kit. Most true.

Omnes. How!

Y. Wild. Sir, may I never——

O. Wild. Peace, monster!—One question more: your maiden name?

Kit. Sybthorp.

O. Wild. Lydia, from Abingdon, in the county of Berks?

Kit. The same.

O. Wild. As I suspected. So then the whole story is true, and the monster is married at last.

Y. Wild. Me, Sir! By all that's—

O. Wild. Eternal dumbness seize thee, measureless lyar!

Y. Wild. If not me, hear this gentleman—Marquis—

Pap. Not I; I'll be drawn into none of your scrapes: it is a pit of your own digging; and so get out as well as you can. Mean time I'll shift for myself. [*Exit.*

O. Wild. What evasion now, monster?

M. God. Deceiver!

O. Wild. Lyar!

M. God. Impostor!

Y. Wild. Why, this is a general combination to distract me; but I will be heard. Sir, you are grosly imposed upon: the low contriver of this woman's shallow artifice I shall soon find means to discover; and as to you, Madam, with whom I have been suddenly surprised into a contract, I most solemnly declare this is the first time I ever set eyes on you.

O. Wild. Amazing confidence! Did not I bring her at your own request?

Y. Wild. No.

M. God.

M. God. Is not this your own letter?

Y. Wild. No.

Kit. Am not I your wife?

Y. Wild. No.

O. Wild. Did not you own it to me?

Y. Wild. Yes—that is—no, no.

Kit. Hear me.

Y. Wild. No.

M. God. Anſwer me.

Y. Wild. No.

O. Wild. Have not I—

Y. Wild. No, no, no. Zounds! you are all mad; and if I ſtay, I ſhall catch the infection.

[*Exit.*

Enter Sir James Elliot and Miſs Grantham.

Omnes. Ha, ha, ha!

M. Gr. Finely perform'd.

O. Wild. You have kept your promiſe, and I thank you, Madam.

M. Gr. My medicine was ſomewhat rough, Sir; but in deſperate caſes, you know—

O. Wild. If his cure is completed, he will gratefully acknowledge the cauſe; if not, the puniſhment comes far ſhort of his crimes. It is needleſs to pay you any compliments, Sir James; with that lady you can't fail to be happy. I ſhan't venture to hint a ſcheme I have greatly at heart, till we have undeniable proofs of the ſucceſs of our operations. To the ladies, indeed, no character is ſo dangerous as that of a lyar:

> They in the faireſt frames can fix a flaw,
> And vanquiſh females whom they never ſaw.

F I N I S.

*Knight and Compton, Printers, Middle-ſtreet,
Cloth Fair.*

THE

P A T R O N:

A

COMEDY

IN THREE ACTS:

PERFORMED AT THE

THEATRE IN THE HAY-MARKET;

WRITTEN BY

SAMUEL FOOTE, Esq.

A NEW EDITION.

LONDON:
PRINTED FOR W. LOWNDES, No. 76, FLEET STREET.
1794.

Price One Shilling and Sixpence.

GRANVILLE LEVESON GOWER,

EARL GOWER,

Lord Chamberlain of his Majefty's Houfhold.

My Lord,

THE following little Comedy, founded on a ftory of M. Marmontell's, and calculated to ex- pofe the frivolity and ignorance of the pre- tenders to learning, with the infolence and vanity of their fuperficial, illiberal protectors, can be addreffed to no nobleman with more propriety than to Lord Gower; whofe judgment, though elegant, is void of affectation; and whofe pa- tronage, though powerful, is deftitute of all fa- ftidious parade. It is with pleafure, my Lord, that the Public fees your Lordfhip placed at the head of that department which is to decide,

without

without appeal, on the moft popular domain in the whole republic of letters; a fpot that has always been diftinguifhed with affection, and cultivated with care, by every ruler the leaft attentive to either chaftifing the morals, polifhing the manners, or, what is of equal importance, rationally amufing the leifure of the people.

The Patron, my Lord, who now begs your protection, has had the good fortune to be well received by the public; and, indeed, of all the pieces that I have had the honour to offer them, this feems to me to have the faireft claim to their favour.

But the play, ftripp'd of thofe theatrical ornaments for which it is indebted to your Lordfhip's indulgence, muft now plead it's own caufe; nor will I, my Lord, with an affected humility, echo the trite, coarfe, though claffical compliment, of *Optimus patronus, peffimus poeta:* for if this be really true of the laft, the firft can have but fmall pretenfions to praife; patronizing bad poets being, in my poor opinion, full as pernicious to the progrefs of letters, as neglecting the good.

In humble hopes, then, my Lord, of not being thought the meaneft in the Mufes train, I have taken the liberty to prefix your name to this dedication, and publicly to acknowledge my obligations to your Lordfhip; which, let me boaft too, I have had the happinefs to receive, untainted by the infolence of domeftics, the delays

lays of office, or the chilling fuperiority of rank; mortifications which have been too often experienced by much greater writers than myfelf, from much lefs men than your Lordfhip.

My Lord, I have the honour to be, with the greateft refpect and gratitude,

Your Lordfhip's moft obliged,

and moft devoted,

humble fervant.,

Weft-End,
June 20, 1764.

SAMUEL FOOTE.

Dramatis

Dramatis Personæ.

Sir Thomas Lofty, Sir Peter Pepperpot,	} Mr. Foote.
Dick Bever,	Mr. Death.
Frank Younger,	Mr. Davis
Sir Roger Dowlas,	Mr. Palmer.
Mr. Rust,	Mr. Weston.
Mr. Dactyl,	Mr. Granger.
Mr. Puff,	Mr. Hayes.
Mr. Staytape,	Mr. Brown.
Robin,	Mr. Parsons.
John,	Mr Lewis.
Two Blacks.	
Miss Juliet,	Mrs. Granger.

THE

P A T R O N.

ACT I.

SCENE THE STREET.

Enter Bever and Younger.

YOUNGER.

No, Dick, you muſt pardon me.

BEVER.

Nay, but to ſatisfy your curioſity.

YOUNGER.

I tell you, I have not a jot.

BEVER.

Why then to gratify me.

YOUNGER.

At rather too great an expence.

BEVER.

To a fellow of your obſervation and turn, I
ſhould think, now, ſuch a ſcene a moſt delicate
treat.

YOUNGER.

Delicate! Palling, nauſeous, to a dreadful degree. To a lover, indeed, the charms of the
niece may palliate the uncle's fulſome formality.

BEVER.

The uncle! ay, but then you know he is only
one of the group.

YOUNGER.

YOUNGER.

That's true; but the figures are all finiſh'd a-like:—a *maniere*, a tireſome ſameneſs throughout.

BEVER.

There you will excuſe me; I am ſure there is no want of variety.

YOUNGER.

No! then let us have a detail. Come, Dick, give us a bill of the play.

BEVER.

Firſt, you know, there's Juliet's uncle.

YOUNGER.

What, Sir Thomas Lofty! the modern Midas, or rather (as fifty dedications will tell you) the Pollio, the Atticus, the patron of genius, the protector of arts, the paragon of poets, decider on merit, chief juſtice of taſte, and ſworn appraiſer to Apollo and the tuneful Nine. Ha, ha.—Oh, the tedious, inſipid, inſufferable coxcomb!

BEVER.

Nay, now, Frank, you are too extravagant. He is univerſally allow'd to have taſte; ſharp-judging Adriel, and the muſe's friend, himſelf a muſe.

YOUNGER.

Taſte! by who? underling bards, that he feeds; and broken bookſellers, that he bribes. Look ye, Dick, what raptures you pleaſe, when Miſs Lofty is your theme; but expect no quarter for the reſt of the family. I tell thee, once for all, Lofty is a rank impoſtor, the bufo of an illiberal, mercenary tribe; he has neither genius to create, judgment to diſtinguiſh, or generoſity to reward; his wealth has gain'd him flattery from the indigent

digent, and the haughty infolence of his pretence, admiration from the ignorant. *Voilà le
portrait de votre oncle.* Now on to the next.

BEVER.

The ingenious and erudite Mr. Ruft.

YOUNGER.

What, old Martin, the medal-monger?

BEVER.

The fame, and my rival in Juliet.

YOUNGER.

Rival! what, Ruft? why fhe's too modern for
him by a couple of centuries. Martin! why he
likes no heads but upon coins. Married! the
mummy! Why 'tis not above a fortnight ago
that I faw him making love to the figure without a nofe in Somerfet-Gardens: I caught him
ftroaking the marble plaits of her gown, and
afked him if he was not afhamed to take fuch
liberties with ladies in public.

BEVER.

What an inconftant old fcoundrel it is!

YOUNGER.

Oh, a Dorimant. But how came this about?
what could occafion the change? was it in the
power of flefh and blood to feduce this adorer of
virtù from his marble and porphyry?

BEVER.

Juliet has done it; and, what will furprize you,
his tafte was a bawd to the bufinefs.

YOUNGER.

Pr'ythee explain.

BEVER.

Juliet met him laft week at her uncle's: he was
a little pleafed with the Greek of her profile; but,

on

on a clofer enquiry, he found the turn-up of her nofe to exactly refemble the buft of the princefs Popæa.

YOUNGER.

The chafte moiety of the amiable Nero.

BEVER.

The fame.

YOUNGER.

Oh, the deuce! then your bufinefs was done in an inftant.

BEVER.

Immediately. In favour of the tip, he offered *carte blanche* for the reft of the figure, which (as you may fuppofe) was inftantly caught at.

YOUNGER.

Doubtlefs. But who have we here?

BEVER.

This is one of Lofty's companions, a Weft-Indian of an over-grown fortune. He faves me the trouble of a portrait. This is Sir Peter Pepperpot.

Enter Sir Peter Pepperpot and two blacks.

Sir PETER.

Carelefs fcoundrels! harkee, rafcals! I'll banifh you home, you dogs! you fhall back, and broil in the fun. Mr. Bever, your humble; Sir, I am your entirely devoted.

BEVER.

You feem moved; what has been the matter, Sir Peter?

Sir PETER.

Matter! why, I am invited to dinner on a barbicu, and the villains have forgot my bottle of cayenne.

YOUNGER.

YOUNGER.

Unpardonable.

Sir PETER.

Ay, this country has fpoil'd them; this fame chriftening will ruin the colonies.———Well, dear Bever, rare news? boy; our fleet is arrived from the Weft.

BEVER.

It is?

Sir PETER.

Ay, lad; and a glorious cargo of turtle. It was lucky I went to Brighthelmftone; I nicked the time to a hair; thin as a lath, and a ftomach as fharp as a fhark's: never was in finer condition for feeding.

BEVER.

Have you a large importation, Sir Peter?

Sir PETER.

Nine; but feven in excellent order: the captain affures me they greatly gain'd ground on the voyage.

BEVER.

How do you difpofe of them?

Sir PETER.

Four to Cornhill, three to Almack's, and the two fickly ones I fhall fend to my borough in Yorkfhire.

YOUNGER.

Ay! what, have the provincials a relifh for turtle?

Sir PETER.

Sir, it is amazing how this country improves in turtle and turnpikes; to which (gives me leave to fay) we, from our part of the world, have not a little contributed. Why, formerly, Sir, a brace of bucks on the mayor's annual day was thought a pretty moderate bleffing. But we, Sir, have

polifh'd

their palates. Why, Sir, not the meaneſt member of my corporation but can diſtinguiſh the
paſh from the pee.

YOUNGER.

Indeed!

Sir PETER.

Ay, and ſever the green from the ſhell with
the ſkill of the ableſt anatomiſt.

YOUNGER.

And they are fond of it?

Sir PETER.

Oh, that the conſumption will tell you. The
ſtated allowance is ſix pounds to an alderman, and
five to each of their wives.

BEVER.

A plentiful proviſion.

Sir PETER.

But there was never known any waſte: the
mayor, recorder, and rector, are permitted to eat
as much as they pleaſe.

YOUNGER.

The entertainment is pretty expenſive.

Sir PETER.

Land-carriage and all. But I contrived to
ſmuggle the laſt that I ſent them.

BEVER.

Smuggle! I don't underſtand you.

Sir PETER.

Why, Sir, the raſcally coachman had always
charged me five pounds for the carriage.
Damn'd dear! Now my cook going at the
ſame time into the country, I made him clap a
capuchin upon the turtle, and for thirty ſhillings
put him an inſide paſſenger in the Doncaſter Fly.

YOUNGER.

A happy expedient.

BEVER.

BEVER.

Oh, Sir Peter has infinite humour.

Sir PETER.

Yes, but the frolick had like to have proved fatal.

YOUNGER.

How fo?

Sir PETER.

The maid at the Rummer, at Hatfield, popp'd her head into the coach, to know if the company would have any breakfaſt: Ecod, the turtle, Sir, laid hold of her noſe, and flapp'd her face with his fins till the poor devil fell into a fit. Ha, ha, ha.

YOUNGER.

Oh, an abſolute Rabelais.

BEVER.

What, I reckon, Sir Peter, you are going to the Square?

Sir PETER.

Yes; I extremely admire Sir Thomas. You know this is his day of aſſembly; I ſuppoſe you will be there: I can tell you, you are a wonderful favourite.

BEVER.

Am I?

Sir PETER.

He ſays, your natural genius is fine; and when poliſh'd by his cultivation, will ſurprize and aſtoniſh the world.

BEVER.

I hope, Sir, I ſhall have your voice with the public.

Sir PETER.

Mine! O fie, Mr. Bever.

BEVER.

Come, come, you are no inconſiderable patron.

Sir PETER.

Sir PETER.

He, he, he. Can't fay but I love to encourage the arts.

BEVER.

And have contributed largely yourfelf.

YOUNGER.

What, is Sir Peter an author?

Sir PETER.

O fie! what me? a mere dabbler; have blotted my fingers, 'tis true:—fome fonnets, that have not been thought wanting in falt.

BEVER.

And your epigrams.

Sir PETER.

Not entirely without point.

BEVER.

But come, Sir Peter, the love of the arts is not the fole caufe of your vifits to the houfe you are going to.

Sir PETER.

I don't underftand you.

BEVER.

Mifs Juliet, the niece.

Sir PETER.

O fie! what chance have I there? Indeed, if Lady Pepperpot fhould happen to pop off—

BEVER.

I don't know that. You are, Sir Peter, a dangerous man; and, were I a father, or uncle, I fhould not be a little fhy of your vifits.

Sir PETER.

Pfha! dear Bever, you banter.

BEVER.

And (unlefs I am extremely out in my guefs) that lady—

Sir PETER.

Sir PETER.

Hey! what, what, dear Bever?

BEVER.

But if you fhould betray me—

Sir PETER,

May I never eat a bit of green fat, if I do!

BEVER.

Hints have been dropp'd.

Sir PETER,

The devil! come a little this way,

BEVER.

Well made; not robuft and gigantic, 'tis true, but extremely genteel.

Sir PETER.

Indeed!

BEVER,

Features, not entirely regular; but marking, with an air now, fuperior; greatly above the — you underftand me?

Sir PETER.

Perfectly. Something noble; expreffive of— fafhion.

BEVER.

Right.

Sir PETER.

Yes, I have been frequently told fo.

BEVER.

Not an abfolute wit; but fomething infinitely better: an *enjouement*, a fpirit, a—

Sir PETER.

Gaiety. I was ever fo, from a child.

BEVER.

In fhort, your drefs, addrefs, with a thoufand other particulars that at prefent I can't recollect.

Sir PETER.

Why, dear Bever, to tell thee the truth, I have always admired Mifs Juliet, and a delicate creature

creature fhe is: fweet as a fugar-cane, ftrait as a
bamboo, and her teeth as white as a negro's.

BEVER.

Poetic, but true. Now only conceive, Sir
Peter, fuch a plantation of perfections to be de-
voured by that caterpillar Ruft.

Sir PETER.

A liquorifh grub! Are pine-apples for fuch
muckworms as he? I'll fend him a jar of
citrons and ginger, and poifon the pipkin.

BEVER.

No, no.

Sir PETER.

Or invite him to dinner, and mix rat's-bane
along with his curry.

BEVER.

Not fo precipitate; I think we may defeat him
without any danger.

Sir PETER.

How, how?

BEVER.

I have a thought—but we muft fettle the plan
with the lady. Could not you give her the hint,
that I fhould be glad to fee her a moment.

Sir PETER.

I'll do it directly.

BEVER.

But don't let Sir Thomas perceive you.

Sir PETER.

Never fear. You'll follow?

BEVER.

The inftant I have fettled matters with her;
but fix the old fellow fo that fhe may not be
mifs'd.

Sir PETER.

Sir PETER.

I'll nail him, I warrant; I have his opinion to beg on this manuscript.

BEVER.

Your own?

Sir PETER.

No.

BEVER.

Oh ho! what something new from the doctor, your chaplain?

Sir PETER.

He! no, no. O Lord, he's eloped.

BEVER.

How?

Sir PETER.

Gone. You know he was to dedicate his volume of fables to me: so I gave him thirty pounds to get my arms engraved, to prefix (by way of print) to the frontispiece; and, O grief of griefs! the doctor has moved off with the money. I'll send you Mifs Juliet. [*Exit.*

BEVER.

There, now, is a fpecial protector! The arts, I think, can't but flourifh under fuch a Mecænas.

YOUNGER.

Heaven vifits with a tafte the wealthy fool.

BEVER.

True; but then, to juftify the difpenfation,

From hence the poor are cloath'd, the hungry fed.
Fortunes to bookfellers, to authors bread.

YOUNGER.

The diftribution is, I own, a little unequal: and here comes a moft melancholy inftance; poor Dick Dactyl, and his publifher Puff.

Enter

Enter Dactyl and Puff.

PUFF.

Why, then, Mr. Dactyl, carry them to somebody else; there are people enough in the trade: but I wonder you would meddle with poetry; you know it rarely pays for the paper.

DACTYL.

And how can one help it, Mr. Puff? Genius impels, and when a man is once lifted in the service of the Mufes—

PUFF.

Why let him give them warning as foon as he can. A pretty fort of fervice, indeed! where there are neither wages nor vails. The Mufes! And what, I fuppofe, this is the livery they give. Gadzooks, I had rather be a waiter at Ranelagh.

BEVER.

The poet and publifher at variance! What is the matter, Mr. Dactyl?

DACTYL.

As Gad fhall judge me, Mr. Bever, as pretty a poem, and fo polite; not a mortal can take any offence; all full of panegyric and praife.

PUFF.

A fine character he gives of his works. No offence! the greateft in the world, Mr. Dactyl. Panegyric and praife! and what will that do with the public? Why, who the devil will give money to be told that Mr. Such-a-one is a wifer or better man than himfelf? No, no; 'tis quite and clean out of nature. A good foufing fatire, now, well powder'd with perfonal pepper, and feafoned with the fpirit of party; that demolifhes a confpicuous character, and finks him below

our

our own level; there, there, we are pleafed;
there we chuckle, and grin, and tofs the half-
crowns on the counter.

DACTYL.

Yes, and fo get cropp'd for a libel.

PUFF.

Cropp'd! ay, and the luckieft thing that can
happen to you. Why, I would not give two
pence for an author that is afraid of his ears.
Writing, writing is, (as I may fay,) Mr. Dactyl,
a fort of warfare, where none can be victor that
is the leaft afraid of a fcar. Why, zooks, Sir, I
never got falt to my potridge till I mounted at
the Royal Exchange.

BEVER.

Indeed!

PUFF.

No, no; that was the making of me. Then
my name made a noife in the world. Talk of
forked hills, and of Helicon! romantic and fa-
bulous ftuff. The true Caftalian ftream is a
fhower of eggs, and a pillory the poet's Par-
naffus.

DACTYL.

Ay, to you indeed it may anfwer; but what do
we get for our pains?

PUFF.

Why, what the deuce would you get? food,
fire, and fame. Why you would not grow fat!
a corpulent poet is a monfter, a prodigy! No,
no; fpare diet is a fpur to the fancy; high feeding would but founder your Pegafus.

DACTYL.

Why, you impudent, illiterate rafcal! who is
it you dare treat in this manner?

PUFF.

PUFF.

Heyday! what is the matter now?

DACTYL.

And is this the return for all the obligations
you owe me? But no matter? the world, the
world shall know what you are, and how you
have used me.

PUFF.

Do your worst; I despise you.

DACTYL.

They shall be told from what a dunghill you
sprang. Gentlemen, if there be faith in a sinner,
that fellow owes every shilling to me.

PUFF.

To thee!

DACTYL.

Ay, Sirrah, to me. In what kind of way did
I find you? then where and what was your state?
Gentlemen, his shop was a shed in Moorfields;
his kitchen a broken pipkin of charcoal; and
his bed-chamber, under the counter.

PUFF.

I never was fond of expence; I ever minded
my trade.

DACTYL.

Your trade! and pray with what stock did
you trade? I can give you the catalogue; I believe it won't overburthen my memory. Two
odd volumes of Swift; the Life of Moll Flanders,
with cuts; the Five Senses, printed and coloured
by Overton; a few classics, thumb'd and blotted
by the boys of the Charterhouse; with the Trial
of Dr. Sacheverel.

PUFF.

Malice!

DACTYL.

DACTYL.

Then, Sirrah, I gave you my Canning: it was she firſt ſet you afloat.

PUFF.

A grub.

DACTYL.

And it is not only my writings: you know, Sirrah, what you owe to my phyſic.

BEVER.

How! a phyſician?

DACTYL.

Yes, Mr. Bever; phyſic and poetry. Apollo is the patron of both: *Opiferque per orbem dicor.*

PUFF.

His phyſic!

DACTYL.

My phyſic! ay, my phyſic: why, dare you deny it, you raſcal! What, have you forgot my powders for flatulent crudities?

PUFF,

No.

DACTYL.

My coſmetic lozenge, and ſugar plumbs?

PUFF.

No.

DACTYL.

My coral for cutting of teeth, my potions, my lotions, my pregnancy drops, with my paſte for ſuperfluous hairs?

PUFF.

No, no; have you done?

DACTYL.

No, no, no; but I believe this will ſuffice for for the preſent.

PUFF.

PUFF.

Now would not any mortal believe that I owed my all to this fellow.

BEVER.

Why, indeed, Mr. Puff, the balance does feem in his favour.

PUFF.

In his favour! why you don't give any credit to him: a reptile, a bug, that owes his very being to me.

DACTYL.

I, I, I!

PUFF.

You, you! What, I fuppofe, you forget your garret in Wine-office-court, when you furnifh'd paragraphs for the Farthing-poft at twelve-pence a dozen.

DACTYL.

Fiction.

PUFF.

Then, did not I get you made collector of ca-fualties to the Whitehall and St. James's? but that poft your lazinefs loft you. Gentlemen, he never brought them a robbery till the highwayman was going to be hang'd; a birth till the chriften-ing was over; nor a death till the hatchment was up.

DACTYL.

Mighty well!

PUFF.

And now, becaufe the fellow has got a little in flefh, by being puff to the play-houfe this winter, (to which, by the bye, I got him appointed,) he is as proud and as vain as Voltaire. But I fhall foon have him under; the vacation will come.

DACTYL.

Let it.

PUFF.

PUFF.

Then I fhall have him fneaking and cringing, hanging about me, and begging a bit of tranflation.

DACTYL.

I beg, I, for tranflation!

PUFF.

No, no, not a line; not if you would do it for two-pence a fheet. No boil'd beef and carrot at mornings; no more cold pudding and porter. You may take your leave of my fhop.

DACTYL.

Your fhop! then at parting I will leave you a legacy.

BEVER.

O fie, Mr. Dactyl!

PUFF.

Let him alone.

DACTYL.

Pray, gentlemen, let me do myfelf juftice.

BEVER.

Younger, reftrain the publifher's fire.

YOUNGER.

Fie, gentlemen, fuch an illiberal combat—it is a fcandal to the republic of letters.

BEVER,

Mr. Dactyl, an old man, a mechanic, beneath—

DACTYL.

Sir, I am calm; that thought has reftored me. To your infignificancy you are indebted for fafety. But what my generofity has faved, my pen fhall deftroy.

PUFF.

Then you muft get fomebody to mend it.

DACTYL.

Adieu!

PUFF.

PUFF.

Farewel!

[Dactyl and Puff exeunt severally.

BEVER.

Ha, ha, ha! come, let us along to the square.

Blockheads with reason wicked wits abhor,
But dunce with dunce is barb'rous civil war.

[Exeunt.

END OF THE FIRST ACT.

ACT

ACT II.

SCENE CONTINUES.

Enter Bever and Younger.

YOUNGER.

POOR Dactyl! and dwells such mighty rage in little men? I hope there is no danger of blood-shed.

BEVER.

Oh, not in the least: the *gens vatum*, the nation of poets, though an irritable, are yet a placable people. Their mutual interests will soon bring them together again.

YOUNGER.

But shall not we be late? The critical senate is by this time assembled.

BEVER.

I warrant you, frequent and full; where

> Stately Bufo, puff'd by ev'ry quill,
> Sits, like Apollo, on his forked hill.

But you know I must wait for Miss Lofty; I am now totally directed by her. She gives me the key to all Sir Thomas's foibles, and prescribes the most proper method to feed them; but what good purpose that will produce——

YOUNGER.

YOUNGER.

Is she clever, adroit?

BEVER.

Doubtless. I like your asking the question of me.

YOUNGER.

Then pay an implicit obedience: the ladies, in these cases, generally know what they are about. The door opens.

BEVER.

It is Juliet, and with her old Rust. Enter, Frank: you know the knight, so no intruduction is wanted. [*Exit Younger.*] I should be glad to hear this reverend piece of lumber make love; the courtship must certainly be curious. Good-manners, stand by; by your leave I will listen a little. [*Bever retires.*]

Enter Juliet and Rust.

JULIET.

And your collection is large?

RUST.

Most curious and capital. When, Madam, will you give me leave to add your charms to my catalogue?

JULIET.

O dear! Mr. Rust, I shall but disgrace it. Besides, Sir, when I marry, I am resolv'd to have my husband all to myself: now, for the possession of your heart I shall have too many competitors.

RUST,

How, Madam! were Prometheus alive, and would animate the Helen that stands in my hall, she should not cost me a sigh.

JULIET.

JULIET.

Ay, Sir, there lies my greateft misfortune.
Had I only thofe who are alive to contend with,
by affiduity, affection, cares, and careffes, I might
fecure my conqueft: though that would be difficult; for I am convinced, were you, Mr. Ruft,
put up by Chriftie to auction, the Apollo Belvidere would not draw a greater number of
bidders.

RUST.

Would that were the cafe, Madam, fo I might
be thought a proper companion to the Venus de
Medicis.

JULIET.

The flower of rhetoric, and pink of politenefs.
But my fears are not confined to the living; for
every nation and age, even painters and ftatuaries,
confpire againft me. Nay, when the Pantheon
itfelf, the very goddeffes rife up as my rivals,
what chance has a mortal like me.——I fhall certainly laugh in his face. [Afide.]

RUST.

She is a delicate fubject.——Goddeffes, Madam! zooks, had you been on Mount Ida when
Paris decided the conteft, the Cyprian queen had
pleaded for the pippin in vain.

JULIET.

Extravagant gallantry.

RUST.

In you, Madam, are concentered all the beauties
of the Heathen mythology: the open front of
Diana; the luftre of Pallas's eyes,——

JULIET,

JULIET.

Oh, Sir!

RUST.

The chromatic mufic of Clio, the blooming
graces of Hebè, the empereal port of queen Juno,
with the delicate dimples of Venus.

JULIET.

I fee, Sir, antiquity has not engrofs'd all your
attention: you are no novice in the nature of
women.   Incenfe, I own, is grateful to moft of
my fex; but there are times when adoration may
be difpenfed with.

RUST.

Ma'am!

JULIET.

I fay, Sir, when we women willingly wave our
rank in the fkies, and wifh to be treated as
mortals.

RUST.

Doubtlefs, Madam: and are you wanting in
materials for that? No, Madam; as in dignity
you furpafs the Heathen divinities, fo in the
charms of attraction you beggar the queens of
the earth. The whole world, at different periods,
has contributed it's feveral beauties to form
you.

JULIET.

The deuce it has!   [Afide.]

RUST.

See, there, the ripe Afiatic perfection, join'd to
the delicate foftnefs of Europe! In you, Madam,
I burn to poffefs Cleopatra's alluring glances, the
Greek profile of queen Clytemneftra, the Roman
nofe of the emprefs Popæa—

JULIET.

JULIET.

With the majeftic march of queen Befs.
Mercy on me, what a wonderful creature am I!

RUST

In fhort, Madam, not a feature you have, but
recals to my mind fome trait in a medal or buft.

JULIET.

Indeed! Why, by your account, I muft be an
abfolute olio, a perfect falamongundy of charms.

RUST.

Oh, Madam, how can you demean, as I may
fay, undervalue—

JULIET.

Value! there is the thing; and to tell you the
truth, Mr. Ruft, in that word Value lies my
greateft objection.

RUST.

I don't underftand you.

JULIET.

Why then I will explain myfelf. It has been
faid, and I believe with fome fhadow of truth,
that no man is a hero to his *valet de chambre*:
now, I am afraid, when you and I grow a little
more intimate, which I fuppofe muft be the cafe
if you proceed on your plan, you will be horribly
difappointed in your high expectations, and foon
difcover this Juno, this Cleopatra, and princefs
Popæa, to be as arrant a mortal as madam your
mother.

RUST.

Madam, I, I, I—

JULIET.

JULIET.

Your patience a moment. Being therefore
defirous to preferve your devotion, I beg, for the
future, you would pleafe to adore at a diftance.

RUST.

To Endymion, Madam, Luna once liftened.

JULIET.

Ay, but he was another kind of a mortal : you
may do very well as a votary; but for a hufband
—mercy upon me!

RUST.

Madam, you are not in earneft, not ferious!

JULIET.

Not ferious! Why have you the impudence
to think of marrying a goddefs ?

RUST.

I fhould hope—

JULIET.

And what fhould you hope? I find your devotion refembles that of the world : when the
power of finning is over, and the fprightly firft-
runnings of life are rack'd off, you offer the vapid
dregs to your deity. No, no; you may, if you
pleafe, turn monk in my fervice. One vow, I
believe, you will obferve better than moft of
them, chaftity.

RUST.

Permit me—

JULIET.

Or, if you muft marry, take your Julia, your
Portia, or Flora, your Fum-fam from China, or
your Egyptian Ofiris. You have long paid your
addreffes to them.

RUST.

RUST.

Marry! what, marble?

JULIET.

The propereſt wives in the world; you can't chooſe amiſs; they will ſupply you with all that you want.

RUST.

Your uncle has, Madam, conſented.

JULIET.

That is more than ever his niece will. Con-ſented! and to what? to be ſwath'd to a moulder-ing mummy; or be lock'd up, like your medals, to canker and ruſt in a cabinet! No, no; I was made for the world, and the world ſhall not be robb'd of it's right.

BEVER.   [*Aſide.*

Bravo, Juliet! Gad, ſhe's a fine ſpirited girl.

JULIET.

My profile, indeed! No, Sir, when I marry, I muſt have a man that will meet my full face.

RUST.

Might I be heard for a moment?

JULIET.

To what end? You ſay, you have Sir Thomas Lofty's conſent; I tell you, you can never have mine. You may ſcreen me from, or expoſe me to, my uncle's reſentment; the choice is your own: if you lay the fault at my door, you will, doubtleſs, greatly diſtreſs me; but take the blame on yourſelf, and I ſhall own myſelf extremely obliged to you.

RUST.

RUST.

How! confefs myfelf in the fault?

JULIET.

Ay; for the beft thing that a man can do, when he finds he can't be beloved, is to take care he is not heartily hated. There is no other alternative.

RUST.

Madam, I fha'n't break my word with Sir Thomas.

JULIET.

Nor I with myfelf. So there's an end of our conference. Sir, your very obedient.

RUST.

Madam, I, I, don't—that is, let me—But no matter. Your fervant.   [*Exit*.

JULIET.

Ha, ha, ha!

Enter Bever from behind.

BEVER.

Ha, ha, ha! Incomparable Juliet! How the old dotard trembled and tottered; he could not have been more inflam'd, had he been robb'd of his Otho.

JULIET.

Ay; was ever goddefs fo familiarly ufed? In my confcience, I began to be afraid that he would treat me as the Indians do their dirty divinities; whenever they are deaf to their prayers, they beat and abufe them.

BEVER.

But, after all, we are in an aukward fituation.

JULIET.

JULIET.

How fo?

BEVER.

I have my fears.

JULIET.

So have not I.

BEVER.

Your uncle has refolved that you fhould be married to Ruft.

JULIET.

Ay, he may decree; but it is I that muft execute.

BEVER.

But fuppofe he has given his word.

JULIET.

Why then let him recal it again.

BEVER.

But are you fure you fhall have courage enough—

JULIET.

To fay No? That requires much refolution, indeed.

BEVER.

Then I am at the height of my hopes.

JULIET.

Your hopes! Your hopes and your fears are ill-founded alike.

BEVER.

Why, you are determined not to be his.

JULIET.

Well, and what then?

BEVER.

What then! why then you will be mine.

JULIET.

Indeed! and is that the natural confequence? Whoever won't be his, muft be your's. Is that the logic of Oxford?

BEVER.

Madam, I did flatter myfelf—

JULIET.

Then you did very wrong, indeed, Mr. Bever:
you should ever guard against flattering yourself;
for of all dangerous parasites, self is the worst.

BEVER.

I am astonish'd!

JULIET.

Astonish'd! your are mad, I believe! Why, I
have not known you a month. It is true, my
uncle says your father is his friend ; your fortune,
in time, will be easy; your figure is not remarkably faulty; and as to your understanding, pass-
able enough for a young fellow who has not seen
much of the world: but when one talks of a
husband—Lord, it's quite another sort of a—
Ha, ha, ha! Poor Bever, how he stares! he stands
like a statue!

BEVER.

Statue, indeed, Madam; I am very near petrified.

JULIET.

Even then you will make as good a husband as
Rust. But go, run, and join the assembly
within : be attentive to every word, motion, and
look of my uncle's; be dumb when he speaks,
admire all he says, laugh when he smirks, bow
when he sneezes; in short, fawn, flatter, and
cringe; don't be afraid of over-loading his stomach, for the knight has a noble digestion, and
you will find some there who will keep you in
countenance.

BEVER.

I fly. So then, Juliet, your intention was only
to try—

JULIET.

Don't plague me with impertinent questions :
march! obey my directions. We must leave the
issue

issue to Chance; a greater friend to mankind than they are willing to own. Oh, if any thing new should occur, you may come into the drawing room for further instructions. [*Exeunt severally.*

SCENE,

A ROOM IN SIR THOMAS LOFTY's HOUSE.

Sir Thomas, Rust, Puff, Dactyl, and others, discovered sitting.

Sir THOMAS.

Nothing new to-day from Parnassus?

DACTYL.

Not that I hear.

Sir THOMAS.

Nothing critical, philosophical, or political?

PUFF.

Nothing.

Sir THOMAS.

Then in this *disette*, this dearth of invention, give me leave, gentlemen, to distribute my stores. I have here in my hand a little, smart, satyrical epigram; new, and prettily pointed: in short, a production that Martial himself would not have blush'd to acknowledge.

RUST.

Your own, Sir Thomas?

Sir THOMAS.

O fie! no; sent me this morning, anonymous

DACTYL.

Pray, Sir Thomas, let us have it.

ALL.

By all means; by all means.

Sir THOMAS.

Sir THOMAS.

To Phillis.

Think'st thou, fond Phillis, Strephon told thee true,
Angels are painted fair to look like you:
Another story all the town will tell;
Phillis paints fair—to look like an-gel.

ALL.
Fine! fine! very fine!

DACTYL.
Such an ease and simplicity.

PUFF.
The turn so unexpected and quick.

RUST.
The satire so poignant.

Sir THOMAS.
Yes; I think it possesses, in an eminent degree, the three great epigrammatical requisites; brevity, familiarity, and severity.

> Phillis paints fair—to look like an-gel.

DACTYL.
Happy! Is the Phillis, the subject, a secret?

Sir THOMAS.
Oh, dear me! nothing personal; no; an impromptu; a mere *jeu d'esprit.*

PUFF.
Then, Sir Thomas, the secret is out; it is your own.

DACTYL.
That was obvious enough.

PUFF.
Who is there else could have written it?

RUST.
True, true.

Sir THOMAS.

Sir THOMAS.

The name of the author is needlefs. So it is an acquifition to the republic of letters, any gentleman may claim the merit that will.

PUFF.

What a noble contempt!

DACTYL.

What greatnefs of mind!

RUST.

Scipio and Lælius were the Roman Loftys. Why, I dare believe Sir Thomas has been the making of half the authors in town: he is, as I may fay, the greateft manufacturer; the other poets are but pedlars, that live by retailing his wares.

ALL.

Ha, ha, ha! well obferv'd, Mr. Ruft.

Sir THOMAS.

Ha, ha, ha! *Molle atque facetum.* Why, to purfue the metaphor, if Sir Thomas Lofty was to call in his poetical debts, I believe there would be a good many bankrupts in the Mufe's Gazette.

ALL.

Ha, ha, ha!

Sir THOMAS.

But, *à propos*, gentlemen; with regard to the eclipfe: you found my calculation exact?

DACTYL.

To a digit.

Sir THOMAS.

Total darknefs, indeed! and birds going to rooft! Thofe philomaths, thofe almanackmakers, are the moft ignorant rafcals—

PUFF.

proprietor; and feems defirous of collecting from this learned affembly fome rhetorical flowers, which he hopes to ftrew, with honour to himfelf, and advantage to the company, in Leadenhall Street. [*Enter Sir Roger Dowlas.*] Sir Roger, be feated. This gentleman has, in common with the greateft orator the world ever faw, a fmall natural infirmity; he flutters a little: but I have prefcrib'd the fame remedy that Demofthenes ufed, and don't defpair of a radical cure. Well, Sir, have you digefted thofe general rules?

Sir ROGER.

Pr—ett—y well, I am obli—g'd to you, Sir Thomas.

Sir THOMAS.

Have you been regular in taking your tincture of fage, to give you confidence for fpeaking in public?

Sir ROGER.

Y—es, Sir Thomas.

Sir THOMAS.

Did you open at the laft general court?

Sir ROGER.

I attem—p—ted fo—ur or fi—ve times.

Sir THOMAS.

What hindered your progrefs?

Sir ROGER.

The pe—b—bles.

Sir THOMAS.

Oh, the pebbles in his mouth   But they are only put in to practife in private; you fhould take them out when you are addreffing the public.

Sir ROGER.

Yes; I will for the fu—ture.

Sir THOMAS.

Sir THOMAS.

Well, Mr. Ruft, you had a *tête-à-tête* with my niece. A propos, Mr. Bever, here offers a fine occasion for you; we shall take the liberty to trouble your Mufe on their nuptials. O Love! O Hymen! here prune thy purple wings; trim thy bright torch. Hey, Mr. Bever?

BEVER.

My talents are at Sir Thomas Lofty's direction; tho' I muft defpair of producing any performance worthy the attention of fo complete a judge of the elegant arts.

Sir THOMAS.

Too modeft, good Mr. Bever. Well, Mr. Ruft, any new acquifition, fince our laft meeting, to your matchlefs collection?

RUST.

Why, Sir Thomas, I have both loft and gained fince I faw you.

Sir THOMAS.

Loft! I am forry for that.

RUST.

The curious farcophagus, that was fent me from Naples by Signior Belloni—

Sir THOMAS.

You mean the urn that was fuppofed to contain the duft of Agrippa!

RUST.

Suppofed! no doubt but it did.

Sir THOMAS.

I hope no finifter accident to that ineftimable relic of Rome.

RUST.

It's gone.

Sir THOMAS.

Gone! oh, illiberal! What, ftolen, I fuppofe, by fome connoiffeur?

RUST.

RUST.

Worfe, worfe! a prey, a martyr to ignorance: a houfemaid, that I hired laft week, miftook it for a broken green chamber-pot, and fent it away in the duft-cart.

Sir THOMAS.

She merits impaling.   Oh, the Hun!

DACTYL.

The Vandal!

ALL.

The Vifigoth!

RUST.

But I have this day acquired a treafure that will in fome meafure make me amends.

Sir THOMAS.

Indeed! what can that be?

PUFF.

That muft be fomething curious, indeed.

RUST.

It has coft me infinite trouble to get it.

DACTYL.

Great rarities are not had without pains.

RUST.

It is three months ago fince I got the firft fcent of it, and I have been ever fince on the hunt; but all to no purpofe.

Sir THOMAS.

I am quite upon thorns till I fee it.

RUST.

And yefterday, when I had given it over, when all my hopes were grown defperate, it fell into my hands, by the moft unexpected and wonder-ful accident.

Sir THOMAS.

Quod optanti divum promittere nemo
Auderet, volvenda dies en attulit ultro.

Mr. Bever, you remark my quotation?

BEVER.

BEVER.

Moſt happy. Oh, Sir, nothing you ſay can be loſt.

RUST.

I have brought it here in my pocket; I am no churl; I love to pleaſure my friends.

Sir THOMAS.

You are, Mr. Ruſt, extremely obliging.

ALL.

Very kind, very obliging, indeed.

RUST.

It was not much hurt by the fire.

Sir THOMAS.

Very fortunate.

RUST.

The edges are ſoil'd by the link; but many of the letters are exceedingly legible.

Sir ROGER.

A li—ttle roo—m, if you p—leaſe.

RUST.

Here it is; the precious remains of the very North-Britain that was burnt at the Royal-Exchange.

Sir THOMAS.

Number forty-five?

RUST.

The ſame.

BEVER.

You are a lucky man, Mr. Ruſt.

RUST.

I think ſo. But, Gentlemen, I hope I need not give you a caution: huſh—ſilence—no words on this matter.

DACTYL.

You may depend upon us.

RUST.

For as the paper has not ſuffered the law, I don't know whether they may not ſeize it again.

Sir THOMAS.

Sir THOMAS.

With us you are fafe Mr. Ruft. Well, young gentleman, you fee we cultivate all branches of fcience.

BEVER.

Amazing, indeed! But when we confider you, Sir Thomas, as the directing the ruling planet, our wonder fubfides in an inftant. Science firft faw the day with Socrates in the Attic portico; her early years were fpent with Tully in the Tufculan fhade; but her ripe, maturer hours, fhe enjoys with Sir Thomas Lofty, near Cavendifh-Square.

Sir THOMAS.

The moft claffical compliment I ever received. Gentlemen, a philofophical repaft attends your acceptance within. Sir Roger, you'll lead the way. [*Exeunt all but Sir Thomas and Bever.*] Mr. Bever, may I beg your ear for a moment? Mr. Bever. the friendfhip I have for your father, fecured you at firft a gracious reception from me; but what I then paid to an old obligation, is now, Sir, due to your own particular merit.

BEVER.

I am happy, Sir Thomas, if—

Sir THOMAS.

Your patience. There is in you, Mr. Bever, a fire of imagination, a quicknefs of apprehenfion, a folidity of judgment, join'd to a depth of difcretion, that I never yet met with in any fubject at your time of life.

BEVER.

I hope I fhall never forfeit—

Sir THOMAS.

I am fure you never will; and to give you a convincing proof that I think fo, I am now going to truft you with the moft important fecret of my whole life.

BEVER.

BEVER.

Your confidence does me great honour.

Sir THOMAS.

But this muſt be on a certain condition.

BEVER.

Name it.

Sir THOMAS.

That you give me your ſolemn promiſe to comply with one requeſt I ſhall make you.

BEVER.

There is nothing Sir Thomas Lofty can aſk,
that I ſhall not chearfully grant.

Sir THOMAS.

Nay, in fact, it will be ſerving yourſelf.

BEVER.

I want no ſuch inducement.

Sir THOMAS.

Enough. But we can't be too private. [*Shuts
the door.*] Sit you down. Your Chriſtian name,
I think, is—

BEVER.

Richard.

Sir THOMAS.

True; the ſame as your father's. Come, let us
be familiar. It is, I think, dear Dick, acknowledged, that the Engliſh have reached the higheſt
pitch of perfection in every department of writing but one—the dramatic.

BEVER.

Why the French critics are a little ſevere.

Sir THOMAS.

And with reaſon. Now, to reſcue our credit,
and at the ſame time give my country a model,
[*ſhews a manuſcript*] ſee here.

BEVER.

A play?

Sir THOMAS.

Sir THOMAS.

A *chef d' oeuvre*.

BEVER.

Your own?

Sir THOMAS.

Speak lower. I am the author.

BEVER.

Nay, then there can be no doubt of it's merit.

Sir THOMAS.

I think not. You will be charm'd with the subject.

BEVER.

What is it, Sir Thomas?

Sir THOMAS.

I shall surprize you. The story of Robinson Crusoe. Are not you struck?

BEVER.

Most prodigiously.

Sir THOMAS.

Yes; I knew the very title would hit you. You will find the whole fable is finely conducted, and the character of Friday, *qualis ab incepto*, nobly supported throughout.

BEVER.

A pretty difficult task.

Sir THOMAS.

True; that was not a bow for a boy. The piece has long been in rehearsal at Drury-lane play-house, this night is to make its appearance.

BEVER.

To-night?

Sir THOMAS.

This night.

BEVER.

I will attend, and engage all my friends to support it.

Sir THOMAS.

That is not my purpose; the piece will want no such assistance.

BEVER.

BEVER.

I beg pardon.

Sir THOMAS.

The manager of that houſe (who you know is a writer himſelf), finding all the anonymous things he produced (indeed ſome of them wretched enough, and very unworthy of him) placed to his account by the public, is determined to exhibit no more without knowing the name of the author.

BEVER.

A reaſonable caution.

Sir THOMAS.

Now, upon my promiſe (for I appear to patronize the play) to announce the author before the curtain draws up, Robinſon Cruſoe is advertiſed for this evening.

BEVER.

Oh, then, you will acknowledge the piece to be your's?

Sir THOMAS.

No.

BEVER.

How then?

Sir THOMAS.

My deſign is to give it to you.

BEVER.

To me!

Sir THOMAS.

To you.

BEVER.

What, me the author of Robinſon Cruſoe!

Sir THOMAS.

Ay.

BEVER.

Lord, Sir Thomas, it will never gain credit: ſo compleat a production the work of a ſtripling! Beſides, Sir, as the merit is your's, why rob yourſelf of the glory?

Sir THOMAS.

Sir THOMAS.

I am entirely indifferent to that.

BEVER.

Then why take the trouble?

Sir THOMAS.

My fondnefs for letters, and love of my country. Befides, dear Dick, though the *pauci & felecti*, the chofen few, know the full value of a performance like this, yet the ignorant, the profane, (by much the majority,) will be apt to think it an occupa-tion ill-fuited to my time of life.

BEVER.

Their cenfure is praife.

Sir THOMAS.

Doubtlefs. But, indeed, my principal motive is my friendfhip for you. You are now a candidate for literary honours, and I am determin'd to fix your fame on an immoveable bafis.

BEVER.

You are moft exceffively kind; but there is fomething fo difingenuous in ftealing reputation from another man—

Sir THOMAS.

Idle punctilio!

BEVER.

It puts me fo in mind of the daw in the fable—

Sir THOMAS.

Come, come, dear Dick, I won't fuffer your modefty to murder your fame. But the com-pany will fufpect fomething; we will join them, and proclaim you the author. There, keep the copy; to you I confign it for ever; it fhall be a fecret to lateft pofterity. You will be fmother'd with praife by our friends; they fhall all in their bark to the playhoufe, and there

Attendant fail,
Purfue the triumph, and partake the gale.

END OF THE SECOND ACT.

ACT III.

SCENE CONTINUES.

Enter Bever Reading.

So ends the firſt act. Come, now for the ſecond. "Act the ſecond, ſhewing"—the coxcomb has prefaced every act with an argument too, in humble imitation, I warrant, of Monſ. Diderot— "ſhewing the fatal effects of diſobedience to parents;" with, I ſuppoſe, the diverting ſcene of a gibbet; an entertaining ſubject for comedy. And the blockhead is as prolix—every ſcene as long as a homily. Let's ſee; how does this end? "Exit Cruſoe, and enter ſome ſavages, dancing a ſaraband." There's no bearing this abominable traſh. [*Enter Juliet.*] So, Madam; thanks to your advice and direction, I am got into a fine ſituation.

JULIET.

What is the matter now, Mr Bever?

BEVER.

The Robinſon Cruſoe.

JULIET.

Oh, the play that is to be acted to-night. How ſecret you were? Who in the world would have gueſs'd you was the author?

BEVER.

Me, Madam!

JULIET.

Your title is odd; but to a genius every ſubject is good.

BEVER.

You are inclined to be pleaſant.

JULIET.

Within they have been all prodigious loud in the praiſe of your piece; but I think my uncle rather more eager than any.

BEVER.

BEVER.

He has reafon; for fatherly fondnefs goes far.

JULIET.

I don't underftand you.

BEVER.

You don't!

JULIET.

No.

BEVER.

Nay, Juliet, this is too much; you know it is none of my play.

JULIET.

Whofe then?

BEVER.

Your uncle's.

JULIET.

My uncle's! then how, in the name of wonder, came you to adopt it?

BEVER.

At his earneft requeft. I may be a fool; but remember, Madam, you are the caufe.

JULIET.

This is ftrange; but I can't conceive what his motive could be.

BEVER.

His motive is obvious enough; to fcreen him-felf from the infamy of being the author.

JULIET.

What, is it bad, then?

BEVER.

Bad! moft infernal!

JULIET.

And you have confented to own it?

BEVER.

Why, what could I do? he in a manner com-pell'd me.

JULIET.

I am extremely glad of it.

BEVER.

BEVER.

Glad of it! why, I tell you, 'tis the moſt dull, tedious, melancholy—

JULIET.

So much the better.

BEVER.

The moſt flat piece of frippery that ever Grub-ſtreet produced.

JULIET.

So much the better.

BEVER.

It will be damn'd before the third act.

JULIET.

So much the better.

BEVER.

And I ſhall be hooted and pointed at where-ever I go.

JULIET.

So much the better.

BEVER.

So much the better! zounds! ſo, I ſuppoſe, you would ſay if I was going to be hang'd. Do you call this a mark of you friendſhip?

JULIET.

Ah, Bever, Bever! you are a miſerable poli-tician. Do you know, now, that this is the luckieſt incident that ever occurr'd?

BEVER.

Indeed!

JULIET.

It could not have been better laid, had we planned it ourſelves.

BEVER.

You will pardon my want of conception: but theſe are riddles—

JULIET.

That at preſent I have not time to explain. But what makes you loit'ring here? Paſt ſix o'clock, as I live! Why, your play is begun; run, run,

run, to the houfe. Was ever author fo little
anxious for the fate of his piece?

BEVER.

My piece!

JULIET.

Sir Thomas! I know by his walk. Fly, and
pray all the way for the fall of your play. And, do
you hear, if you find the audience too indulgent,
inclined to be milky, rather than fail, fqueeze in
a little acid yourfelf. Oh, Mr. Bever, at your return let me fee you, before you go to my uncle;
that is, if you have the good luck to be damn'd.

BEVER.

You need not doubt that.   *Exit.*

Enter Sir Thomas Lofty.

Sir THOMAS.

So, Juliet; was not that Mr. Bever?

JULIET.

Yes, Sir.

Sir THOMAS.

He is rather tardy; by this time his caufe is
come on. And how is the young gentleman affected? for this is a trying occafion.

JULIET.

He feems pretty certain, Sir.

Sir THOMAS.

Indeed, I think he has very little reafon to fear :
I confefs I admire the piece ; and feel as much for
it's fate as if the work was my own.

JULIET.

That I moft fincerely believe. I wonder, Sir,
you did not choofe to be prefent.

Sir THOMAS.

Better not. My affections are ftrong, Juliet,
and my nerves but tenderly ftrung; however, intelligent people are planted, who will bring me
every act a faithful account of the procefs.

JULIET.

JULIET.

That will anfwer your purpofe as well.

Sir THOMAS.

Indeed, I am paffionately fond of the arts, and therefore can't help—did not fomebody knock? no. My good girl, will you ftep, and take care that when any body comes the fervants may not be out of the way. [*Exit Juliet.*] Five and thirty minutes paft fix ; by this time the firft act muft be over: John will be prefently here. I think it can't fail; yet there is fo much whim and caprice in the public opinion, that—This young man is un-known; they'll give him no credit. I had better have own'd it myfelf: Reputation goes a great way in thefe matters: people are afraid to find fault; they are cautious in cenfuring the works of a man who—hufh! that's he: no; 'tis only the fhutters. After all, I think I have chofe the beft way: for, if it fucceeds to the degree I expect, it will be eafy to circulate the real name of the author; if it falls, I am concealed, my fame fuffers no— There he is. [*Loud knocking.*] I can't conceive what kept him fo long. [*Enter John.*] So, John; well; and—but you have been a monftrous while.

JOHN.

Sir, I was wedged fo clofe in the pit that I could fcarcely get out.

Sir THOMAS.

The houfe was full then?

JOHN.

As an egg, Sir.

Sir THOMAS.

That's right. Well John, and did matters go fwimmingly? hey?

JOHN.

Exceedingly well, Sir.

Sir THOMAS.

Exceedingly well. I don't doubt it. What, vaft clapping and roars of applaufe, I fuppofe.

JOHN.

JOHN.

Very well, Sir.

Sir THOMAS.

Very well, Sir! You are damn'd coftive, I think.
But did not the pit and boxes thunder again?

JOHN.

I can't fay there was over much thunder.

Sir THOMAS.

No! Oh, attentive, I reckon. Ay, attention!
that is the true, folid, fubftantial applaufe. All
elfe may be purchafed; hands move as they are
bid: but when the audience is hufhed ftill, afraid
of lofing a word, then—

JOHN.

Yes, they were very quiet indeed, Sir.

Sir THOMAS.

I like them the better, John; a ftrong mark of
their great fenfibility. Did you fee Robin?

JOHN.

Yes, Sir; he'll be here in a trice; I left him
lift'ning at the back of the boxes, and charged
him to make all the hafte home that he could.

Sir THOMAS.

That's right, John; very well; your account
pleafes me much, honeft John. [*Exit John.*] No,
I did not expect the firft act would produce any
prodigious effect. And, after all, the firft act is
but a mere introduction; juft opens the bufinefs,
the plot, and gives a little infight into the characters: fo that if you but engage and intereft the
houfe, it is as much as the beft writer can flatt---
[*knocking without*] Gadfo! what, Robin already!
why the fellow has the feet of a Mercury. [*Enter
Robin.*] Well, Robin, and what news do you bring?

ROBIN.

Sir, I, I, I,——

Sir THOMAS.

Stop, Robin, and recover your breath. Now,
Robin.

ROBIN.

There has been a woundy uproar below.

Sir THOMAS.

An uproar! what, at the playhouſe?

ROBIN.

Ay.

Sir THOMAS.

At what?

ROBIN.

I don't know: belike at the words the play-folk were talking.

Sir THOMAS.

At the players! how can that be? Oh, now I begin to conceive. Poor fellow, he knows but little of plays. What, Robin, I ſuppoſe, hallowing, and clapping, and knocking of ſticks?

ROBIN.

Hallowing! ay, and hooting too.

Sir THOMAS.

And hooting!

ROBIN.

Ay, and hiſſing to boot.

Sir THOMAS.

Hiſſing! you muſt be miſtaken.

ROBIN.

By the maſs, but I am not.

Sir THOMAS.

Impoſſible! Oh, moſt likely ſome drunken, diſorderly fellows, that were diſturbing the houſe and interrupting the play; too common a caſe; the people were right: they deſerv'd a rebuke. Did not you hear them cry, Out, out, out?

ROBIN.

Noa; that was not the cry; 'twas Off, off, off!

Sir THOMAS.

That was a whimſical noiſe. Zounds! that muſt be the players. Did you obſerve nothing elſe?

ROBIN.

ROBIN.

Belike the quarrel firſt began between the gentry and a black-a-moor man.

Sir THOMAS.

With Friday! The public taſte is debauched; honeſt nature is too plain and ſimple for their vitiated palates! [*Enter Juliet.*] Juliet, Robin brings me the ſtrangeſt account; ſome little diſturbance; but I ſuppoſe it was ſoon ſettled again. Oh, but here comes Mr. Staytape, my taylor; he is a rational being; we ſhall be able to make ſomething of him. [*Enter Staytape.*] So, Staytape; what, is the third act over already?

STAYTAPE.

Over, Sir! no; nor never will be.

Sir THOMAS.

What do you mean?

STAYTAPE.

Cut ſhort.

Sir THOMAS.

I don't comprehend you.

STAYTAPE.

Why, Sir, the poet has made a miſtake in meaſuring the taſte of the town; the goods, it ſeems, did not fit; ſo they returned them upon the gentleman's hands.

Sir THOMAS.

Rot your affectation and quaintneſs, you puppy! ſpeak plain.

STAYTAPE.

Why, then, Sir, Robinſon Cruſoe is dead.

Sir THOMAS.

Dead!

STAYTAPE.

Ay; and, what is worſe, will never riſe any more. You will ſoon have all the particulars; for there were four or five of your friends cloſe at my heels.

Sir THOMAS.

Sir THOMAS.

Staytape, Juliet, run and stop them; say I am gone out; I am sick; I am engaged: but, whatever you do, be sure you don't let Bever come in. Secure of the victory, I invited them to the celebr—

STAYTAPE.

Sir, they are here.

Sir THOMAS.

Confound—

Enter Puff, Dactyl, and Rust.

RUST.

A, truly, Mr. Puff, this is but a bitter beginning; then the young man must turn himself to some other trade.

PUFF.

Servant, Sir Thomas; I suppose you have heard the news of—

Sir THOMAS.

Yes, yes; I have been told it before.

DACTYL.

I confess, I did not suspect it; but there is no knowing what effect these things will have till they come on the stage.

RUST.

For my part, I don't know much of these matters; but a couple of gentlemen near me, who seem'd sagacious enough too, declared that it was the vilest stuff they ever had heard, and wondered the players would act it.

DACTYL.

Yes; I don't remember to have seen a more general dislike.

PUFF.

I was thinking to ask you, Sir Thomas, for your interest with Mr. Bever about buying the copy: but now no mortal would read it. Lord, Sir, it would not pay for paper and print.

RUST.

RUST.

I remember Kennet, in his Roman Antiquities, mentions a play of Terence's, Mr. Dactyl, that was terribly treated; but that he attributes to the people's fondnefs for certain funambuli, or rope-dancers; but I have not lately heard of any famous tumblers in town: Sir Thomas, have you?

Sir THOMAS.

How fhould I; do you fuppofe I trouble my head about tumblers?

RUST.

Nay, I did not——

BEVER, *fpeaking without.*

Not to be fpoke with! Don't tell me, Sir; he muft, he fhall.

Sir THOMAS.

Mr. Bever's voice. If he is admitted in his prefent difpofition, the whole fecret will certainly out. Gentlemen, fome affairs of a moft interefting nature makes it impoffible for me to have the honour of your company to-night; therefore I beg you would be fo good as to——

RUST.

Affairs! no bad news? I hope Mifs Julè is well.

Sir THOMAS.

Very well; but I am moft exceedingly——

RUST.

I fhall only juft ftay to fee Mr. Bever. Poor lad! he will be moft horribly down in the mouth: a little comfort won't come amifs.

Sir THOMAS.

Mr. Bever, Sir! you won't fee him here.

RUST.

Not here! why I thought I heard his voice but juft now.

Sir THOMAS.

You are miftaken Mr. Ruft; but——

RUST.

RUST.

May be fo; then we will go. Sir Thomas, my compliments of condolence, if you pleafe, to the poet.

Sir THOMAS.

Ay, ay.

DACTYL.

And mine; for I fuppofe we fha'n't fee him foon.

PUFF.

Poor gentleman! I warrant he won't fhew his head for thefe fix months.

RUST.

Ay, ay: indeed, I am very forry for him; fo tell him, Sir.

DACTYL *and* PUFF.

So are we.

RUST.

Sir Thomas, your fervant. Come, Gentlemen. By all this confufion in Sir Thomas, there muft be fomething more in the wind than I know; but I will watch, I am refolved.   *Exeunt.*

BEVER, *without.*

Rafcals, ftand by! I muft, I will fee him.

Enter BEVER.

So, Sir; this is delicate treatment, after all I have fuffered.

Sir—THOMAS.

Mr. Bever, I hope you don't—that is—

BEVER.

Well, Sir Thomas Lofty, what think you now of your Robinfon Crufoe? a pretty performance!

Sir THOMAS.

Think, Mr. Bever! I think the public are blockheads; a tafteless, a ftupid, ignorant tribe; and a man of genious deferves to be damn'd who writes any thing for them. But courage, dear Dick! the principals will give you what the peo-

ple

ple refuse; the closet will do you that justice the
stage has denied: print your play.

BEVER.

My play! zounds, Sir, 'tis your own.

Sir THOMAS.

Speak lower, dear Dick; be moderate, my
good, dear lad!

BEVER.

Oh, Sir Thomas, you may be easy enough;
you are safe and secure, removed far from that
precipice that has dashed me to pieces.

Sir THOMAS.

Dear Dick, don't believe it will hurt you.
The critics, the real judges, will discover in that
piece such excellent talents—

BEVER.

No, Sir Thomas, no. I shall neither flatter
you nor myself; I have acquired a right to speak
what I think. Your play, Sir, is a wretched
performance; and in this opinion all mankind
are united.

Sir THOMAS.

May be not.

BEVER.

If your piece had been greatly received, I
would have declared Sir Thomas Lofty the author; if coldly, I would have owned it myself:
but such disgraceful, such contemptible treatment! I own, the burthen is too heavy for me;
so, Sir, you must bear it yourself.

Sir THOMAS.

Me, dear Dick! what to become ridiculous in
the decline of my life; to destroy in one hour the
fame that forty years has been building! that was
the prop, the support of my age! Can you be
cruel enough to desire it?

BEVER.

Zounds! Sir, and why must I be your
crutch? Would you have me become a volun-
tary

tary victim? No, Sir, this cause does not merit
a martyrdom.

Sir THOMAS.

I own myself greatly oblig'd; but persevere,
dear Dick, persevere; you have time to recover
your fame: I beg it with tears in my eyes.
Another play will—

BEVER.

No, Sir Thomas; I have done with the stage:
the Muses and I meet no more.

Sir THOMAS.

Nay, there are various roads open in life.

BEVER.

Not one, where your piece won't pursue me.
If I go to the bar, the ghost of this cursed comedy
will follow, and hunt me in Westminster-hall:
nay, when I die, it will stick to my memory, and
I shall be handed down to posterity with the author of Love in a Hollow Tree.

Sir THOMAS.

Then marry: you are a pretty smart figure;
and your poetical talents—

BEVER.

And what fair would admit of my suit, or
family wish to receive me? Make the case your
own, Sir Thomas; would you?

Sir THOMAS.

With infinite pleasure.

BEVER.

Then give me your niece; her hand shall seal
up my lips.

Sir THOMAS.

What, Juliet? willingly   But are you serious,
do you really admire the girl?

BEVER.

Beyond what words can express. It was by her
advice I consented to father your play.

Sir THOMAS.

Sir THOMAS.

What, is Juliet appriz'd? Here, Robin, John, run and call my niece hither this moment. That giddy baggage will blab all in an inftant.

BEVER.

You are miftaken; fhe is wifer than you are aware of.

Enter Juliet.

Sir THOMAS.

Oh, Juliet! you know what has happen'd.

JULIET.

I do, Sir.

Sir THOMAS.

Have you reveal'd this unfortunate fecret.

JULIET.

To no mortal, Sir Thomas.

Sir THOMAS.

Come, give me your hand. Mr. Bever, child, for my fake, has renounced the ftage, and the whole republic of letters; in return I owe him your hand.

JULIET.

My hand! what, to a poet hooted, hiffed, and exploded! You muft pardon me, Sir.

Sir THOMAS.

Juliet, a trifle: the moft they can fay of him, is, that he is a little wanting in wit; and he has fo many brother writers to keep him in countenance, that now-a-days that is no reflection at all.

JULIET.

Then, Sir, your engagement to Mr. Ruft.

Sir THOMAS.

I have found out the rafcal; he has been more impertinently fevere on my play, than all the reft put together; fo that, I am determined he fhall be none of the man.

Enter

Enter Ruſt.

RUST.

Are you ſo, Sir? what, then, I am to be ſacrificed, in order to preſerve the ſecret that you are a blockhead? But you are out in your politics; before night it ſhall be known in all the coffeehouſes in town.

Sir THOMAS.

For Heaven's ſake, Mr. Ruſt!

RUST.

And to-morrow I will paragraph you in every news-paper; you ſhall no longer impoſe on the world; I will unmaſk you; the lion's ſkin ſhall hide you no longer.

Sir THOMAS.

Juliet! Mr. Bever! what can I do?

BEVER.

Sir Thomas, let me manage this matter. Harkee, old gentleman, a word in your ear: you remember what you have in your pocket?

RUST.

Hey! how! what?

BEVER.

The curioſity that has coſt you ſo much pains.

RUST.

What, my Æneas! my precious relict of Troy!

BEVER.

You muſt give up that, or the lady.

JULIET.

How, Mr. Bever!

BEVER.

Never fear; I am ſure of my man.

RUST.

Let me conſider—As to the girl, girls are plenty enough; I can marry whenever I will: but my paper, my phœnix, that ſprings freſh from the flames, that can never be match'd.—Take her.

BEVER.

BEVER.

And, as you love your own fecret, be careful
of ours.

RUST.

I am dumb.

Sir THOMAS.

Now, Juliet.

JULIET.

You join me, Sir, to an unfortunate bard; but,
to procure your peace—

Sir THOMAS.

You oblige me for ever.   Now the fecret dies
with us four.   My fault.   I owe him much:

Be it your care to fhew it ;
And blefs the man, tho' I have damn'd the poet.

Exeunt Omnes.

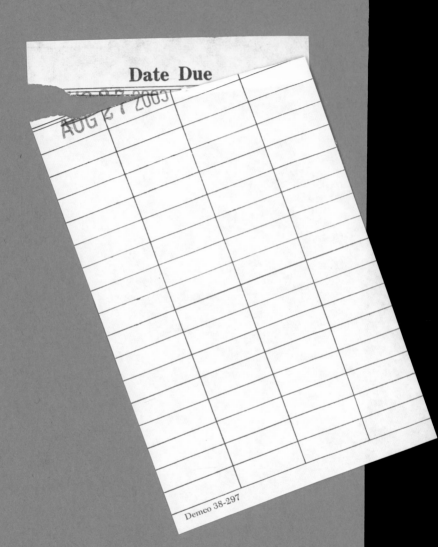

Date Due

AUG 27 2003

Demco 38-297